Ultimate Family
PUZZLE
Book 1

Ultimate Family

PUZZLE

Book 1

igloo

First published in 2006 by Igloo Books Ltd
Igloo Books Ltd
Cottage Farm
Sywell
Northants, NN6 0B
info@igloo-books.com

www.igloo-books.com

ISBN 1-84561-317-1
Printed in China

Project Management by Metro Media Ltd

Coordinator: Adam Phillips
Production: Victoria Chow
Text design & layout: Kurt Young, Tom Lynton, Neil Earp,
David Boyle & Andy Huckle
Cover design: Dan Tyler & Kurt Young
Puzzles created by: Puzzlecraft

Welcome to the Ultimate Family Puzzle Book 1!

All the family can enjoy the *Ultimate Family Puzzle Book*, as it has something to suit everyone. Whether your preference is for number puzzles or word puzzles, both can be found here, alongside mazes, Sudoku and many more.

There are three levels of difficulty in this book. Easy puzzles are marked with one star and – as the name suggests – are the most simple puzzles to do. These are suitable for the youngest child or the puzzle beginner. The moderate puzzles are that little bit harder, and have been highlighted with two stars for those who feel that the easy puzzles do not provide enough of a challenge.

Then finally there are the challenging puzzles, which are marked with three stars. These are for serious puzzlers only and represent the peak of difficulty. So, something for all the family to sit down together and enjoy!

BLOCKBUSTERS

★★★

Complete the square by using each number and symbol provided in the top row ONCE only in every other row and column to equal the given answer. The first column and all the - signs have been put in to give you a start!

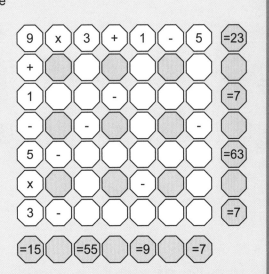

9	x	3	+	1	-	5	=23
+					=7
1		-			=7
-		-			=63
5	-				=63
x			-		
3	-				=7
=15	=55	=9	=7		

WORD FIT

★★★

Can you fit all the places of work into the grid below?

4 letter words	5 letter words	6 letter words	7 letter words	8 letter words
Firm	Docks	Market	Barbers	Refinery
Mill	Forge	Office	Cannery	
Mint	Works	School	Concern	
Shop			Embassy	
			Factory	

80s MOVIES QUIZ

★★★

1. Who played a naval hero in No Way Out?

....

2. Which 80s film featured Emily Lloyd at the seaside?

....

3. In which 80s classic did Tom Cruise play a character called Maverick?

....

4. What was the title of the film about the life of Dian Fossey?

....

5. Who played Superman's cousin in 1984?

....

ADD THREE TO THREE

★★

Can you add three letters to the three words in red below to make another word which solves the clue? For example, by adding three letters to the clue 'BAN this fruit', you can make the word BANANA.

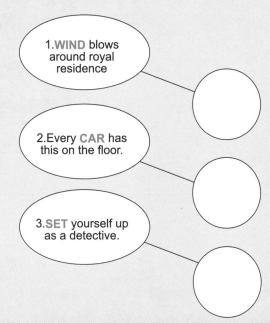

1. **WIND** blows around royal residence

2. Every **CAR** has this on the floor.

3. **SET** yourself up as a detective.

NOURISHING NINE

★★

How many words of four letters or more can you track down in this game? At least one 'nourishing' word will contain all nine letters and all words must contain the central letter. Use each letter once only. No words with capital letters, foreign words, hyphens, or plurals and verb forms ending in -s are allowed.

R I L
C G
K A C N

WORD SPLITZ

Each row of ten letters can be split into two five-letter rivers. These words read from left to right and are in order.

For example SMOKOSUENK can be split to reveal SKUNK and MOOSE.

1. C F O L R Y T D E H
2. L S E O I I R N E E
3. S R H T I O N U R E
4. V T R O E L N G A T

KAKURO

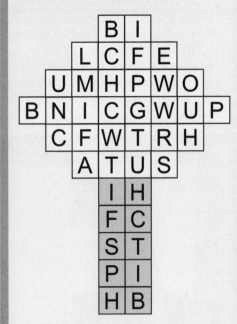

In Kakuro the numbers in the black squares refer to the SUMS of the digits 1–9 which you are to fill into the empty spaces. The number ABOVE the diagonal line refers to the empty spaces directly to the RIGHT of that number. A number BELOW the diagonal line refers to the empty spaces directly BELOW that number. No zeros are used here and a digit can only appear once in any particular digit combination.

NATURE TRAIL

Find the plant that is growing inside the tree by removing all the letters that appear more than twice.

THE HIDDEN PLANT IS

....

STEP LADDER

Starting with the top word, change one letter at a time to make a new word at every step until you have reached the bottom word.

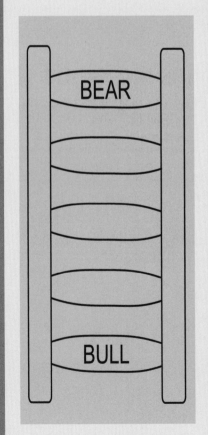

BEAR

BULL

AWARDS WORDSEARCH

The grid contains 14 words associated with awards hidden vertically, horizontally or diagonally. Can you find them all?

BELT
CROWN
DEGREE
GARLAND
GARTER
LAUREL
MEDAL

MONEY
PLAQUE
PRESENT
STAR
STRIPE
TITLE
WREATH

B	E	L	T	I	T	G	H
Z	R	D	E	P	A	T	E
D	N	A	L	R	A	G	U
E	W	H	T	E	U	U	Q
G	O	E	R	S	D	A	A
R	R	W	M	E	D	A	L
E	C	M	O	N	E	Y	P
E	P	I	R	T	S	A	V

NOBLE HAZE TWIT (1)		
STOMP ME (7)	THE LINK IS	
NETTLE CHI (3,6)		
KNEADING LAW MAD (4,3,7)		

HOLLYWOOD ANAGRAMS

On the left are four anagrams of films or film people. The number and length of words to find is shown in brackets. The four anagram solutions are all linked in some way, can you find the link?

KAKURO

In Kakuro the numbers in the black squares refer to the SUMS of the digits 1–9 which you are to fill into the empty spaces. The number ABOVE the diagonal line refers to the empty spaces directly to the RIGHT of that number. A number BELOW the diagonal line refers to the empty spaces directly BELOW that number. No zeros are used here and a digit can only appear once in any particular digit combination.

SUDOKU

To solve, fill in the grid so that every row, column and box contains the numbers 1 through 9.

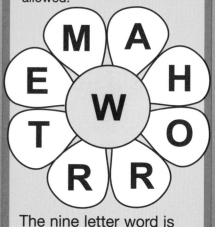

	3	2			8	1		
		8				3	7	4
	7	6	5				1	
	8			4		1		3
		7	3					
2	5		1			4	8	
						7	6	
7		4	9	1	6	5		
3	6				5			

NATURAL NINE

Try and become king of the jungle in this natural puzzle. How many words of four letters or more can you track down? At least one will use all nine letters and all contain the central letter W. Use each letter once only. No words with capitals, foreign words, hyphens, or plurals are allowed.

The nine letter word is

....

PUSSYCAT STANDARD: 8 words
PANTHER STANDARD: 16 words
LION STANDARD: 24 words

ODD ONE OUT

Can you spot the odd one out in this selection of countries?

ARROWS

Put the following numbers in the arrows below:

1 1 1 1 1 2 2 2

Be careful though.

The total numbers in the three arrows pointing at each other must add up to 7.

The total numbers in the arrows which are back to back must add up to 3.

ADDING GRIDS

Place any digits 0 to 9 into the empty circles. When complete each row should add up to the figures on the right and each column to the figures below. The shaded numbers are the total of the diagonal circles.

				11
				18
0	2		7	11
6	6	2		16
				12
15	13	12	17	18

SHEEP WORDSEARCH ⭐⭐

The grid contains 14 words associated with sheep hidden vertically, horizontally or diagonally. The unused letters spell out another connected word.

S	H	E	P	H	E	R	D
L	F	K	C	L	W	X	E
A	L	E	O	E	A	W	E
R	O	N	I	R	E	M	R
Z	C	T	H	S	O	L	B
A	K	T	L	D	L	O	F
C	N	L	O	C	N	I	L
A	C	H	E	V	I	O	T

ANTHRAX
BREED
CHEVIOT
EWES
FLEECE
FLOCK
FOLD
HERD

KENT   LINCOLN
LAMB   MERINO
LARZAC   SHEPHERD

NATUREGRAMS ⭐⭐

Solve each clue, then rearrange the five letters in every answer to form a set of three mammals.

CLUES:
1. Force out
2. Engaging in
3. Filled greatly

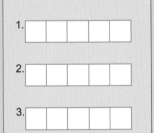

1. ☐☐☐☐☐
2. ☐☐☐☐☐
3. ☐☐☐☐☐

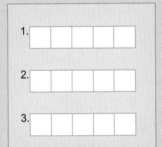

1. ☐☐☐☐☐
2. ☐☐☐☐☐
3. ☐☐☐☐☐

WORD WHEEL ⭐⭐

For each of the circles, can you find two letters which when placed in the middle will form three six-letter words?

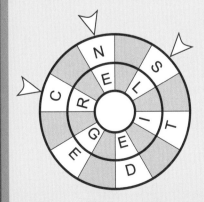

CODED CROSSWORD ⭐⭐⭐

Each number in the grid represents a different letter of the alphabet. Can you fill in the grid using the given letters to get you started?

21	10	10	16	23	2	■	21	12	15	16	16	6
12	■	15	■	15	■	6	■	17	■	26	■	21
12	14	11	16	16	3	16	■	11	24	9	2	12
9	■	2	■	21	■	13	■	24	■	12	■	2
12	17	16	21	13	■	10	9	18	8	2	16	13
2	■	■	15	■	25	■	■	16	■	■	4	■
■	6	15	21	4	18	13	25	11	24	22	12	■
5	■	16	■	■	19	■	24	■	■	22		
21	11	2	2	13	9	21	■	23	21	1	15	16
18	■	2	■	8	■	24	■	25	■	21	■	21
18	15	25	13	4	■	23	25	20	16	13	16	22
16	■	24	■	19	■	16	■	16	■	7	■	15
22	9	12	8	16	12	■	18	13	21	12	12	4

1	2	3	4	5	6 P	7	8	9	10 F	11	12	13
14 L	15	16	17	18	19	20	21	22 D	23	24	25	26

BITS AND PIECES ⭐⭐⭐

The tiles in the top grid are all jumbled up. Can you rearrange them in the grid below using only one tile from each column to reveal four related words and their theme?

C	WE	X	A	DO
OV	LO	CO	E	ER
T	ER	U	IN	G
S	U	A	T	RS
TR	O	TH	SE	T

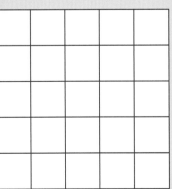

LITTLE TOUGHIE

Across
4 Assistant's terribly dear display (6)
5 'You dirty little...' (3)
6 Record for going round a circuit (3)
8 Surprised a mother with last letter (6)
Down
1 A vehicle following car across the desert? (7)
2 Fellow in middle of Irish Sea (3)
3 Dad juggling with tees must be calmed down! (7)
7 Scotsman needs it to keep dry? (3)

PLACE THE PLACES

To solve the puzzle, place the letters from the place in capitals into the empty spaces in the grid. Four everyday words should be formed reading across the grid and three everyday words reading down.

C R O A T I A

CHAIN REACTION

Solve this puzzle by creating a 'chain reaction' of 20 five-letter words that run left to right, beginning in the upper-left hand corner, using the 19 two-letter tiles in the middle. A two-letter tile that ends one begins the next. Each tile will only be used once. The single letters already entered are the middle letters of the words you are to form. Start by finishing the word that begins EAG_ _.

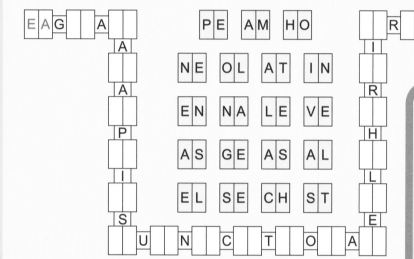

HALT WORDSEARCH

The grid contains 14 words that mean halt hidden vertically, horizontally or diagonally. The unused letters spell out another connected word.

ARREST   IMPEDE
BLOCK   LAPSE
BREAK   QUIT
CEASE   RECESS
CHECK   REST
DELAY   STOP
IMPASSE   SUSPEND

```
I B L O C K I K
M L A P S E M C
P T S S T O P E
A I P S S D E H
S U S P E N D C
S Q A L R C E U
E K A E R B E S
E Y E S A E C R
```

ANAGRAM LADDERS

Solve the anagrams below to reveal the names of seven jobs. The shaded row in the middle will then reveal the name of another job.

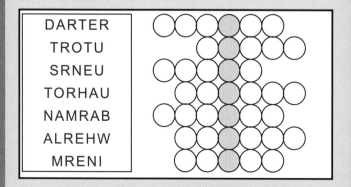

DARTER
TROTU
SRNEU
TORHAU
NAMRAB
ALREHW
MRENI

OCCUPATIONS

How many words of four letters or more can you track down in this game? At least one will be a nine letter occupation and all contain the central letter. Use each letter once only. No words with capitals, foreign words, hyphens, or plurals and verb forms ending in -s are allowed.

GOOD: 15 words
VERY GOOD: 20 words
EXCELLENT: 28 words

PYRAMID OF APPLES

Fill in the apples with numbers. The number in each apple must equal the sum of the two apples below it.

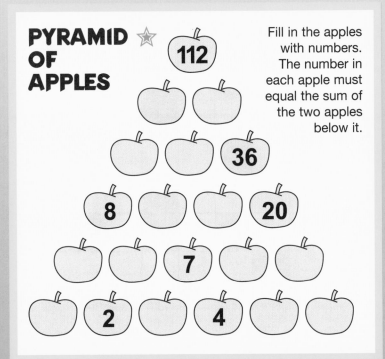

BIRD BOXES

Shade in all the numbers from 1 to 5 to reveal a hidden bird.

9	6	2	4	3	8	9	6	9	5	9	6
7	8	5	9	1	9	7	8	6	1	8	9
5	9	1	3	5	7	9	8	6	3	8	7
2	8	2	6	4	8	7	7	9	4	6	7
4	7	5	8	1	6	9	6	8	2	9	2
3	6	7	6	7	1	2	4	7	5	1	7
1	8	8	9	9	5	6	9	8	4	9	3
6	9	6	7	6	3	8	9	7	8	6	8

SKELETON CROSSWORD

Below is an incomplete quick crossword grid. Can you solve the puzzle by fitting the answers to the clues correctly into the grid, along with the remaining blocks and clue numbers? A few blocks have been shaded to give you a start. The puzzle has been rotated by 180 degrees.

Across
2 Convinces (7)
7 Malarial fever (4)
8 Layers of rock (6)
9 Tidy (4)
10 Other/different (4)
12 North European language (6)
14 Tranquil (6)
16 Shortened girl's name (4)
18 Farewell (2-2)
19 A set of clothes (6)
20 Type of bean (4)
21 From a Scandinavian country (7)

Down
1 Hang in folds (5)
3 Embarrassing display of emotion (5)
4 Despicable person (6)
5 To suddenly surprise (7)
6 French for white (5)
8 An enclosed space (3)
11 Fairies (7)
13 Complete (6)
14 Sailing vessel (5)
15 Chew and swallow (3)
16 Foundation (5)
17 Growl (5)

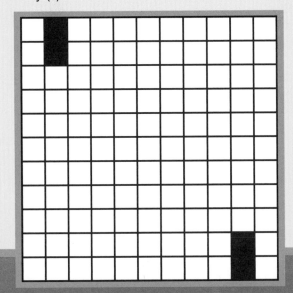

ON TARGET

Put the answers to the clues in the grid starting from the outside. Each answer has five letters and ends with the central letter L. When you've finished the outer ring will reveal the name of a sport (7).

1 Large group of fish (5)
2 Place providing accommodation (5)
3 Edible internal parts of an animal (5)
4 A track (5)
5 Part of a flower (5)
6 Before, to the time when (5)
7 Cave-dwelling goblin (5)

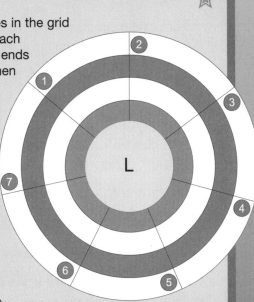

JIG GRID

Can you fit the blocks back into the grid to reveal, reading from left to right, six occupations?

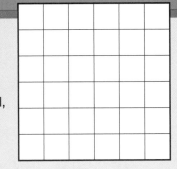

BAR		DOC		AUTH
CLER		F A		M
		J O		
OR		R		KER
A N				MER
I C		I N E R		

CULT TV SHOWS SQUIRCLE ★★

Put vowels in the circles and consonants in the squares to make words in all the vertical columns. Definitions of these words are given. When this has been done, the first and third horizontal lines will make two UK cult TV shows.

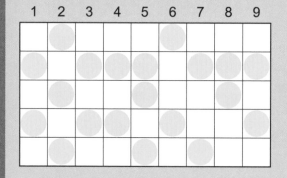

	1	2	3	4	5	6	7	8	9

DEFINITIONS
1 Rest
2 Rub out
3 Shooting lure
4 Noblemen
5 Make a fabric
6 Small poisonous snake
7 Long narrow hill
8 Evil spirit
9 Flat brimless cap

CROSSWORD ★

Across
1 Totting up (6)
5 Plaything (3)
6 A vegetable (3)
7 Small child (3)
8 Travel over snow (3)
9 Operate machine (3)
10 A cure (6)

Down
1 Painter (6)
2 The hours between dusk and dawn (7)
3 God of the sea (7)
4 Hardly ever (6)

QUICK QUIZ QUESTIONS ★★

Can you get all of these quiz questions correct?

WHOSE REAL NAME IS.......	
1. ROBERT ZIMMERMAN ?	
2. REGINALD DWIGHT ?	
3. PAUL HEWSON ?	
4. GORDON SUMMNER ?	
5. RICHARD STARKEY ?	
6. DAVID HAYWARD-JONES ?	

FIVE SNEAKY SNAKES ★★★

Can you add five letters to each of the words in capitals in the snakes below, to make another word which solves the clue? For example, by adding five letters to the clue 'A revolt can make you REEL', you can make the word REBELLION. Each of the answers share a common theme.

1. Paint this Scottish city RED.
2. Proverbially NEAT place to carry coal.
3. Goldsmith's vicar came from a WILD place.
4. LAD finds the land of fabulous wealth.
5. Old car's destination in fancy RIG.

GEOGRAMS ★★

Solve each clue, then rearrange the six letters in every answer to form a set of three countries.

CLUES:
1 Set of programs
2 Cook in liquid
3 Have a lofty goal

1.
2.
3.

1.
2.
3.

COUNTING CRITTERS

Can you find the number that is represented by each animal face? You will find the total of the numbers below each column and to the right of each row.

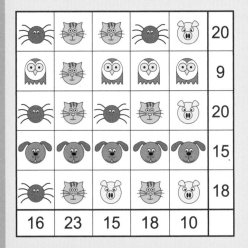

spider	cat	cat	spider	pig	20
owl	cat	owl	owl	owl	9
spider	cat	spider	cat	mouse	20
dog	dog	dog	dog	dog	15
spider	cat	mouse	cat	pig	18
16	23	15	18	10	

dog =
cat =
owl =
spider =
pig =

NURSERY BLOCKS

Rearrange each column of letters and write them in the grid to reveal the first two lines of a well known nursery rhyme. Some of the letters have been put in to give you a head start.

Grid contains: O, T, B, ., D, .

```
      T              O
    N E          O     O C
  F O C H      K W M E E
  S H O U R E E N O O R
  A T U E K L T H R Y K
```

HOLLYWOOD ANAGRAMS

Here are four anagrams of films or film people. The number and length of words to find is shown in brackets. The four anagram solutions are all linked in some way – can you find the link?

MOTH SANK
(3, 5)

SHETLAND OWNING ZEN
(6, 10)

MOORLAND BARN (6, 6)

DOMINANT HUFFS (6, 7)

THE LINK IS .....

....

CAGED ANIMALS

An animal has escaped from the zoo. To put him back in his cage answer the eight clues and put them in the grid starting from the outermost circle. When this is done the central circles starting clockwise from number nine will reveal the name of the animal who escaped.

1 Calf meat (4)
2 Shows a program (4)
3 War-torn country (4)
4 Bill of fare (4)
5 A cab (4)
6 Growl of lion (4)
7 Finished (4)
8 Primary color (4)

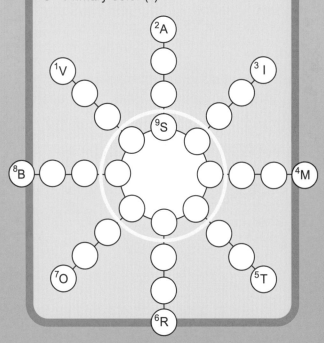

ZOO HUNT

An animal has escaped from the zoo and is hiding somewhere in the grid. If you cross out all the letters that appear more than twice, the remaining letters will spell out the missing creature.

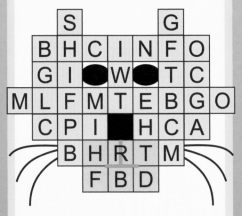

```
  S        G
B H C I N F O
G I ● W ● T C
M L F M T E B G O
C P I ■ H C A
  B H R T M
    F B D
```

THE MISSING CREATURE IS A

....

NOURISHING NINE

How many words of four letters or more can you track down in this game? At least one word will contain all nine letters and all words must contain the central letter. Use each letter once only. No words with capital letters, foreign words, hyphens, or plurals and verb forms ending in -s are allowed.

```
  N F   T
 A   G N
  T E I
```

UNDERDONE: 8 words
MEDIUM: 13 words
WELL DONE: 18 words

SUDOKU

To solve, fill in the grid so that every row, column and box contains the numbers 1 through 9.

3		4	9	5	1		7	6
8			6	2		4	3	
	7			4	3	9	2	1
4	6			8	2	3		9
1	5	8	3	9	4			7
2				5	1	8	4	
9	4	5		7		6	1	3
7		2	4	3	6	5		8
	8	3	5	1	9	7		2

NATURE TRAIL

Find the plant that is growing inside the tree by removing all the letters that appear more than twice.

```
      N B
    W S H O
  K F S C N P
B A M O M K T F
  C E P R H S
    N L O I
      M C
      P L
      B K
      F Y
      H O
```

THE HIDDEN PLANT IS A

....

COOKIES WORDSEARCH

The grid contains 16 cookie words hidden vertically, horizontally or diagonally. Can you find them all?

BREAD   GINGER   RICE
CHIP   LEMON   RICH
COFFEE   NICE   SHORT
CRACKER   ORANGE   THIN
DATE   PLAIN   WAFER
                        WATER

W	H	P	P	E	O	R	D
A	C	E	L	T	W	L	A
T	I	O	R	A	N	G	E
E	R	O	F	D	I	I	R
R	H	E	P	F	C	N	B
S	R	I	C	E	E	G	N
T	H	I	N	O	M	E	L
C	R	A	C	K	E	R	S

BATTLESHIPS

There are four ships hidden in the grid. Look at the key to see which ships you have to find. The numbers on the grid tell you how many squares of each row or column part of a ship is found in. To get you started we've put a few parts of ships (in red) and a few squares with no ships (in black).

HINTS: Begin by shading in all the misses (all the columns which have a zero in them) as there are no ships here. When you have found a full ship you can shade all the blocks around that ship as misses because none of the ships are touching.

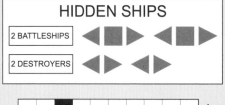
HIDDEN SHIPS

2 BATTLESHIPS

2 DESTROYERS

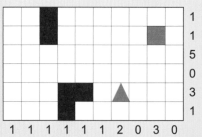

Column totals: 1 1 1 1 1 1 2 0 3 0
Row totals: 1 1 5 0 3 1

NINE NUMBERS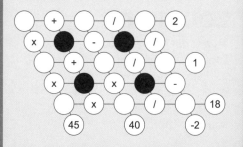

Try to fill in the missing numbers. Use the numbers 1 to 9 to complete the equations. Each number is only used once. Each row and column is an equation with the totals given below and to the right.

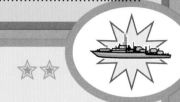

BITS AND PIECES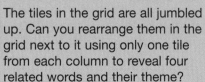

The tiles in the grid are all jumbled up. Can you rearrange them in the grid next to it using only one tile from each column to reveal four related words and their theme?

ST	P	G	RI	R
S	TE	TR	C	K
EN	HA	O	E	K
KL	AR	RP	E	N
P	IN	S	O	SE

OCCUPATIONS

How many words of four letters or more can you track down in this game? At least one will be a nine letter occupation and all contain the central letter. Use each letter once only. No words with capitals, foreign words, hyphens, or plurals and verb forms ending in -s are allowed.

GOOD: 15 words
VERY GOOD: 22 words
EXCELLENT: 31 words

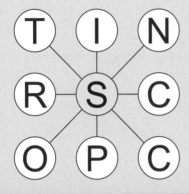

80s UK TV QUIZ

1. Which 80s TV drama starred Jeremy Irons and Anthony Andrews?

....

2. Who was the male star of the sitcom To the Manor Born?

....

3. Which actor played Rene in the sitcom 'Allo 'Allo!?

....

4. What was the style of music featured in The Beiderbecke Connection TV series?

....

5. Whose Video Show ended in 1980?

....

KAKURO

In Kakuro the numbers in the black squares refer to the SUMS of the digits 1–9 which you are to fill into the empty spaces. The number ABOVE the diagonal line refers to the empty spaces directly to the RIGHT of that number. A number BELOW the diagonal line refers to the empty spaces directly BELOW that number. No zeros are used here and a digit can only appear once in any particular digit combination.

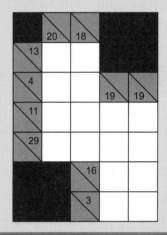

LITTLE TOUGHIE

Across
4 Club included in letter for discussion (6)
5 He's a bit of a loafer (3)
6 Strike to get a sunburn! (3)
8 Bird that is a new recruit (6)

Down
1 Puts things right with regard to couples (7)
2 What gifted speakers have? (3)
3 First-class beer served up with royal accompaniments (7)
7 It's shelled from a ship, oddly (3)

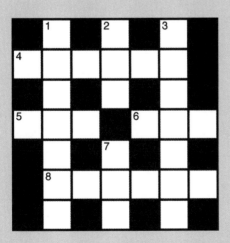

TREE NUMBER PIC ✩✩

Can you create a picture from the grid below? Each number represents a group of shaded squares, so for example [3][2] means that on this row there is a group of 3 red squares to the left of a group of 2 green squares. The numbers are always in order, so [3][2] means a group of 3 red squares to the left of a group of 2 green squares in that row, and [5][3] means a block of 5 green squares above a block of 3 red squares in that column.

SKELETON CROSSWORD

Below is an incomplete quick crossword grid. Can you solve the puzzle by fitting the answers to the clues correctly into the grid, along with the remaining blocks and clue numbers? A few blocks have been shaded to give you a start. The puzzle has been rotated by 180 degrees.

Across
1 Large bundle of hay (4)
4 Member of boy's organisation (5)
8 Addicted to drink (2,3,6)
9 High regard (6)
11 Facial feature (4)
13 Shelter for cows (4)
14 Tiers (6)
17 Past one's prime (4,3,4)
19 Wear away (5)
20 Stitched join in fabric (4)

Down
2 Perform on stage (3)
3 Small hole for lace (6)
4 Expression used to frighten away (4)
5 Consequence (7)
6 Underlying topic (5)
7 Round roof (4)
10 Underwater missile (7)
12 Grows narrower at one end (6)
13 Bankrupt (5)
15 A seasoning (4)
16 Eyesore (4)
18 Broadcasting authority (3)

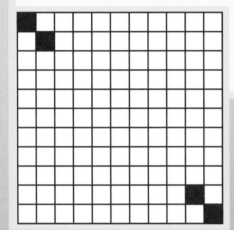

BIRD BOXES

Shade in all the even numbers to reveal a hidden bird.

1	27	15	7	27	11	3	19	9	33	17	9
23	36	2	31	10	40	16	8	22	7	31	5
19	20	5	3	28	21	2	29	12	25	9	23
27	6	24	9	34	23	4	7	6	17	11	27
15	14	17	35	12	7	1	11	32	37	19	29
1	8	25	33	19	31	29	13	11	38	13	24
33	20	30	27	5	7	9	33	3	4	21	18
17	5	21	3	13	35	23	15	21	14	10	26

ON TARGET

Put the answers to the clues in the grid starting from the outside. Each answer has five letters and ends with the central letter H. When you've finished the outer ring will reveal the name of a UK soccer team (7).

1 American farm (5)
2 Soil (5)
3 Muslim name for God (5)
4 End of life (5)
5 Nationality of Dave Allen (5)
6 Cry of horse (5)
7 Symbolic diagram (5)

QUICK MOVIE QUIZ

1. Which actor plays Ace Ventura Pet Detective?

....

2. Name the actor who plays Spider-Man.

....

3. What is the name of the school which Harry Potter attends?

....

4. What piece of furniture must you climb through to reach Narnia?

....

5. What animals are the inhabitants of Jurassic Park?

....

RIDDLE WORDS

Can you answer these word riddles with types of weather?

? Which type of weather also means to take by force? ?	
? Which bad weather occurs when you call for a taxi? ?	
Which sunny word also means intelligent?	
? Which type of weather also means extremely fast? ?	

LETTER STEW

Use all the given letters in the stew to spell three words meaning small.

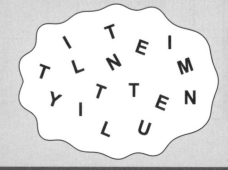

ADD THREE TO THREE ⭐⭐

Can you add three letters to the three words in red below to make another word which solves the clue? For example, by adding three letters to the clue 'BAN this fruit', you can make the word BANANA.

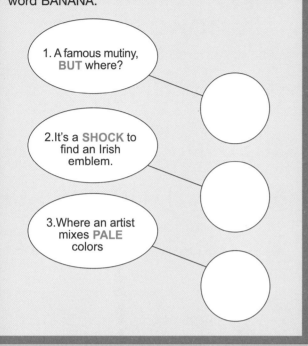

1. A famous mutiny, **BUT** where?

2. It's a **SHOCK** to find an Irish emblem.

3. Where an artist mixes **PALE** colors

COMMON WORDS ⭐⭐⭐

Your task here is to determine the answers to each set of tricky definitions below, as well as the word that is contained in all five of the set's answers. For example if the five solutions were ERRAND, TERRIBLE, MERRY MEN, PREFERRED and PERRY, the word in the central circle would be ERR.

CLUES:
1 Oaklet
2 Horn
3 Distained
4 Maned myth
5 Goat of note

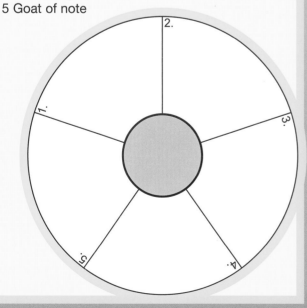

SUDOKU ⭐⭐⭐

To solve, fill in the grid so that every row, column and box contains the numbers 1 through 9.

	7	9						
				5				
4		8		9				7
1	6					5	8	
			4					
				3	2	1		
7					3			
			6	1	9			
	8		5				2	

PLACE THE PLACES ⭐⭐

To solve the puzzle, place the letters from the place in capitals into the empty spaces in the grid. Four everyday words should be formed reading across the grid and three everyday words reading down.

A R C A D E

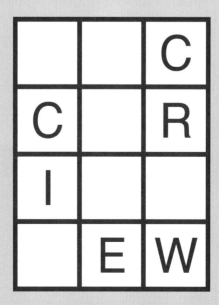

REBUS TOWER ⭐⭐⭐

Can you work out which common phrases are represented by each of the three diagrams in the tower below?

X TOAST

MATES

CENTURIONS

YOKELS

POLMUMICE

BLOCKBUSTERS

Complete the square by using each number and symbol provided in the top row ONCE only in every other row and column to equal the given answer. The first column and all the - signs have been put in to give you a start!

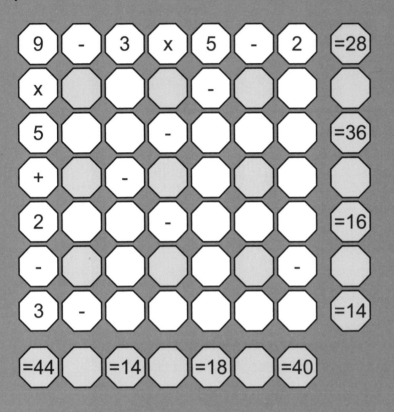

WORD SPLITZ

Each row of ten letters can be split into two five-letter dances. These words read from left to right and are in order.

For example

SMOKOSUENK

can be split to reveal SKUNK and MOOSE.

1. WTAALNTZGO
2. SPOALMKBAA
3. FLLIINGMBO
4. CRUOMNGABA

BITS AND PIECES

The tiles in the top grid are all jumbled up. Can you rearrange them in the grid below using only one tile from each column to reveal four related words and their theme?

SC	A	G	LA	S
T	AR	AS	A	E
G	G	ST	GO	ND
C	O	T	L	N
HA	L	T	I	W

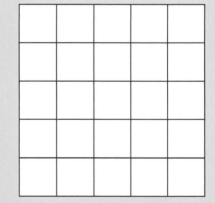

CROSSWORD

Across
2 To angle (4)
4 Of great height (4)
5 A room for books (7)
6 Peel (4)
7 Immediately following (4)

Down
1 Spread out from the center (7)
2 Flower seller (7)
3 Sign of the zodiac (7)

ZOO HUNT

An animal has escaped from the zoo and is hiding somewhere in the grid. If you cross out all the letters that appear more than twice, the remaining letters will spell out the missing creature.

```
    F         G
K R C M K C I
Z O ● N ● O Z
L F Y H P F B M H
N E K ■ N P A
  M P R P O
    C K H
```

THE MISSING CREATURE IS A

....

HOLLYWOOD ANAGRAMS

Below are four anagrams of films or film people. The number and length of words to find are shown in brackets. The four anagram solutions are all linked in some way – can you find the link?

ANNIVERSARY PIG VAT (6, 7, 4)	
ENTHRAL ITEM (3, 8)	THE LINK IS .....
WORDSWORTH FLEA (3, 2, 3, 6)	....
FISHERIES MAMA GOO (7, 2, 1, 6)	

THREE FOUR ALL

The object is to find two four-letter words using the letters given in each word without changing the order of the letters. For example, if the given word were PRICES, the first word might be PIES, the second might be RICE.

OINTMENT	_ _ _ _	_ _ _ _
DEBONAIR	_ _ _ _	_ _ _ _
SUGARED	_ _ _ _	_ _ _ _

PICTURE PHRASES

The images below represent three well known phrases. Look carefully and see if you can work out what they are.

1.

JACK

2.
FUNNY   FUNNY
WORDS   WORDS
WORDS   WORDS

3.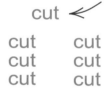
cut ←
cut   cut
cut   cut
cut   cut

SPORTS EQUIPMENT WORDSEARCH

The grid contains 13 items of sports equipment hidden vertically, horizontally or diagonally. The unused letters spell out another piece of equipment.

E	L	D	R	U	H	J	S
E	R	E	M	M	A	H	E
L	L	A	B	V	O	B	L
C	B	T	E	R	A	S	T
Y	E	L	T	T	U	H	S
C	I	S	O	I	A	O	I
N	O	N	I	T	K	E	H
P	D	I	S	C	U	S	W

BALL
BATON
CYCLE
DISCUS
HAMMER
HURDLE
JAVELIN

POST
SHOES
SHORTS
SHUTTLE
SKITTLE
WHISTLE

NOURISHING NINE

How many words of four letters or more can you track down in this game? At least one 'nourishing' word will contain all nine letters and all words must contain the central letter. Use each letter once only. No words with capital letters, foreign words, hyphens, or plurals and verb forms ending in -s are allowed.

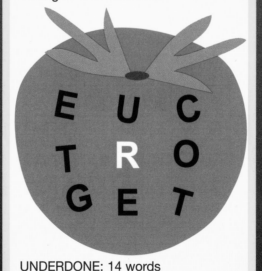

E U C
T R O
G E T

UNDERDONE: 14 words
MEDIUM: 23 words
WELL DONE: 35 words

SWEETIE TEASE

Can you work out the answer to this teaser?

Jill ate 50 sweets in five days, each day eating 3 more than on the previous day. How many sweets did she eat on each day?

DAY 1 =	DAY 2 =	DAY 3 =	DAY 4 =	DAY 5 =

KAKURO ★★★

In Kakuro the numbers in the black squares refer to the SUMS of the digits 1–9 which you are to fill into the empty spaces. The number ABOVE the diagonal line refers to the empty spaces directly to the RIGHT of that number. A number BELOW the diagonal line refers to the empty spaces directly BELOW that number. No zeros are used here and a digit can only appear once in any particular digit combination.

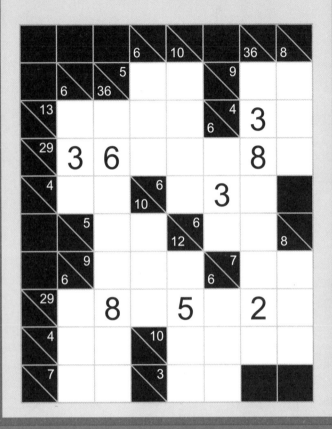

CLUB HOUSE ★★★

Hidden in the grid are six F1 racing drivers. Can you find them all?

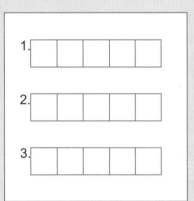

NATUREGRAMS ★★

Solve each clue, then arrange the five letters in every answer to form a set of three fish.

CLUES:
1 Yellow fossil resin
2 Listens
3 English romantic poet

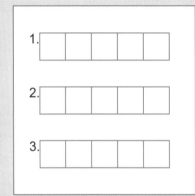

ARROWS ★

Put the following numbers in the arrows below:

2 3 4 5 6 6 7 8

Be careful though.
The total numbers in the 3 arrows pointing at each other must add up to 14.

The total numbers in the arrows which are back to back must add up to 10.

PLACE THE PLACES ★★

To solve the puzzle, place the letters from the place in capitals into the empty spaces in the grid. Four everyday words should be formed reading across the grid and three everyday words reading down.

A E G E A N

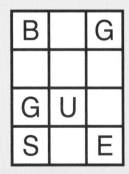

CODED CROSSWORD

Each number in the grid represents a different letter of the alphabet. Can you fill in the grid using the given letters to get you started?

Crossword grid (numbers):

6		4		2		19		16		14
19	7	7	10	18	21	11	12	19	15	2	17	23
	18		18		9		6		19		19	
11	8	22	6	10	11	2	16		8	11	8	2
			8		15		2		5		13	
24	19	8	1	17	2	1		16	19	25	2	10
	9			1		17				15		
2	26	6	19	17		1	2	2	7	2	16	15
	6		16		3		15		11			
10	11	14	16		11	8	15	2	10	20	19	17
	10		6		8		2		19		9	
10	2	25	10	11	4	2	10	19	15	18	10	16
	1		2		16		16		2		2	

Key grid:

1	2	3	4	5	6	7	8 P	9 N	10	11	12	13
14	15	16	17	18	19	20	21	22	23 R	24	25	26

NATURAL NINE

Try and become king of the jungle in this natural puzzle.
How many words of four letters or more can you track down? At least one will use all nine letters and all contain the central letter E. Use each letter once only. No words with capitals, foreign words, hyphens, or plurals are allowed.

The nine letter word is

....

PUSSYCAT STANDARD: 6 words, PANTHER STANDARD: 9 words, LION STANDARD:13 words.

NINE NUMBERS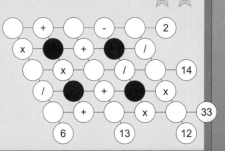

Try to fill in the missing numbers. Use the numbers 1 to 9 to complete the equations. Each number is only used once. Each row and column is an equation with the totals given below and to the right.

ODD ONE OUT

Can you spot the odd one out in this collection of letters?

E a i u t O

SUDOKU

To solve, fill in the grid so that every row, column and box contains the letters a to i.

		a		f				
c	i	d	g	e	a		h	f
						a		g
	i	f			a	g		
	a			b	e			c
d		b	h	a		f	i	e
						i		a
		d	i				e	h
i		h		g	f			d

FLOWERY PHRASES

We have described a well-known saying using flowery language. Can you uncover the more familiar form? For example, 'An eruption in the cook pot' would be 'A Flash in the pan'.

> The most accurate and reliable method of ascertaining and validating the quality and consistency of the duff category of thickened nutriments resides in the act of consumption and deglutition.

ON TARGET

Put the answers to the clues in the grid starting from the outside. Each answer has five letters and ends with the central letter D. When you've finished, the outer ring will reveal the name of a UK soccer team (7).

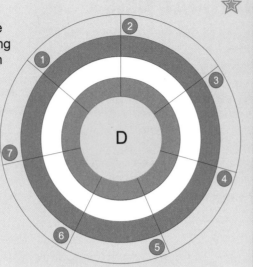

1 Swift (5)

2 Was in pain (5)

3 Nude (5)

4 Pasted (5)

5 Became more bearable (5)

6 Evaluated (5)

7 Dish of vegetables (5)

HIDDEN COLORS

To find the color, shade in the all the odd numbers.

36	50	10	16	21	34	37	24	32	14	18	46
48	6	13	44	33	26	15	22	8	12	30	38
16	2	35	4	9	27	45	12	32	38	36	14
30	52	23	14	22	6	30	36	28	20	28	20
1	19	39	26	46	32	50	47	31	7	40	38
29	2	3	2	12	40	6	17	10	41	16	34
11	25	43	34	2	18	10	5	20	19	22	42
24	4	44	4	26	8	42	18	24	28	48	8

NUMBER HEX

Can you correctly enter six numbers into the Number Hex grid using the clues below? All are whole numbers below 10 and no two numbers are the same.

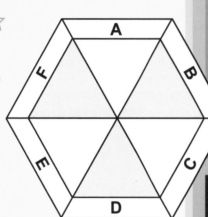

CLUES:
A is twice D
E is one third of B
F and C add up to B (C is even)
The six numbers add up to 24
E is an odd number

SUDOKU

To solve this fiendish puzzle, fill in the grid so that every row, column and box contains the numbers 1 through 9.

1				7				
	2	5	8	1	6			
	9	5				2		
			7		6			
9				5			3	
				9				4
	6				4	7	9	
			8					
7		1					2	8

ADD A LETTER

Add one letter to each word in capitals to create a new word that answers the clue. The order of the letters does not need to be changed. For example – 'I BET it's more superior' would be BEST.

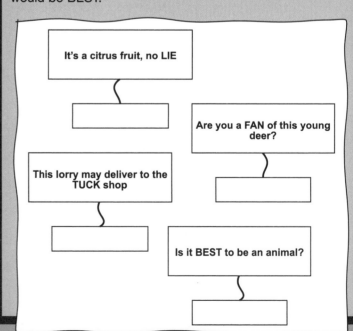

It's a citrus fruit, no LIE

Are you a FAN of this young deer?

This lorry may deliver to the TUCK shop

Is it BEST to be an animal?

PETS WORDSEARCH

The grid contains 13 pets hidden vertically, horizontally or diagonally. Can you find them all?

BUDGIE
CANARY
DOGS
DONKEY
FISH
GERBIL
HAMSTER
HORSE
KITTEN
MACAW
PARROT
PUPPY
TORTOISE

F	M	P	A	R	R	O	T
I	A	Y	E	K	N	O	D
S	C	A	N	A	R	Y	L
H	A	M	S	T	E	R	I
O	W	D	O	G	S	M	B
R	E	I	G	D	U	B	R
S	S	P	U	P	P	Y	E
E	N	E	T	T	I	K	G

KITCHEN SQUIRCLE

Put vowels in the circles and consonants in the squares to make words in all the vertical columns. Definitions of these words are given. When this has been done, the first and fifth horizontal lines will make the names of three kitchen appliances.

DEFINITIONS

1 Group of sheep
2 Long narrow hill
3 Work out from evidence
4 Consume fluids
5 Large aquatic bird
6 Precise
7 Police trainee
8 Edible organs
9 Very fat

1	2	3	4	5	6	7	8	9

CHAIN REACTION

Solve this puzzle by creating a 'chain reaction' of 20 five-letter words that run left to right, beginning in the upper-left hand corner, using the 19 two-letter tiles in the middle. A two-letter tile that ends one begins the next. Each tile will only be used once. The single letters already entered are the middle letters of the words you are to form. Start by finishing the word that begins DRA_ _.

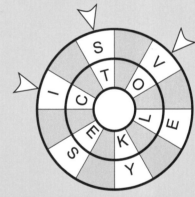

WORD FIT

Can you fit all the sea fish into the grid below?

3 letter words
Dab
Ray

4 letter words
Bass
Chad
Goby
Hake
Shad
Sild
Tuna

5 letter words
Coley
Skate
Sprat

6 letter words
Blenny
Salmon
Turbot

7 letter words
Haddock
Halibut
Sardine

8 letter words
Flounder
Mackerel

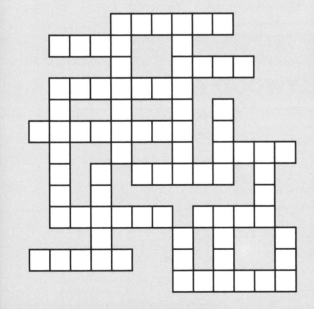

WORD WHEEL

For each of the circles, can you find two letters which, when placed in the middle, will form three six-letter words?

PLACE THE PLACES

To solve the puzzle, place the letters from the place into the empty spaces in the grid. Four everyday words should be formed, reading across the grid and three everyday words reading down.

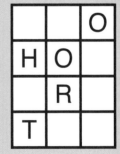

NEWPORT

SUDOKU

To solve, fill in the grid so that every row, column and box contains the numbers 1 through 9.

2	5		4	8		7		6
6	9		5			1		2
		4		6			3	5
1			6			3		9
4		7	3	1	9	2		
3	8				7	6	1	
5	3		7		8	9	6	1
8	7	1		9			4	
9	4	6	1		2	5	8	

ANAGRAM LADDERS

Solve the anagrams below to reveal the names of seven vehicles. The shaded row in the middle will then reveal the name of another mode of transport.

ROTOM
MART
RCA
CKURT
TRAC
DEPMO
ROYRL

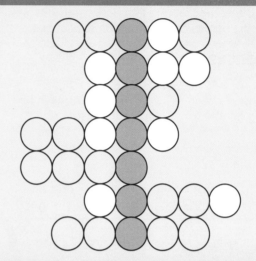

BIRD BOXES

Shade in all the consonants to reveal a hidden bird. For this puzzle, 'Y' shouldn't be considered as a vowel.

A	B	O	E	A	E	U	K	A	E	P	I
E	U	A	U	I	O	I	L	I	O	C	O
I	X	O	L	R	D	E	C	V	T	H	U
O	F	E	Y	E	F	A	U	I	E	W	E
M	S	I	B	A	P	U	E	A	O	M	A
U	A	O	C	K	J	O	I	J	X	N	E
I	E	U	Q	O	G	I	U	A	E	I	U
U	O	I	E	U	E	A	E	O	U	A	O

NINE NUMBERS ⭐⭐⭐

Each row and column is an equation with the totals given below and to the right. You must use the numbers 1 to 9 to complete the equations using each number only once.

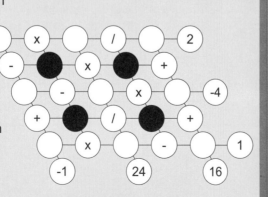

HOLLYWOOD ANAGRAMS ⭐⭐⭐

To the right are four anagrams of films or film people. The number and length of words to find are shown in brackets. The four anagram solutions are all linked in some way – can you find the link?

| ENERGY COOL EGO (6, 7) |
| LAZIER CHEWS (6, 5) |
| NOW CHEERIER POETS (5,11) |
| EEL NAG (3, 3) |

THE LINK IS .....

OPPOSITES ATTRACT

Arrange the tiles below to create two pairs of four letter words. Each pair has words with opposite meanings.

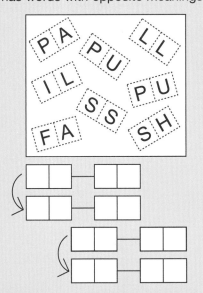

NOURISHING NINE

How many words of four letters or more can you track down in this game? At least one 'nourishing' word will contain all nine letters and all words must contain the central letter. Use each letter once only. No words with capital letters, foreign words, hyphens, or plurals and verb forms ending in -s are allowed with this puzzle.

UNDERDONE: 14 words, MEDIUM: 20 words, WELL DONE: 26 words

M R D

U C S

K I T

MOVIE HOUSE

Hidden in the grid are six Tom Cruise films. Can you find them all?

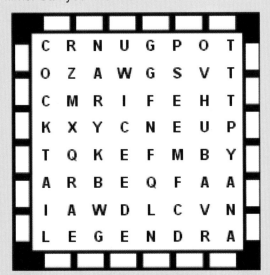

C	R	N	U	G	P	O	T
O	Z	A	W	G	S	V	T
C	M	R	I	F	E	H	T
K	X	Y	C	N	E	U	P
T	Q	K	E	F	M	B	Y
A	R	B	E	Q	F	A	A
I	A	W	D	L	C	V	N
L	E	G	E	N	D	R	A

CODED CROSSWORD

Each number in the grid represents a different letter of the alphabet. Can you fill in the grid using the given letters to get you started?

| 1 | 2 | 3 | 4 | 5 | 6 | 7 I | 8 | 9 | 10 | 11 | 12 | 13 N |
| 14 | 15 | 16 | 17 | 18 | 19 | 20 L | 21 | 22 | 23 | 24 | 25 | 26 |

LETTER SWAP

Can you replace a letter from each word with a letter from the boxes below to reveal a well known saying? Each letter is used only once.

AT NEWER RAIDS CUT IS POUTS

B V R I T N

ODD ONE OUT

Can you spot the odd one out in this sequence of words?

mouth
EAR CHIN
eye ANKLE
nose

KAKURO ⭐⭐⭐

In Kakuro the numbers in the black squares refer to the SUMS of the digits 1–9 which you are to fill into the empty spaces. The number ABOVE the diagonal line refers to the empty spaces directly to the RIGHT of that number. A number BELOW the diagonal line refers to the empty spaces directly BELOW that number. No zeros are used here and a digit can only appear once in any particular digit combination.

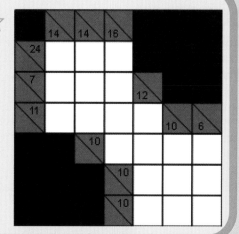

SWEET NUMBER PIC ⭐⭐⭐

Can you create a picture from the grid below? Each number represents a group of shaded squares, so for example **3 2** means that on this row there is a group of 3 black squares to the left of a group of 2 black squares, with one or more white squares in between (there must be at least one white square in between the groups.

The numbers are always in order, so **4 2** means a group of 4 black squares to the left of a group of 2 black squares in that row, and **5/3** means a block of 5 black squares above a block of 3 black squares in that column.

			1	1	1			
2	3	5	2	2	2	5	3	2

2								
3								
5								
1 1								
1 2								
4								
5								
3								
2								

CAGED ANIMALS ⭐

An animal has escaped from the zoo. To put him back in his cage answer the eight clues and put them in the grid starting from the outermost circle. When this is done the central circle, starting clockwise from number nine, will reveal the name of the animal who escaped.

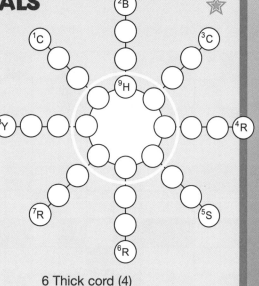

1 To block (4)
2 Shrub (4)
3 Fruit of fir or pine (4)
4 Peel (4)
5 A bullet (4)
6 Thick cord (4)
7 Wealthy (4)
8 Toy on a string (4)

NATURAL NINE ⭐⭐

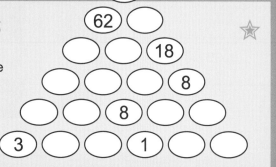

Try and become king of the jungle in this natural puzzle. How many words of four letters or more can you track down? At least one will use all nine letters and all contain the central letter T. Use each letter once only. No words with capitals, foreign words, hyphens, or plurals are allowed.

The nine letter word is...

PYRAMID OF EGGS ⭐

Fill in the eggs with numbers. The number in each egg must equal the sum of the two eggs below it.

Pyramid values: 108 / 62, (blank) / (blank), (blank), 18 / (blank), (blank), (blank), 8 / (blank), (blank), 8, (blank), (blank) / 3, (blank), (blank), 1, (blank)

FIVE SNEAKY SNAKES ⭐⭐⭐

Can you add five letters to each of the words in capitals in the snakes below, to make another word which solves the clue? For example, by adding five letters to the clue 'A revolt can make you REEL', you can make the word REBELLION. Each of the answers shares a common theme.

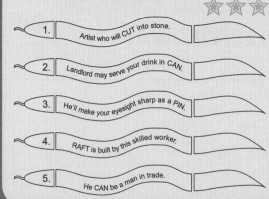

1. Artist who will CUT into stone.
2. Landlord may serve your drink in CAN.
3. He'll make your eyesight sharp as a PIN.
4. RAFT is built by this skilled worker.
5. He CAN be a man in trade.

GEOGRAMS ★★

Solve each clue, then rearrange the six letters in every answer to form a set of three cities. CLUES: 1. Emotional plays, 2. Creature, 3. Aircraft

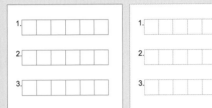

COMMON WORDS ★★★

Your task here is to determine the answers to the set of tricky definitions below, as well as the word that is contained in all five answers. For example, if the five solutions were ERRAND, TERRIBLE, MERRY MEN, PREFERRED and PERRY, the word in the central circle would be ERR.

Clues:
1 Genius
2 Taxed
3 Casablanca actor
4 Restriction
5 Choo-choos!

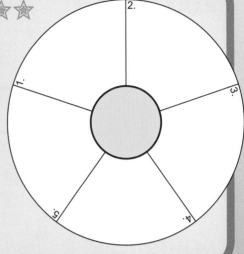

SUDOKU ★★

To solve, fill in the grid so that every row, column and box contains the numbers 1 through 9.

								2
	2			9				
5			4	7			8	
			1	3			5	8
	3			9		4	2	
				7			3	9
	8	7					4	
2			7	1	5	8		
3		6			4	2		7

ARROWS ★

Put the following numbers in the arrows below:

2 3 4 5 6 7 7 8

Be careful though. The total numbers in the three arrows pointing at each other must add up to 13.

The numbers in the arrows which are back to back must add up to 10.

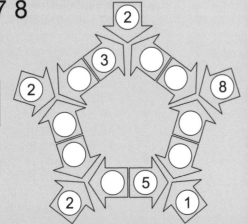

CROSSWORD ★★

Across
2 The common people (6)
5 Magnetic recording strip (4)
6 Cream cake (6)
7 Chair (4)
8 Specialist UK army regiment (3)
11 Sit for photograph (4)
13 Thinly scattered (6)
14 Scorch (4)
15 Perspires (6)

Down
1 Satisfy fully (4)
2 Encounters (5)
3 Stitched join in fabric (4)
4 Ancient copyist (6)
7 Muscle cramps (6)
9 Glasses (5)
10 Challenge (4)
12 Male deer (4)

ZOO HUNT

An animal has escaped from the zoo and is hiding somewhere in the grid. If you cross out all the letters that appear more than twice, the remaining letters will spell out the missing creature.

THE MISSING CREATURE IS A

....

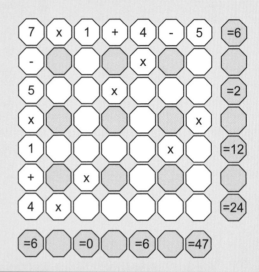

BLOCKBUSTERS

Complete the square by using each number and symbol provided in the top row ONCE only in every other row and column to equal the given answer. The first column and all the x signs have been put in to help you!

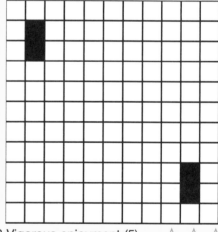

REBUS TOWER

Can you work out which common phrases are represented by each of the three diagrams in the tower below?

WAY PUBLIC

TIMING

TIM ING

TEKCIT

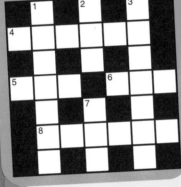

LITTLE TOUGHIE

Across

4 To exist and enjoy possessions is to be good (6)
5 Loaf for the swan (3)
6 Marines will carry a pile-driver (3)
8 Saint grows old in phases (6)

Down

1 Great regret concerning the TV detective (7)
2 It'll carry a name for chasing game (3)
3 Delayed story when sitting up in bed (7)
7 A lot of talk can be anaesthetic (3)

Across

1 Sun specs (4,7)
7 Make a point in sport (5)
8 Upright (5)
11 Feel remorse for (3)
12 Having a husky voice (6)
14 Recess in church (4)
16 Carry (4)
18 Agreement between states (6)
21 Or nearest offer (3)
22 Listens to (5)
25 Piece of garlic (5)
26 In disarray (11)

Down

1 Disastrous (4)
2 Uncommon (4)

SKELETON CROSSWORD

Below is an incomplete quick crossword grid. Can you solve the puzzle by fitting the answers to the clues correctly into the grid, along with the remaining blocks and clue numbers? A few blocks have been shaded to give you a start. This puzzle has been rotated by 180 degrees.

3 Vigorous enjoyment (5)
4 Love affair (5)
5 System of sound reproduction (6)
6 Formally withdraw (6)
9 Light tap (3)
10 American female singer (4)
13 Eyesore (4)
14 Be plentiful (6)
15 Frame once used as punishment (6)
17 Rocky hill top (3)
19 Run away to marry (5)
20 Used to refer to things nearby (5)
23 Skating jump (4)
24 Travelled very quickly (4)

ADD THREE TO THREE ⭐⭐

Can you add three letters to the three words in red below to make another word which solves the clue? For example, by adding three letters to the clue 'BAN this fruit', you can make the word BANANA.

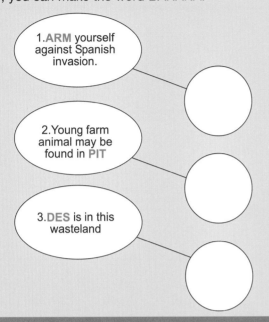

1. **ARM** yourself against Spanish invasion.

2. Young farm animal may be found in **PIT**

3. **DES** is in this wasteland

MALE ACTORS WORDSEARCH ⭐⭐

The grid contains 11 male actors hidden vertically, horizontally or diagonally. The unused letters spell out another connected word.

BURTON
CHAPLIN
CONNERY
EASTWOOD
GABLE
GRANT
HAWKINS
HOFFMAN
MASON
PACINO
PECK

```
E C O N N E R Y
N A H N O S A M
A G S A I N E K
M A R T P C W C
F B M A W L A E
F L A N N O I P
O E B U R T O N
H A W K I N S D
```

LETTER STEW ⭐

Use all the given letters in the stew to spell three words meaning bad.

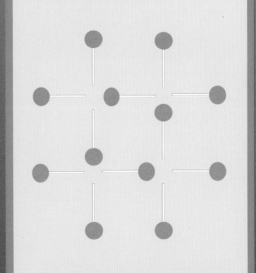

W
E O K E
C I L R D
I V P O

ADD A LETTER ⭐

Add one letter to each word in capitals to create a new word that answers the clue. The orders of the letters does not need to be changed.

For example – 'I BET it's more superior' would be BEST.

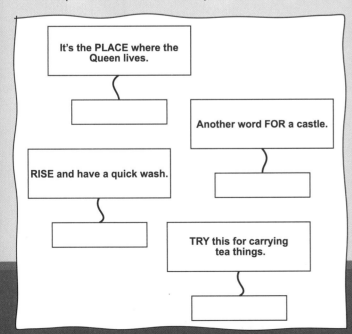

It's the PLACE where the Queen lives.

Another word FOR a castle.

RISE and have a quick wash.

TRY this for carrying tea things.

LOLLIPOPS ⭐

By moving three of the lollipops below can you make three equal sided squares?

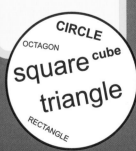

ODD ONE OUT ⭐

Can you spot the odd one out in this selection of words?

CIRCLE
OCTAGON
square cube
triangle
RECTANGLE

MATCHING PAIR

Only two of the pictures below match exactly, the others are different. Can you find the matching pair?

1. 2. 3.
4. 5. 6.

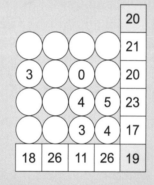

DIZZY DICTATION

Jeff's new secretary is having some trouble with dictation. Can you work out what he is trying to say in the following sentences?

1. HALVE EWE SCENE THERE SUNS WILED GNU HARE STILE?

2. CHEEP SHOOS MITE CAWS SOAR FEAT.

3. WHETHER FORK ASTERS GUEST THEIR WOOD BEE REIN HAY, LANDS NO.

ADDING GRIDS

Place any digits 0 to 9 into the empty circles. When complete each row should add up to the figures on the right and each column to the figures below. The shaded numbers are the total of the diagonal circles.

				20
				21
3		0		20
		4	5	23
	3	4	17
18	26	11	26	19

GEOGRAMS

Solve each clue, then rearrange the five letters in each answer to form three rivers.
CLUES: 1 Mass of bubbles, 2 One who lubricates, 3 Written proposals

1. ☐☐☐☐☐   1. ☐☐☐☐☐
2. ☐☐☐☐☐   2. ☐☐☐☐☐
3. ☐☐☐☐☐   3. ☐☐☐☐☐

A'MAZE'ING NUMBERS

Try to make your way through the maze. The number at the beginning of each row and column tells you exactly how many squares you will have to cross through in order to reach the finish. No diagonal moves are allowed.

Solving hint: To begin, shade any box that you determine will not be used, and place a dot in any box that you know must be used.

SUDOKU

To solve, fill in the grid so that every row, column and box contains the numbers 1 through 9.

	7				8	2		
		5						
9			5	1	6			7
				2	3		6	9
		7		8		1		
	3							
						9	3	5
	8			5			7	6

CROSSWORD

Across

1 Believed likely (9)

6 People from the Middle East (5)

7 Termite (3)

8 Dismiss (4)

10 Writing implements (4)

13 Kick with front of foot (3)

14 Bulb used in cooking (5)

16 Level lines (9)

Down

1 Makes tight (5)

2 Mediterranean for instance (3)

3 Loosen the tension (4)

4 To track down (5)

5 Pen point (3)

9 Shout of encouragement (5)

11 Vocal performances (5)

12 A score in soccer (4)

13 Summit (3)

15 Frozen water (3)

HIDDEN COLORS

Shade in all the numbers that can be divided exactly by four to reveal a hidden color.

19	26	11	22	25	39	9	5	43	37	44	2
48	8	28	42	34	6	17	31	27	34	12	11
4	1	33	18	23	41	22	39	10	1	20	14
40	38	41	24	12	8	31	14	4	32	28	38
24	25	2	8	17	6	26	35	20	30	32	27
16	13	21	40	36	16	18	3	36	24	12	29
30	21	7	4	29	9	42	10	15	17	15	35
13	37	19	20	28	16	33	23	5	7	43	3

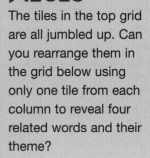

DANCE NUMBER PIC

Can you create a picture from the grid below? Each number represents a group of shaded squares, so for example **3 2** means that on this row there is a group of 3 black squares to the left of a group of 2 black squares, with one or more white squares in between (there must be at least one white square in between the groups.

The numbers are always in order, so **4 2** means a group of 4 black squares to the left of a group of 2 black squares in that row, and **5** means a block of 5 black squares above a **3** block of 3 black squares in that column.

BITS AND PIECES

The tiles in the top grid are all jumbled up. Can you rearrange them in the grid below using only one tile from each column to reveal four related words and their theme?

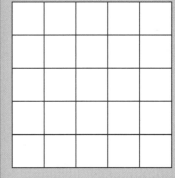

B	F	S	I	LL
T	LO	FO	E	L
CO	W	L	BE	IP
F	L	W	L	P
DA	U	UE	DI	RS

NOURISHING NINE

How many words of four letters or more can you track down in this game? At least one word will contain all nine letters and all words must contain the central letter. Use each letter once only. No words with capital letters, foreign words, hyphens, or plurals and verb forms ending in -s are allowed.

UNDERDONE: 9 words, MEDIUM: 14 words, WELL DONE: 19 words

(Dance Number Pic grid with column clues 3,3,2/3/2,1/1,1,8,1,1,5,1/1,2/2 and row clues across the top: 1 3 3 / 1 1 1 1 1 3 / 3 1 3 1 8 1 3 1 1 0)

CODED CROSSWORD ★★★

Each number in the grid represents a different letter of the alphabet. Can you fill in the grid using the given letters to get you started?

	4		12		12		25		2		6	
21	23	10	15	5	21	10	7	6	21	13	13	19
	7		20		16		9		17		15	
21	10	10	7	10	23	8	26		2	13	23	26
			16		21		25		26		8	
8	21	16	22	26	17	25		8	17	21	7	16
	10			19		2				16		
25	3	26	26	14		14	21	6	20	21	22	26
	13		24		25		17		16			
8	26	26	14		11	21	17	17	7	15	17	25
	10		26		7		7		18		7	
6	7	17	6	23	5	1	26	17	26	16	6	26
	6		10		25		17		25		26	

1	2	3	4	5	6	7	8	9	10 T	11	12	13
14	15 O	16 N	17	18	19	20 K	21	22	23	24	25	26

ADD A LETTER ★

Add one letter to each word in capitals to create a new word that answers the clue.

For example - 'I BET it's more superior' would be BEST.

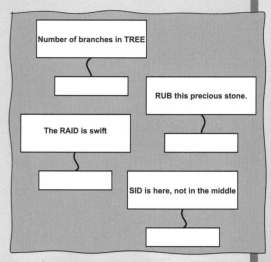

Number of branches in TREE

RUB this precious stone

The RAID is swift

SID is here, not in the middle

JIG GRID ★★★

Can you fit the blocks back into the grid to reveal, reading from left to right, seven tools?

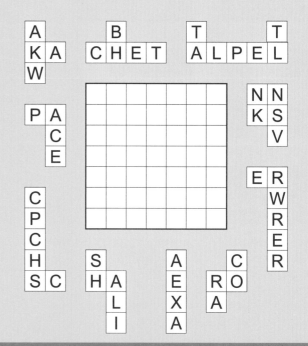

A K A / W
B / C H E T
T A L P E L / T
P A C E
C P C H S
N K / N N S V
E R W R E R
S H A L I
A E X A
C R O / R A

COUNTING CRITTERS ★

Can you find the number that is represented by each animal face? You will find the total of the numbers below each column and to the right of each row.

spider	pig	dog	pig	dog	50
owl	owl	dog	owl	pig	90
spider	cat	cat	cat	spider	85
cat	pig	pig	cat	cat	65
spider	spider	dog	pig	spider	75
100	80	40	75	70	

dog =
cat =
owl =
spider =
pig =

OCCUPATIONS ★★★

How many words of four letters or more can you track down in this game? At least one will be a nine letter occupation and all contain the central letter. Use each letter once only. No words with capitals, foreign words, hyphens, or plurals and verb forms ending in -s are allowed.

GOOD: 8 words
VERY GOOD: 13 words
EXCELLENT: 18 words

S I Y
H C N
I A P

SUDOKU ⭐

To solve, fill in the grid so that every row, column and box contains the numbers 1 through 9.

2	5			7	8			
3	7	6	5	4	9	2	8	1
9	4	8	1			7	5	3
	9	3			7			2
4		2	9	1				6
	1			2	6	8		
7	2	5	6	3	1	9	4	
8	3	4	2					
1	6	9	7	8	4	3		5

PAIR WHEELS ⭐

Place each of the twelve pairs of letters into one of the circles in the grid, so that every line running through the central circle gives you a six-letter word with the middle letters RE.

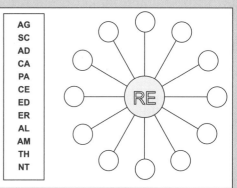

AG
SC
AD
CA
PA
CE
ED
ER
AL
AM
TH
NT

CHAIN REACTION ⭐⭐⭐

Solve this puzzle by creating a 'chain reaction' of 20 five-letter words that run left to right, beginning in the upper-left hand corner, using the 19 two-letter tiles in the middle. A two-letter tile that ends one begins the next. Each tile is only used once. The single letters already entered are the middle letters of the words you are to form. Start by finishing the word that begins BAL_ _.

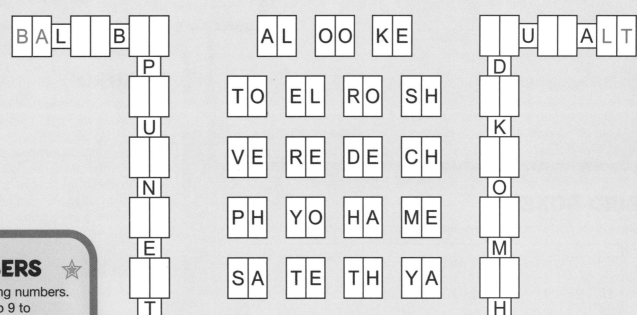

NINE NUMBERS ⭐

Try to fill in the missing numbers. Use the numbers 1 to 9 to complete the equations. Each number is only used once. Each row and column is an equation with the totals given below and to the right.

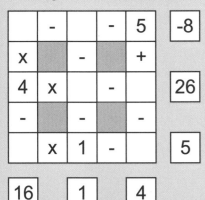

KAKURO ⭐⭐

In Kakuro the numbers in the black squares refer to the SUMS of the digits 1–9 which you are to fill into the empty spaces. The number ABOVE the diagonal line refers to the empty spaces directly to the RIGHT of that number. A number BELOW the diagonal line refers to the empty spaces directly BELOW that number. No zeros are used here and a digit can only appear once in any particular digit combination.

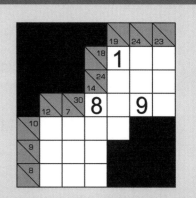

NINE NUMBERS

Try to fill in the missing numbers.
Use the numbers 1 to 9 to complete the equations. Each number is only used once. Each row and column is an equation with the totals given below and to the right.

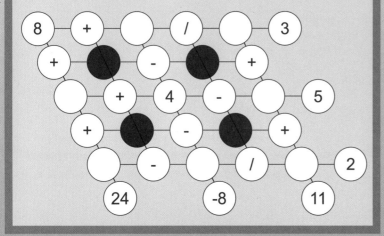

ARROWS

Put the following numbers in the arrows below:

1 1 1 2 2 2 3 3

Be careful though.
The numbers in the three arrows pointing at each other must add up to 8.

The numbers in the arrows which are back to back must add up to 4.

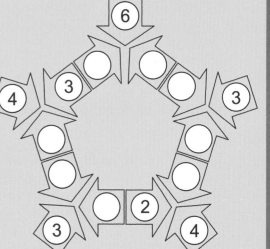

NUMBER HEX

Can you correctly enter six numbers into the Number Hex grid using the clues below? All are whole numbers below 10 and no two numbers are the same.
CLUES: The top half of the grid adds up to 14, Half of the numbers are odd, None of the numbers is greater than 7, E is the same as the number of sides on a square, B is the number of toes on a foot, F is a pair, D is not 1.

KAKURO

In Kakuro the numbers in the black squares refer to the SUMS of the digits 1–9 which you are to fill into the empty spaces. The number ABOVE the diagonal line refers to the empty spaces directly to the RIGHT of that number. A number BELOW the diagonal line refers to the empty spaces directly BELOW that number. No zeros are used here and a digit can only appear once in any particular digit combination.

BIRD BOXES

Shade in all the numbers whose digits add up to 10 to reveal a hidden bird.

73	37	64	20	14	55	91	28	33	13	92	15
15	28	11	17	34	73	43	29	44	20	11	47
30	91	40	18	12	46	16	32	14	45	17	35
21	39	37	19	28	42	30	28	37	64	73	13
12	22	91	17	41	12	26	37	48	21	55	51
21	31	64	55	27	22	16	19	18	50	91	16
27	13	73	38	14	36	31	46	49	25	64	62
15	29	28	82	46	24	11	20	35	17	32	12

MATCH STICKS

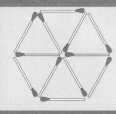

Can you make three equilateral triangles out of the shape on the left by moving just four matches?

WORD FIT

Can you fit all the office items into the grid below?

3 letter words
Pad
Pen

4 letter words
Desk
File
Glue
Pins

5 letter words
Board
Label
Punch
Ruler
Stamp

6 letter words
Binder
Crayon

Ledger
Marker
Rubber
Wallet

7 letter words
Stapler
Stencil

8 letter word
Adhesive

WORD SPLITZ

Each row of ten letters can be split into two five-letter money words. These words read from left to right and are in order. For example, SMOKOSUENK can be split to reveal SKUNK and MOOSE.

① D F I R N A A R N C

② K K R O O P N E K A

③ P R O U U P N D E E

④ P C E E N N N T Y S

PLACE THE PLACES

To solve the puzzle, place the letters from the place in capitals into the empty spaces in the grid. Four everyday words should be formed reading across the grid and three everyday words reading down.

O R I E N T

B		B
		E
A	T	
	A	

ALPHABET SUDOKU

To solve, fill in the grid so that every row, column and box contains the letters a to i.

	c			h	b	f		
		h					d	e
	b		e	a		h		
		a	g	b	h			f
h		d	e	i	g	b		
							i	
b		e			f		g	d
d		i			b			
c				a				e

WORD WALL

Make your way up the wall by changing one letter at a time until you reach the top word.

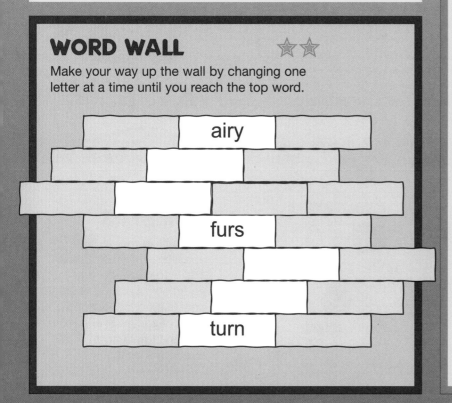

airy

furs

turn

QUICK QUIZ QUESTIONS ⭐⭐

Can you get all of these quiz questions correct?

WHAT ARE THESE PHOBIAS OF?	
1. DEMENTOPHOBIA ?	
2. ACROPHOBIA ?	
3. CLAUSTROPHOBIA ?	
4. CHRONOPHOBIA ?	
5. ARACHNOPHOBIA ?	
6. ZEUSOPHOBIA ?	

CODED CROSSWORD ⭐⭐⭐

Each number in the grid represents a different letter of the alphabet. Can you fill in the grid using the given letters to get you started?

1	2	3	4	5	6	7	8	9	10 L	11	12	13
14	15	16	17 R	18	19	20	21	22 C	23	24	25	26

ZOO HUNT ⭐

An animal has escaped from the zoo and is hiding somewhere in the grid. If you cross out all the letters that appear more than twice, the remaining letters will spell out the missing creature.
THE MISSING CREATURE IS AN …………………..............

```
    C           E
 G  L  K  E  G  M  I
 F  B  ●  M  ●  C  P
G H  I  F  B  O  A  R  F
 K  O  C  ▪  I  R  B
    R  N  O  K  C
       M  B  T
```

NOURISHING NINE ⭐⭐

How many words of four letters or more can you track down in this game? At least one 'nourishing' word will contain all nine letters and all words must contain the central letter. Use each letter once only. No words with capital letters, foreign words, hyphens, or plurals and verb forms ending in -s are allowed.

UNDERDONE: 13 words, MEDIUM: 20 words, WELL DONE: 27 words

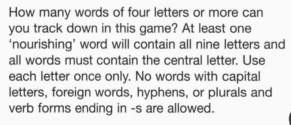

I C I S
H P S
A T O

SUDOKU ⭐

To solve, fill in the grid so that every row, column and box contains the numbers 1 through 9.

9			5	2	6	8	1	
1	7	8			3		2	
5	2	6		8	1		4	9
3	9		8		4	1	7	6
8	1	5		6	7	4		
7			1	9	2	5	3	8
4		2		8	7			3
2	3			5				
6	8	7	4	3	9		5	1

NINE NUMBERS ⭐⭐

Try to fill in the missing numbers. Use the numbers 1 to 9 to complete the equations. Each number is only used once. Each row and column is an equation with the totals given below and to the right.

NURSERY BLOCKS

Rearrange each column of letters and write them in the grid to reveal the first two lines of a well known nursery rhyme. Some of the letters have been put in to give you a head start.

	J				S			T		
F			.					W		
				L			.			

```
            A
  U         A A
O U L K   E N R   N O
C A T C D H I P T I F
C O A L D E E S T A N O E
```

SOUNDS WORDSEARCH

```
L T Q S I G H N
L W O H N G P A
E C H O N O U O
Y E M I H C R M
E E R O N S R T
L P E A L E O I
P B A W L L A C
Q W K R A B R K
```

The grid contains 20 sounds hidden vertically, horizontally or diagonally. Can you find them all?

BARK	HOWL	SNORE
BAWL	MOAN	SNORT
BLARE	PEAL	TICK
CALL	PURR	WHINE
CHIME	RING	YELL
ECHO	ROAR	YELP
HOOT	SIGH	

WORD WHEEL

For each of the circles, can you find two letters which, when placed in the middle, will form three six-letter words?

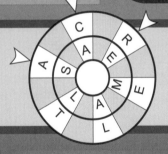
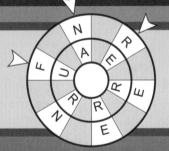

COUNTING CRITTERS

Can you find the number that is represented by each animal face? You will find the total of the numbers below each column and to the right of each row.

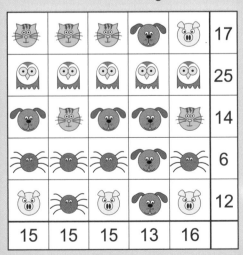

					17
					25
					14
					6
					12
15	15	15	13	16	

🐶 =
🐱 =
🦉 =
🕷 =
🐷 =

HOLLYWOOD ANAGRAMS

Below are four anagrams of films or film people. The number and length of words to find are shown in brackets. The four anagram solutions are all linked in some way – can you find the link?

ALLEY LOUT VAC (4, 8)		
HEADHUNTED SOFA (5, 2, 3, 4)	THE LINK IS	
MONTHLY FLUTE (3, 4, 5)		
GRAVEL HAS OWL (7, 5)		

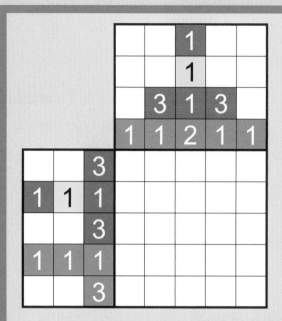

LITTLE FLOWER NUMBER ⭐⭐

Can you create a picture from the grid to the left?

Each number represents a group of shaded squares, so for example `3` `2` means that on this row there is a group of 3 red squares to the left of a group of 2 green squares. The numbers are always in order, so `4` `2` means a group of 4 red squares to the left of a group of 2 green squares in that row, and `5` means a block of 5 green `3` squares above a block of 3 red squares in that column. Groups of squares of the same color cannot be in adjacent squares.

STEP LADDER ⭐

Starting with the top word, change one letter at a time to make a new word at every step until you have reached the bottom word.

HAND

BOND

FOOT

NINE NUMBERS ⭐

Try to fill in the missing numbers. Use the numbers 1 to 9 to complete the equations. Each number is only used once. Each row and column is an equation with the totals given below and to the right.

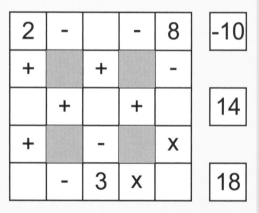

CROSSWORD ⭐

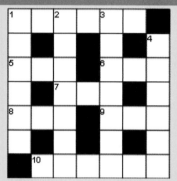

Across
1 Edible shellfish (6)
5 Grow old (3)
6 Rocky ridge (3)
7 Perform on stage (3)
8 An age (3)
9 Young man (3)
10 Academic award (6)

Down
1 A building for worship (6)
2 To remove dirt from (7)
3 Relatively small (7)
4 Walk heavily (6)

BITS AND PIECES ⭐⭐⭐

The tiles in the top grid are all jumbled up. Can you rearrange them in the grid below using only one tile from each column to reveal four related words and their theme?

GE	A	ST	HI	D
S	M	A	O	Z
T	ER	PP	ON	RE
EM	O	AM	L	ND
D	I	P	A	ES

KAKURO ⭐⭐

In Kakuro the numbers in the black squares refer to the SUMS of the digits 1–9 which you are to fill into the empty spaces. The number ABOVE the diagonal line refers to the empty spaces directly to the RIGHT of that number. A number BELOW the diagonal line refers to the empty spaces directly BELOW that number. No zeros are used here and a digit can only appear once in any particular digit combination.

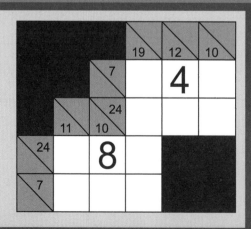

PAIR WHEELS

Place each of the 12 pairs of letters into one of the circles in the grid, so that every line running through the central circle gives you a six-letter word with the middle letters LO.

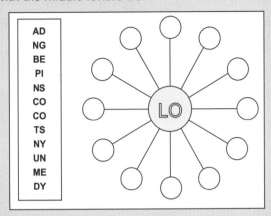

AD
NG
BE
PI
NS
CO
CO
TS
NY
UN
ME
DY

WORD SPLITZ

Each row of ten letters can be split into two five letter countries. These words read from left to right and are in order. For example SMOKOSUENK can be split to reveal SKUNK and MOOSE.

① I I T N A D L Y I A

② J B U A R P A M N A

③ G L I H B A Y N A A

④ M Y A E L M T A E N

COMMON WORDS

Your task here is to determine the answers to each set of tricky definitions below, as well as the word that is contained in all five of the set's answers. For example, if the five solutions were ERRAND, TERRIBLE, MERRY MEN, PREFERRED and PERRY, the word in the central circle would be ERR.

CLUES:
1 Badgers
2 Repair
3 Bizet opera
4 Short time
5 Basic

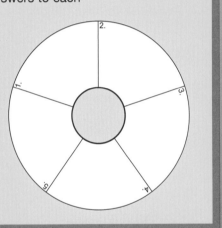

OCCUPATIONS ★★★

How many words of four letters or more can you track down in this game? At least one will be a nine letter occupation and all contain the central letter. Use each letter once only. No words with capitals, foreign words, hyphens, or plurals and verb forms ending in -s are allowed.

GOOD: 11 words, VERY GOOD: 16 words, EXCELLENT: 21 words

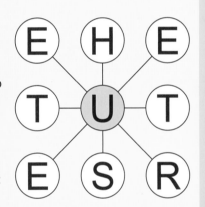

CHAIN REACTION ★★★

Solve this puzzle by creating a 'chain reaction' of 20 five-letter words that run left to right, beginning in the upper-left hand corner, using the 19 two-letter tiles in the middle. A two-letter tile that ends one begins the next. Each tile will only be used once. The single letters already entered are the middle letters of the words you are to form. Start by finishing the word that begins RUC_ _.

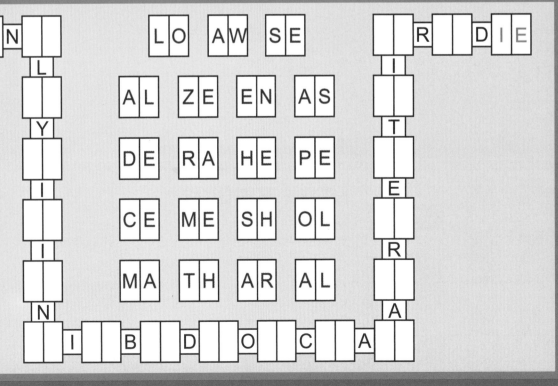

FIVE SNEAKY SNAKES ⭐⭐⭐

Can you add five letters to each of the words in capitals in the snakes below, to make another word which solves the clue? For example, by adding five letters to the clue 'A revolt can make you REEL', you can make the word REBELLION. Each of the answers share a common theme.

1. Game played by workers at the MINT.
2. Riding on this you'll hear a ROAR of waves.
3. Keeper covers the GAPS between these two.
4. RON is on the American football pitch.
5. Horses NIP round in this type of race.

NATURE TRAIL ⭐

Find the plant that is growing inside the tree by removing all the letters that appear more than twice.

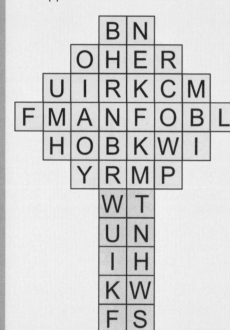

THE HIDDEN PLANT IS A

....

ADD THREE TO THREE

Can you add three letters to the three words in red below to make another word which solves the clue? For example, by adding three letters to the clue 'BAN this fruit' you can make the word BANANA. ⭐⭐

1. Is it a **BIG** part of your nose?
2. Find a small antelope in a **GALE**.
3. **MET** a shooting-star.

REBUS TOWER ⭐⭐⭐

Can you work out which common phrases are represented by each of the three diagrams in the tower?

COAST

COAST
COAST

DAY   THE

KIDNEY

LUNG

HEART   HOME

LITTLE TOUGHIE ⭐⭐⭐

Across
2 Footballer in reverse (4)
4 Get hot in the sun like a loafer? (4)
5 Stick on the edges of a highway (4)
6 Second-grade beer offered in a package (4)
7 In tree, koala causes a stink (4)
8 Sort of end that's over in days (4)

Down
1 Get a man prepared to be a tycoon! (7)
2 You lose control to go like this (7)
3 Part of the union book? (7)

NATURAL NINE

Try and become king of the jungle in this natural puzzle. How many words of four letters or more can you track down? At least one will use all nine letters and all contain the central letter U. Use each letter once only. No words with capitals, foreign words, hyphens, or plurals are allowed.

The nine letter word is ....

PUSSYCAT STANDARD: 7 words,
PANTHER STANDARD: 12 words,
LION STANDARD: 18 words.

A'MAZE'ING NUMBERS

Try to make your way through the maze. The number at the beginning of each row and column tells you exactly how many squares you will have to cross though in order to reach the finish. No diagonal moves are allowed.

Solving hint: To begin, blacken any box that you determine will not be used, and place a dot in any box that you know must be used.

	9	1	1	1	5	1	5	9
4								
3								
3								
3								
5								
3								
3								
3								
6								

SKELETON CROSSWORD

Below is an incomplete quick crossword grid. Can you solve the puzzle by fitting the answers to the clues correctly into the grid, along with the remaining blocks and clue numbers? A few blocks have been shaded to give you a start. This puzzle has been rotated by 180 degrees.

Across

1   Harass (9)
8   To become less in intensity (5)
9   Distinct step in development (5)
10 Pastry dish (3)
11 Exams (5)
13 Asparagus shoot (5)
15 Mislays (5)
18 Dismisses (5)
20 Tap with the hand (3)
21 The outward form (5)
22 Variegated form of quartz (5)
23 Employees of an organisation (9)

Down

2   Written tests (5)
3   Small portable ladder (5)
4   Articles of luggage (5)
5   To playfully vex (5)
6   Lacking flavour (9)
7   Feeling miserable (9)
12 Kick with front of foot (3)
14 Seed eaten as vegetable (3)
16 Hue (5)
17 Glasses (5)
18 Discoloring mark (5)
19 Wooden box (5)

TRUE OR FALSE WORDSEARCH

The grid contains 13 words meaning false, hidden vertically, horizontally or diagonally. The unused letters spell out another related word.

BAFFLE
BUNK
CHARADE
DISGUISE
DUPE
FAKE
FANTASY
FARCE
GARBLE
ILLUSION
MYTH
PRETENCE
PRETEXT

E	C	H	A	R	A	D	E
C	H	T	Y	M	E	A	S
N	O	I	S	U	L	L	I
E	C	R	A	F	B	E	U
T	X	E	T	E	R	P	G
E	B	U	N	K	A	U	S
R	C	T	A	A	G	D	I
P	B	A	F	F	L	E	D

PYRAMID OF BRICKS

Fill in the bricks with numbers. Each brick must equal the sum of the two bricks directly below it.

```
            66
         35
      [ ]    14
   [ ]   9
 [ ]   4
[ ]  3   [ ]  2
```

ANAGRAM LADDERS

Solve the anagrams below to reveal the names of seven car parts. The shaded row in the middle will then reveal the name of another part of a car.

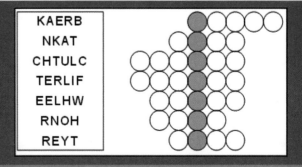

KAERB
NKAT
CHTULC
TERLIF
EELHW
RNOH
REYT

SUDOKU

To solve, fill in the grid so that every row, column and box contains the letters A through I.

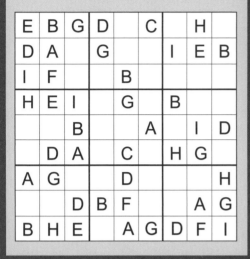

E	B	G	D		C		H	
D	A		G			I	E	B
I	F			B				
H	E	I		G		B		
		B			A		I	D
	D	A		C		H	G	
A	G			D				H
		D	B	F			A	G
B	H	E		A	G	D	F	I

BLOCKBUSTERS

Complete the square by using each number and symbol provided in the top row ONCE only in every other row and column to equal the given answer. The first column and all the x signs have been put in to give you a start!

4	+	5	x	2	-	7	=11
-				x			
2	x						=15
x							
7			x				=17
+		x				x	
5					x		=40
=19		=16		=6		=16	

NATUREGRAMS

Solve each clue, then rearrange the five letters in every answer to form a set of three birds.

CLUES:

1 Italian opera composer

2 Express a welcome

3 Vertebral column

1.

2.

3.

1.

2.

3.

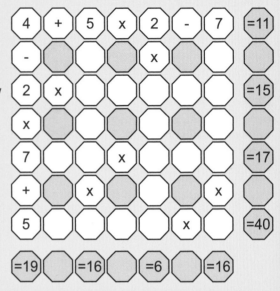

CODED CROSSWORD

Each number in the grid represents a different letter of the alphabet. Can you fill in the grid using the given letters to get you started?

26	6	13	19	7	17		25	7	16	6	2	10
12		1		9		13		20		5		3
2	20	13	22	22	12	2		13	15	15	20	6
6		19		12		2		4		20		18
20	25	4	23	6		25	15	6	19	13	10	6
17				22		18				12		22
	18	9	20	10	12	15	20	17	12	26	23	
26		26				13		25				14
13	11	19	12	2	13	26		23	13	9	23	6
19		25		9		12		3		26		7
19	9	20	6	19		6	24	9	13	10	25	19
25		20		8		4		19		12		13
1	13	22	3	6	4		22	10	13	20	21	22

1	2	3	4	5	6	7	8	9	10	11	12	13
14	15	16	17	18	19	20	21	22	23	24	25	26

EURO TEASE

Can you work out the answer to this teaser?

You have 20 coins to share between 4, following these rules:

- There has to be an even number of coins in each hand.
- The first hand must have twice as many coins as the second.
- The first hand must have the most coins.
- The last hand has less than 5 coins.

Each hand has a different number of coins.

How many coins are in each hand?

HAND 1	HAND 2	HAND 3	HAND 4

 Solutions start on page 189

ARROWS

Put the following numbers in the arrows:

1 1 2 2 2 2 3 3

The total numbers in the 3 arrows pointing at each other must add up to 6.

The total numbers in the arrows which are back to back must add up to 4.

EDIBLE EIGHT

How many words of four letters or more can you track down in this game? At least one 'nourishing' word will contain all eight letters and all words must contain the central letter V. Use each letter once only. No words with capital letters, foreign words, hyphens, or plurals and verb forms ending in -s are allowed.

UNDERDONE: 9 words
MEDIUM: 16 words
WELL DONE: 20 words

RIDDLE WORDS

Can you answer these word riddles with insects?

? Which insect is also a slang term for food?

? Which insect could also be a fault in a machine?

? Which insect is found when you go on a plane?

? Which insect is a mark given for correct work?

ODD ONE OUT

Can you spot the odd one out in this sequence of soccer teams?

Arsenal
REAL MADRID
CHELSEA
ASTON VILLA
Liverpool
Everton

PICTURE PHRASES

The images below represent four well known phrases. Look carefully and see if you can work out what they are.

1. SHCRYAME

2. ICE³

3. BIG BIG IGNORE IGNORE

4. LANGU4AGE

JIG GRID

Can you fit the blocks back into the grid to reveal, reading from left to right, seven musical instruments?

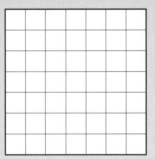

MARA / ANP

CAS / IPE

PIPE / BELL

L / CCOLO

P / BAG / OW

C / WHI / UKU / PI

STLE / ELE

BOOT NUMBER

⭐⭐

Can you create a picture from the grid below? Each number represents a group of shaded squares, so for example **3 2** means that on this row there is a group of 3 black squares to the left of a group of 2 black squares, with one or more white squares in between (there must be at least one white square in-between the groups).

The numbers are always in order, so **4 2** means a group of 4 black squares to the left of a group of 2 black squares in that row, and **5** means a block of 5 black squares above a **3** block of 3 black squares in that column.

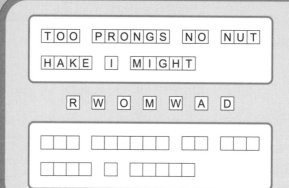

ON TARGET

⭐

Put the answers to the clues in the grid starting from the outside. Each answer has five letters and ends with the central letter T. When you've finished the outer ring, it will reveal the name of a UK soccer team (7).

1 The seaside (5)
2 Vital organ (5)
3 A wading bird (5)
4 The smallest amount (5)
5 To move (5)
6 To burst forth like a volcano (5)
7 Concerning (5)

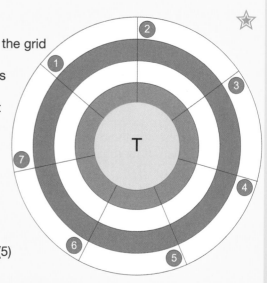

LETTER SWAP

⭐

Can you replace a letter from each word with a letter from the boxes to reveal a well known saying? Each letter is used only once.

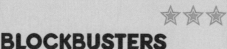

| T O O | P R O N G S | N O | N U T |
| H A K E | I | M I G H T |

| R | W | O | M | W | A | D |

BITS AND PIECES

⭐⭐⭐

The tiles in the top grid are all jumbled up. Can you rearrange them in the grid below using only one tile from each column to reveal four related words and their theme?

OL	E	LE	PI	ER
CE	I	M	V	Y
M	Y	DA	N	E
S	RE	L	L	CS
A	TH	MO	T	S

BLOCKBUSTERS

⭐⭐⭐

Complete the square by using each number and symbol provided in the top row ONCE only in every other row and column to equal the given answer. The first column and all the - signs have been put in to give you a start!

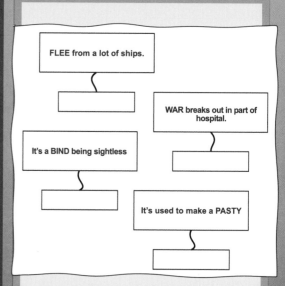

ADD A LETTER

⭐

Add one letter to each word in capitals to create a new word that answers the clue. The orders of the letters does not need to be changed.

For example - 'I BET it's more superior' would be BEST.

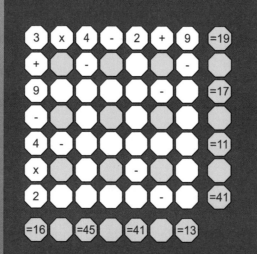

FLEE from a lot of ships.

WAR breaks out in part of hospital.

It's a BIND being sightless.

It's used to make a PASTY

CROSSWORD

Across
1 Startle (8)
6 Non-commissioned officer (3)
7 Paved area beside house (5)
9 Perceived (4)
11 Farewell (2-2)
12 Number in a baseball team (4)
14 Protected bird (4)
16 Monetary unit of India (5)
18 To mimic (3)
19 Rued (8)

Down
1 Hygienic (8)
2 Perch (5)
3 Thick cord (4)
4 Posed (3)
5 Part of face (8)
8 First name of female Russian tennis star (4)
10 Loosen the tension (4)
13 Inappropriate (5)
15 Used to be (4)
17 Pastry dish (3)

LOLLIPOPS

By removing three of the lollipops in the grid below can you make three identical squares?

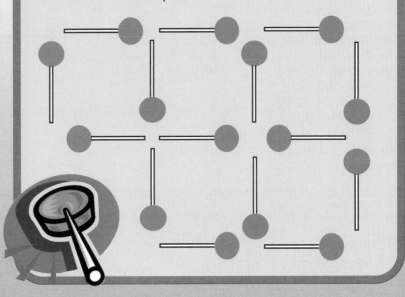

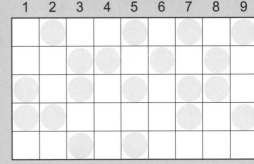

FLOWERY PHRASES

We have described a well-known saying using flowery language. Can you uncover the more familiar form? For example, 'An eruption in the cook pot' would be 'A Flash in the pan'.

> **The spatiotemporal measurements that include the categories of hebdomad and chiliad, and the periodic variations of the hydrospheric areas of the earth caused by lunar gravitational effect, are not known to remain inactive or to hesitate at all in their progression or movement for any known adult male member of the human species.**

CAGED ANIMALS

An animal has escaped from the zoo. To put him back in his cage answer the eight clues and put them in the grid starting from the outermost circle.
When this is done the central circle starting clockwise from number nine will reveal the name of the animal who escaped.

1 Large animal (4)
2 Miss Ford, UK news presenter (4)
3 End of a prayer (4)
4 Female relative (4)
5 Competent (4)
6 District, region (4)
7 A direction (4)
8 Painful (4)

FAMOUS BATTLES SQUIRCLE

Put vowels in the circles and consonants in the squares to make words in all the vertical columns. Definitions of these words are given. When this has been done, the first and third horizontal lines will make the names of two battles.

DEFINITIONS

1 Avarice
2 Permit
3 Depart
4 Cheerful tunes
5 Angry
6 Light footwear
7 Large sea
8 Landowner
9 Interior

	1	2	3	4	5	6	7	8	9

PAIR WHEELS ⭐⭐

Place each of the twelve pairs of letters into one of the circles in the grid, so that every line running through the central circle gives you a six-letter word with the middle letters TT.

BU
LA
ON
EN
EE
OM
SE
ER
BO
LE
KI
BA

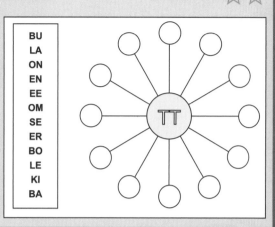
TT

NINE NUMBERS ⭐

Try to fill in the missing numbers. Use the numbers 1 to 9 to complete the equations. Each number is only used once. Each row and column is an equation with the totals given below and to the right.

2	x		-	-6
x		-		-	
6	-		x		10
/		x		x	19
	+	7	+	

| 4 | -21 | 27 |

CHAIN REACTION ⭐⭐⭐

Solve this puzzle by creating a 'chain reaction' of 20 five-letter words that run left to right, beginning in the upper-left hand corner, using the 19 two-letter tiles in the middle. A two-letter tile that ends one begins the next. Each tile will only be used once. The single letters already entered are the middle letters of the words you are to form. Start by finishing the word that begins PAG_ _.

P A G | | G | |

DE | TO | NE

| G | PSY

A
A
L
I
U

R
T
L
A
E

GE | LO | ST | SO
CH | AN | GY | TA
GA | AP | HA | SE
CE | TE | AL | SH

| E | I | P | P | S | A

PLACE THE PLACES ⭐⭐

To solve this one, place the letters from the place in capitals into the empty spaces in the grid. Four everyday words should be formed reading across the grid and three everyday words reading down.

S		
	I	
	D	D
Y	E	

ATHENS

NATURAL NINE ⭐

Try and become king of the jungle in this natural puzzle. How many words of four letters or more can you track down? At least one will use all nine letters and all contain the central letter R. Use each letter once only. No words with capitals, foreign words, hyphens, or plurals are allowed.

The nine letter word is
....

PUSSYCAT STANDARD: 8 words
PANTHER STANDARD: 13 words
LION STANDARD: 20 words.

MOVIE HOUSE ⭐⭐⭐

Hidden in the grid are six popular war films. Can you find them all?

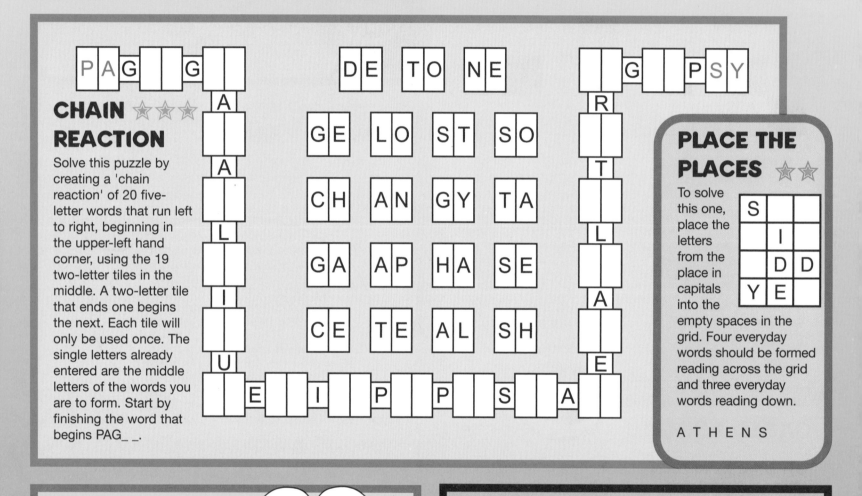

P	S	T	T	D	H	P	Q
M	Z	R	O	A	P	L	Q
P	K	E	H	S	A	M	Z
N	I	D	M	B	T	Y	H
R	U	D	D	O	T	M	T
P	L	A	T	O	O	N	Z
O	U	W	K	T	N	U	C
V	Z	N	Y	Q	Z	K	J

KAKURO ⭐⭐⭐

In Kakuro the numbers in the black squares refer to the SUMS of the digits 1–9 which you are to fill into the empty spaces. The number ABOVE the diagonal line refers to the empty spaces directly to the RIGHT of that number. A number BELOW the diagonal line refers to the empty spaces directly BELOW that number. No zeros are used here and a digit can only appear once in any particular digit combination.

QUICK TV QUIZ ⭐

1. What is the coffee shop in Friends called?

....

2. What is the name of the pub in the UK soap EastEnders?

....

3. What is the dog in Frasier called?

....

4. Which character had his own spin-off TV series after leaving Friends?

....

SUDOKU ⭐⭐

To solve, fill in the grid so that every row, column and box contains the numbers 1 through 9.

6			8	2		3	7	
	3		6	9				
8	1			3		6	4	
	6	5		4	1	2		8
		3		2				
	7							
5					3	8		
	4	8		3			9	1
		5			7		2	

WORD FIT ⭐⭐⭐

Can you fit all the words linked with a quarry into the grid below?

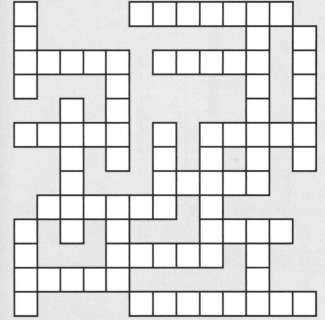

4 letter words
Dust
Fuse
Gold
Lime
Mine
Rock

5 letter words
Blast
Chips
Crane
Flint
Noise
Slate

Spade
Stone

6 letter words
Charge
Danger
Digger
Helmet

7 letter words
Explode

8 letter words
Accident
Detonate

NUMBER HEX ⭐

Can you correctly enter six numbers into the Number Hex grid using the clues below? All are whole numbers below 10 and no two numbers are the same.

CLUES:
1. E is the number of arms on an octopus
2. A multiplied by D equals E
3. A plus D equals B
4. C and F are odd numbers
5. B is three times bigger than A
6. F and C equals D
7. F is bigger than A

WORD SPLITZ

Each row of ten letters can be split into two five-letter cooking words. These words read from left to right and are in order.

For example **SMOKOSUENK** can be split to reveal SKUNK and MOOSE.

1. C D A R R A V E I N
2. G P R O I A L L C H
3. R S O T A E A S T M
4. B G A L S A T E Z E

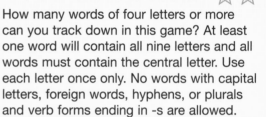

ADDING GRIDS ⭐

Place any digits 0 to 9 into the empty circles. When complete each row should add up to the figures on the right and each column to the figures below. The shaded numbers are the total of the diagonal circles.

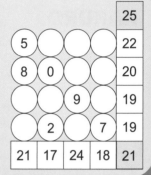

				25
5				22
8	0			20
		9		19
	2		7	19
21	17	24	18	21

NOURISHING NINE ⭐⭐

How many words of four letters or more can you track down in this game? At least one word will contain all nine letters and all words must contain the central letter. Use each letter once only. No words with capital letters, foreign words, hyphens, or plurals and verb forms ending in -s are allowed.

UNDERDONE: 9 words
MEDIUM: 13 words
WELL DONE: 18 words

D I M
Y R A
D I A

SUDOKU ⭐⭐⭐

To solve, fill in the grid so that every row, column and box contains the numbers 1 through 9.

		6					3	
	2			1				7
					5		9	2
			2					
	4		5					9
5						1		3
	7		8					
		1		2				
		3			6	8		

SKELETON CROSSWORD ⭐⭐⭐

Below is an incomplete quick crossword grid. Can you solve the puzzle by fitting the answers to the clues correctly into the grid, along with the remaining blocks and clue numbers? A few blocks have been shaded to give you a start. This puzzle has been rotated by 180 degrees.

Across
1 Gateaux (5)
7 To injure or harm (6)
8 A toothed wheel (7)
9 A play presented in instalments (6)
10 Retained (4)
12 Go back over one's steps (7)
14 Breather (4)
16 Represent, symbolize (6)
18 Tanned hide (7)
19 Breadwinner (6)
20 Person who makes public announcements (5)

Down
2 Astound (5)
3 To arouse to strong feeling (6)
4 After the expected time (4)
5 Afternoon performance (7)
6 Vote into office again (2-5)
7 Armed warship (9)
10 Tied tightly (7)
11 Make ready (7)
13 Opening at top of volcano (6)
15 Strainer (5)
17 Ran off (4)

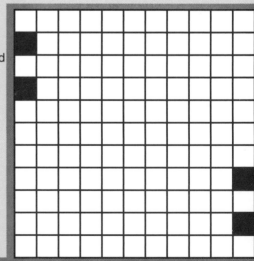

COUNTING CRITTERS ⭐

Can you find the number that is represented by each animal face? You will find the total of the numbers below each column and to the right of each row. Now go figure!

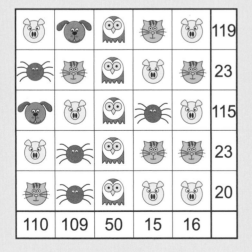

DEER WORDSEARCH

The grid contains 16 words connected with deer hidden vertically, horizontally or diagonally. Can you find them all?

ANTLER
BUCK
DOE
FALLOW
GRASS
HART
HERD
HIDE
HIND
MOOSE
REIN
SHOOT
STAG
STALK
VENISON
WOODS

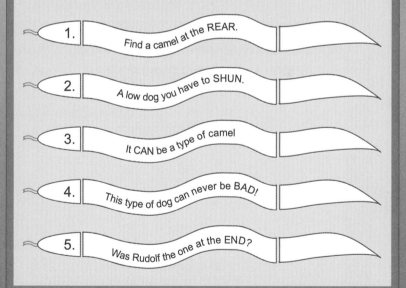

S	S	A	R	G	A	T	S
V	E	N	I	S	O	N	G
N	S	T	A	L	K	S	E
W	O	L	L	A	F	D	F
D	O	E	T	J	I	O	Z
R	M	R	S	H	O	O	T
E	A	B	U	C	K	W	L
H	I	N	D	R	E	I	N

FIVE SNEAKY SNAKES

Can you add five letters to each of the words in capitals in the snakes below, to make another word which solves the clue? For example, by adding five letters to the clue 'A revolt can make you REEL', you can make the word REBELLION. Each of the answers share a common theme.

1. Find a camel at the REAR.

2. A low dog you have to SHUN.

3. It CAN be a type of camel

4. This type of dog can never be BAD!

5. Was Rudolf the one at the END?

REBUS TOWER

Can you work out which common phrases are represented by each of the three diagrams in the tower below?

IFLT

LOOK

OWHER

NATURE TRAIL

Find the plant that is growing inside the tree by removing all the letters that appear more than twice.

THE HIDDEN PLANT IS A

....

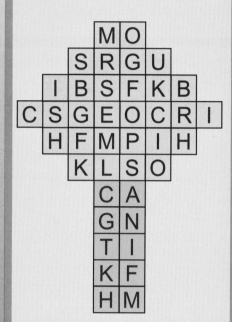

	M	O		
S	R	G	U	
I	B	S	F	K	B

LITTLE TOUGHIE

Across

4 Empty cleaner consumed things (6)

5 Raised cutting tool used to be (3)

6 Downward bulge requiring some massage (3)

8 Round South East, idiot's in a cupboard! (6)

Down

1 What's round bed can spread into valley (7)

2 Taxidermist initially has to pay it? (3)

3 Held up and had a lie-down during action (7)

7 A plaything to Yard (3)

Solutions start on page 189   **49**

OCCUPATIONS

How many words of four letters or more can you track down in this game? At least one will be a nine letter occupation and all contain the central letter. Use each letter once only. No words with capitals, foreign words, hyphens, or plurals and verb forms ending in -s are allowed.

Good 14 words: Very good 19 words: Excellent 27 words

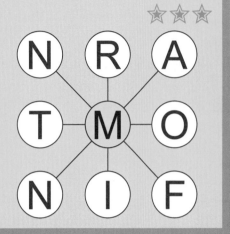

NAME THE DATE

Can you circle the correct date for these famous events?

1. Julius Caesar invaded Britain in...		
55BC	1623	1282

2. The American war of independance began in...		
1777	1877	1977

3. The channel tunnel opened between the UK and France in...		
1994	1894	1974

KAKURO

In Kakuro the numbers in the black squares refer to the SUMS of the digits 1–9 which you are to fill into the empty spaces. The number ABOVE the diagonal line refers to the empty spaces directly to the RIGHT of that number. A number BELOW the diagonal line refers to the empty spaces directly BELOW that number. No zeros are used here and a digit can only appear once in any particular digit combination.

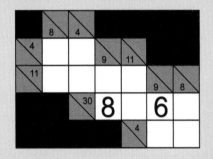

BATTLESHIPS

There are five ships hidden in the grid below. Look at the key to see which ships you have to find. The numbers on the grid tell you how many squares of each row or column part of a ship is found in. To get you started, we've put a few parts of ships (in red) and a few squares with no ships (in black).

HINTS: Begin by shading in all the misses (all the columns which have a nought in them) as there are no ships here. When you have found a full ship you can shade all the blocks around that ship as misses because none of the ships are touching.

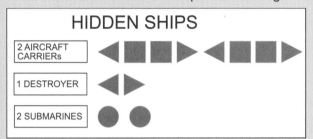

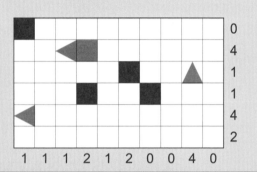

EGYPT WORDSEARCH

The grid contains 14 words associated with Egypt hidden vertically, horizontally or diagonally. The unused letters spell out another connected word.

ANCIENT
DESERT
EPIC
HEAT
HORUS
ISLAM
LEGACY
MAGIC
MYSTERY
MYTH
NILE
ORIENTAL
PYRAMID
TOURIST

```
L P Y R A M I D
T A E H N S U L
S I T C C C D E
I S N N I L E G
R L M G E P S A
U A A Y N I E C
O M Y S T E R Y
T S U R O H T O
```

ADD A LETTER

Add one letter to each word in capitals to create a new word that answers the clue. The order of the letters does not need to be changed.

For example - 'I BET it's more superior' would be BEST.

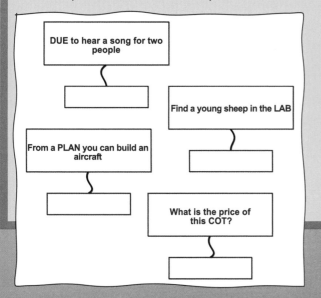

DUE to hear a song for two people

Find a young sheep in the LAB

From a PLAN you can build an aircraft

What is the price of this COT?

COMMON WORDS

Your task here is to determine the answers to each of the tricky definitions below, as well as the word that is contained in all five of the set's answers. For example, if the five solutions were ERRAND, TERRIBLE, MERRY MEN, PREFERRED and PERRY, the word in the central circle would be ERR.

CLUES:
1 Waffler of drama
2 Salad leaves
3 Spike heel
4 Man's man
5 Fool

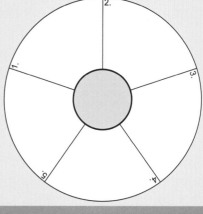

SKELETON CROSSWORD

Below is an incomplete quick crossword grid. Can you solve the puzzle by fitting the answers to the clues correctly into the grid, along with the remaining blocks and clue numbers? A few blocks have been shaded to give you a start. This grid has been rotated by 180 degrees.

Down
1 A good whisky (4)
2 Scottish isle (4)
3 Prepare to eat a meal (3,3,5)
4 The landlord (4)
5 Matted fabric (4)
8 Digging tool (5)
9 Corrodes (5)
11 Conscious of (5)
12 Betting odds (5)
15 Wood choppers (4)
16 One act in variety show (4)
18 Cummerbund (4)
19 Thick slice of cake (4)

Across
6 Device to lift car (4)
7 Loves (6)
8 City road (6)
10 London gallery (4)
13 Alias (7,4)
14 Orient (4)
17 Evaluate (6)
20 Vehicle fuel (6)
21 Monarch of Iran (4)

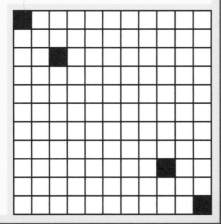

ON TARGET

Put the answers to the clues in the grid starting from the outside. Each answer has five letters and ends with the central letter E. When you've finished, the outer ring will reveal the name of a game (7).

1 Make a point in sport (5)
2 Poke with the elbow (5)
3 Small weight (5)
4 Salad oil (5)
5 Cutting implement (5)
6 Run away to marry (5)
7 Long narrow raised strip (5)

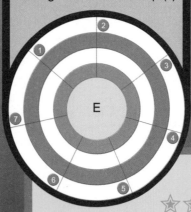

NINE NUMBERS

Try to fill in the missing numbers.
Use the numbers 1 to 9 to complete the equations. Each number is only used once. Each row and column is an equation with the totals given below and to the right.

7	-		+		14
x		-		/	
8	/		-		-1
+		-		-	
	-	6	+		0
61		-8		2	

PAIR WHEELS

Place each of the twelve pairs of letters into one of the circles in the grid, so that every line running through the central circle gives you a six-letter word with the middle letters IT.

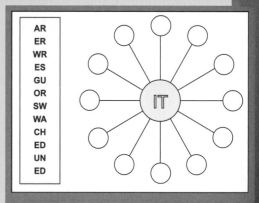

AR
ER
WR
ES
GU
OR
SW
WA
CH
ED
UN
ED

ADD THREE TO THREE

Can you add three letters to the three words in red below to make another word which solves the clue? For example, by adding three letters to the clue 'BAN this fruit', you can make the word BANANA.

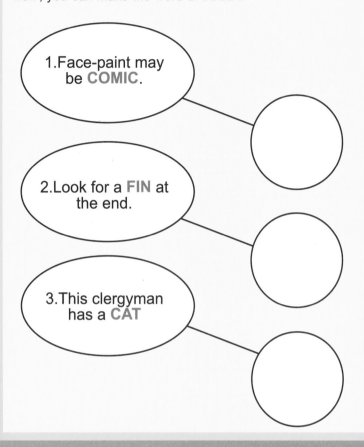

1. Face-paint may be **COMIC**.

2. Look for a **FIN** at the end.

3. This clergyman has a **CAT**

JIG GRID

Can you fit the blocks back into the grid to reveal, reading from left to right, 6 capital cities?

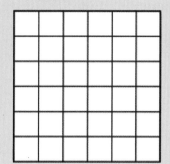

P E K   A T H   N G   R A
B E R   O N   N S
O N   L I N
L O N D
   I   A N K A
L I S B   E

LETTER STEW

Use all the given letters in the stew to spell three words meaning stop.

I D   D E
  E
V E R N   N   T
  E   M
V   E   P
N   E E P
P

SUDOKU

To solve, fill in the grid so that every row, column and box contains the numbers 1 through 9.

3	2	7	6		4	1	8	
	6	4	1	7			5	
5			8		2		7	6
6	7		3	4	8		1	5
1		3		6	7	8		
9	4		2	1			6	7
2	1		5	8		7		4
7	3		4	9		6		8
4		9	7	2			3	1

HOLLYWOOD ANAGRAMS

Below are four anagrams of films or film people. The number and length of words to find is shown in brackets. The four anagram solutions are all linked in some way - can you find the link?

AGITATES DOGS SO (2, 4, 2, 2, 4)		
NACHO TWIN (5, 4)	THE LINK IS	
SYRIA DEER (5, 4)	_____	
TENNIS HIGH (3, 7)		

FIVE SNEAKY SNAKES ⭐⭐⭐

Can you add five letters to each of the words in capitals in the snakes below, to make another word which solves the clue? For example, by adding five letters to the clue 'A revolt can make you REEL', you can make the word REBELLION. Each of the answers shares a common theme.

1. Can you TELL if it's a sputnik?

2. This star-gazer sits on a STONE.

3. SID has this minor planet named after him.

4. The heavens are on FIRE.

5. An ACE astronaut could be called this.

CROSSWORD ⭐

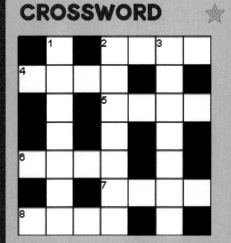

Across
2 A record (4)
4 Large bundle of hay (4)
5 Remain (4)
6 Untruthful person (4)
7 A layer (4)
8 A long time (4)

Down
1 Durable (7)
2 Abandons (7)
3 Loosen (7)

NINE NUMBERS ⭐⭐

Try to fill in the missing numbers.
Use the numbers 1 to 9 to complete the equations. Each number is only used once. Each row and column is an equation with the totals given below and to the right.

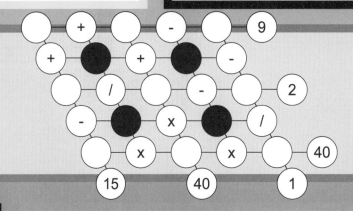

NURSERY BLOCKS ⭐

Rearrange each column of letters and write them in the grid to reveal the first two lines of a well known nursery rhyme. Some of the letters have been put in to give you a head start.

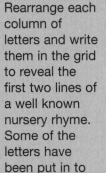

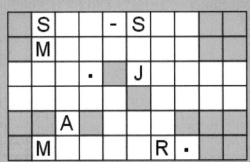

CAGED ANIMALS ⭐

An animal has escaped from the zoo. To put him back in his cage answer the eight clues and put them in the grid starting from the outermost circle. When this is done the central circle starting clockwise from number nine will reveal the name of the animal who escaped.

1 Additional, further (4)
2 Place where money is made (4)
3 Grain store (4)
4 Inferior (4)
5 Immediately following (4)
6 Nil (4)
7 Abominable snowman (4)
8 Lubricates (4)

NATURAL NINE

Try and become king of the jungle in this natural puzzle.
How many words of four letters or more can you track down? At least one will use all nine letters and all contain the central letter R. Use each letter once only. No words with capitals, foreign words, hyphens, or plurals are allowed.

The nine letter word is

....

ANAGRAM LADDERS

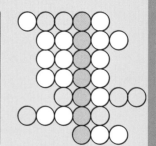

Solve the anagrams on the right to reveal the names of seven items of clothing. The shaded row in the middle will then reveal the name of another clothing item.

```
LWSAH
SRDSE
UTUT
KSAM
BBUSY
CTUNI
IET
```

ON TARGET

Put the answers to the clues in the grid starting from the outside. Each answer has five letters and ends with the central letter Y. When you've finished, the outer ring will reveal the name of a sport (7).

1 Horrible (5)

2 Foe (5)

3 Striped cat (5)

4 One who intimidates weaker

   people (5)

5 Irritate (5)

6 Frozen drink on a stick (5)

7 A truck (5)

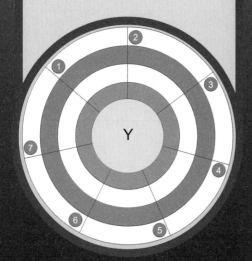

MOVIE HOUSE ★★★

Hidden in the grid are six Best Actress Oscar winners. Can you find them all?

```
L A N G E S A S
T Y Q Z N T A X
G P A L T R O W
U P X X A E W P
R K U N Q B C H
T S D Y I O C B
Y O W Y R R E B
N A M D I K Y N
```

JIG GRID ★★

Can you fit the blocks back into the grid to reveal, reading from left to right, seven birds?

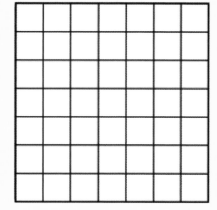

CARTOON CHARACTERS SQUIRCLE

Put vowels in the circles and consonants in the squares to make words in all the vertical columns. Definitions of these words are given. When this has been done, the second and fourth horizontal lines will make three cartoon characters.

DEFINITIONS
1 Pierces with knife
2 Roll of tobacco
3 Senseless or silly
4 Book of maps
5 Very large person
6 Press dough
7 Baffle
8 Brief raid
9 Correct or improve

SUDOKU

To solve, fill in the grid so that every row, column and box contains the letters a to i.

d		h	e			b	g	
		f	b	c			d	
e		b	f		d			i
g								
b	d		i		h			f
f		a		d	e	i		g
		g				f		d
						c	i	b
a				b	c		e	

CODED CROSSWORD ⭐⭐⭐

Each number in the grid represents a different letter of the alphabet. Can you fill in the grid using the given letters to get you started?

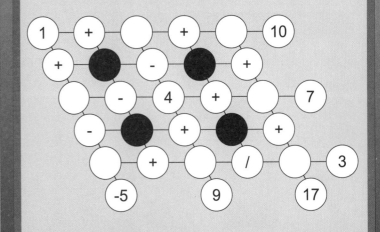

1	2	3	4	5	6	7	8	9	10	11	12	13
14	15	16	17	18	19	20	21	22	23	24	25	26

NINE NUMBERS ⭐⭐

Try to fill in the missing numbers.
Use the numbers 1 to 9 to complete the equations. Each number is only used once. Each row and column is an equation with the totals given below and to the right.

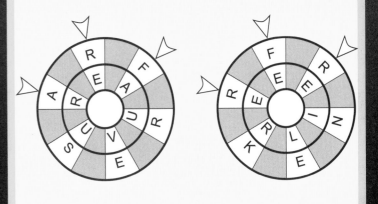

WORD WHEEL ⭐

For each of the circles, can you find two letters which, when placed in the middle, will form three six-letter words?

MATCH STICKS ⭐⭐⭐

Can you make eight equilateral triangles by moving just three matches?

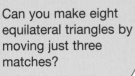

Solutions start on page 189

BITS AND PIECES ★★★

The tiles in the top grid are all jumbled up. Can you rearrange them in the grid below using only one tile from each column to reveal four related words and their theme?

B	R	L	C	D
RE	PR	R	E	W
T	I	W	O	E
S	IL	U	C	S
W	D	E	OO	H

(empty answer grid, 5 columns × 4 rows)

KAKURO ★★★

In Kakuro the numbers in the black squares refer to the SUMS of the digits 1–9 which you are to fill into the empty spaces. The number ABOVE the diagonal line refers to the empty spaces directly to the RIGHT of that number. A number BELOW the diagonal line refers to the empty spaces directly BELOW that number. No zeros are used here and a digit can only appear once in any particular digit combination.

MILITARY PEOPLE WORDSEARCH ★

The grid contains 11 military people hidden vertically, horizontally or diagonally. The unused letters spell out another related word.

R	L	B	A	T	M	A	N
E	T	E	D	A	C	D	I
C	G	U	N	N	E	R	A
I	U	H	U	O	S	A	T
F	A	S	A	R	L	G	P
F	R	O	J	A	M	O	A
O	D	N	A	M	M	O	C
A	D	J	U	T	A	N	T

ADJUTANT   DRAGOON
BATMAN   GUARD
CADET   GUNNER
CAPTAIN   MAJOR
COLONEL   OFFICER
COMMANDO

ZOO HUNT ★

An animal has escaped from the zoo and is hiding somewhere in the grid. If you cross out all the letters that appear more than twice, the remaining letters will spell out the missing creature.

THE MISSING CREATURE IS A

....

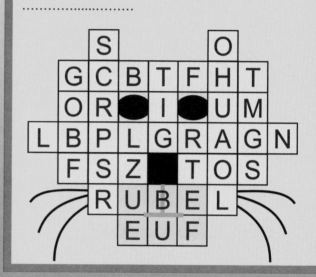

SUN NUMBER PIC ★

Can you create a picture from the grid below? Each number represents a group of shaded squares, so for example 3|2 means that on this row there is a group of 3 yellow squares to the left of a group of 2 yellow squares, with one or more white squares in between (there must be at least one white square in between the groups, or the 3 and 2 would join up to become a 5).

The numbers are always in order, so 4|2 means a group of 4 yellow squares to the left of a group of 2 yellow squares in that row, and 5 over 3 means a block of 5 yellow squares above a block of 3 yellow squares in that column.

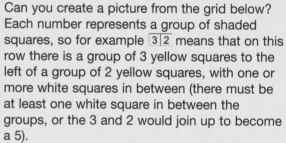

NINE NUMBERS ★

Try to fill in the missing numbers. Use the numbers 1 to 9 to complete the equations. Each number is only used once. Each row and column is an equation with the totals given below and to the right.

2	+		−	3		0
×		+		+		
4	+		−			5
−		+		−		
	−	7	×			−12
3		17		5		

WORD FIT

Can you fit all the words that can precede 'line' into the grid below?

3 letter words
Bar
Hot
Off

4 letter words
Chat
Date

Hard
Land
Main

5 letter words
Front
Plumb
Story

6 letter words
Battle
Bottom
Branch
Firing
Flight
Ledger
Number

7 letter word
Contour

8 letter word
Assembly

NATUREGRAMS

Solve each clue, then rearrange the five letters in every answer to form a set of three fish.

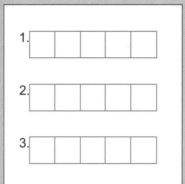

1.

2.

3.

1.

2.

3.

CLUES:
1.Take delight in 2.Long leather strip 3.Private instructor

NOURISHING NINE

How many words of four letters or more can you track down in this game? At least one 'nourishing' word will contain all nine letters and all words must contain the central letter. Use each letter once only. No words with capital letters, foreign words, hyphens, or plurals and verb forms ending in -s are allowed.

UNDERDONE
9 words:
MEDIUM
13 words:
WELL DONE
18 words

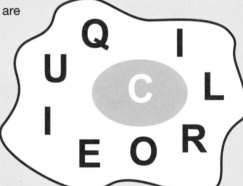

ARROWS

Put the following numbers in the arrows below:

3 4 5 5 6 7 7 8

Be careful though.
The total numbers in the three arrows pointing at each other must add up to 15.

The numbers in the arrows which are back to back must add up to 11.

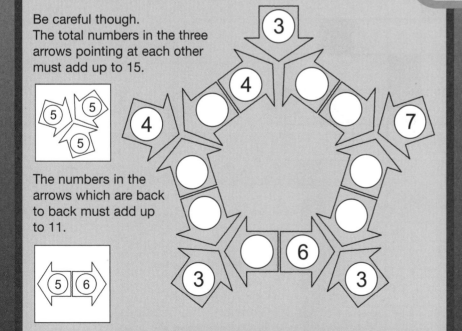

PYRAMID OF EGGS

Fill in the eggs with numbers. Each egg must equal the sum of the two eggs directly below it.

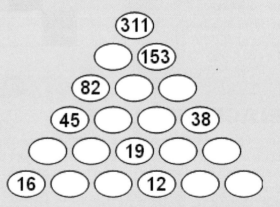

PANTOMIME WORDSEARCH

The grid contains 13 pantomime words vertically, horizontally or diagonally. Can you find them all?

```
N Q U E E N S Q
I I F H C T I W
D D A B N I S L
D C I T I F T E
A R R Y R G E I
L O Y A P U R N
A W W A L I C E
P D O T N A I G
```

ALADDIN	DWARF	QUEEN
ALICE	FAIRY	SINBAD
CROWD	GENIE	SISTER
CURTAIN	GIANT	WITCH
	PRINCE	

CHAIN REACTION

Solve this puzzle by creating a 'chain reaction' of 20 five-letter words that run left to right, beginning in the upper-left hand corner, using the 19 two-letter tiles in the middle. A two-letter tile that ends one word begins the next. Each tile will only be used once. The single letters already entered are the middle letters of the words you are to form. Start by finishing the word that begins WID_ _.

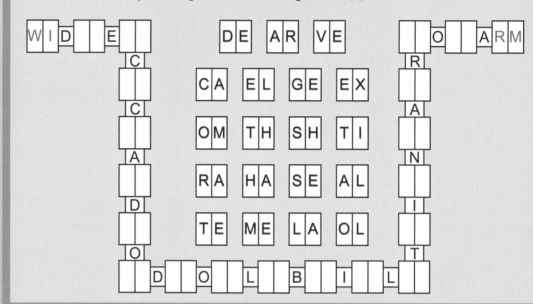

Tiles and grid letters:
WID E   DE AR VE   O A RM
C   CA EL GE EX   R
C   OM TH SH TI   A
A   RA HA SE AL   N
D   TE ME LA OL   I
O   D O L B I L   T

CROSSWORD

Across
1 Piece of lab equipment (4,4)
6 Mediterranean for instance (3)
7 Chaplain (5)
9 A layer (4)
11 Miss Laine the jazz singer (4)
12 Egg on (4)
14 Domesticated (4)
16 The devil (5)
18 Top card (3)
19 Deserted a country (8)

Down
1 Legal precedent (4,4)
2 Condition of something (5)
3 Sort (4)
4 Wicked (3)
5 Clergyman (8)
8 Attractive lily (4)
10 A jot (4)
13 Behave in response (5)
15 Poker stake (4)
17 Golf peg (3)

CAGED ANIMALS

An animal has escaped from the zoo. To put him back in his cage answer the eight clues and put them in the gird starting from the outermost circle. When this is done the central circle starting clockwise from number nine, will reveal the name of the animal that escaped.

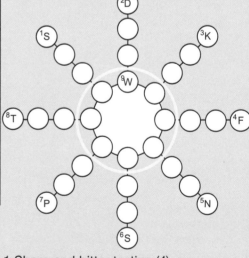

1 Sharp and bitter tasting (4)
2 Sketch (4)
3 Bird from New Zealand (4)
4 Coal for instance (4)
5 Require (4)
6 Pierce with a knife (4)
7 Game played on horseback (4)
8 Brass instrument (4)

PLACE THE PLACES

To solve the puzzle place the letters from the place in capitals into the empty spaces in the grid. Four everyday words should be formed reading across the grid and 3 everyday words reading down.

A L A S K A

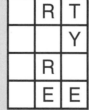

```
R T
  T Y
  R
  E E
```

ALPHAFITS

One of each of the 26 letters of the alphabet has been removed from the crossword grid below. Can you replace them all to fill the crossword with everyday words?

A	B	C	D	E	F	G	H	I	J	K	L	M
N	O	P	Q	R	S	T	U	V	W	X	Y	Z

WHAT COMES FIRST?

Can you work out which word commonly precedes the pairs of words?

1. DROP / MERINGUE

2. STEEPLE / MOUSE

3. HOOD / REDBREAST

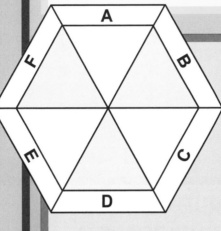

NUMBER HEX

Can you correctly enter six numbers into the Number Hex grid using the clues below? All are whole numbers below 10 and no two numbers are the same.

CLUES:
1. A, D and E add up to F
2. B, C, D and F are odd numbers
3. C and D add up to E
4. D is the smallest number
5. F is the number of days in a week
6. B is not 9

WORD WALL

Make your way up the wall by changing one letter at a time until you reach the top word.

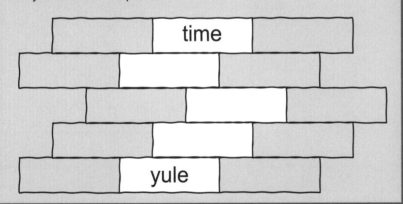

time

yule

SUDOKU

To solve, fill in the grid so that every row, column and box contains the numbers 1 through 9.

	2	1		6	3	8	4	5
5		6	8	4	2	1	7	
	8	4		1		2		9
2			3	5			1	4
		9		2		7	5	8
		5	1	8	7	3		2
6	4				8	9		
9		2				4	8	7
8	1	7	2	9	4	5	3	6

BLOCKBUSTERS

Complete the square by using each number and symbol provided in the top row ONCE only in every other row and column to equal the given answer. The first column and all the + signs have been put in to give you a start!

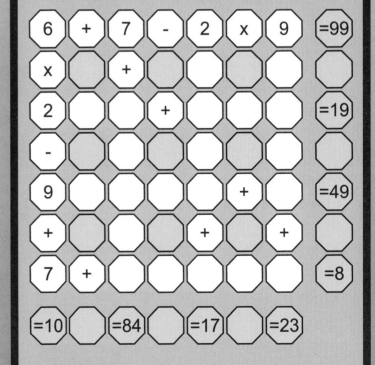

NATURAL NINE

Try and become king of the jungle in this natural puzzle.

How many words of four letters or more can you track down? At least one will use all nine letters and all contain the central letter N. Use each letter once only. No words with capitals, foreign words, hyphens, or plurals are allowed.

The nine letter word is

....

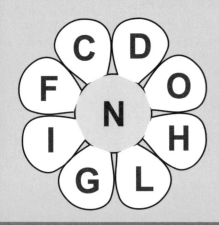

BIRD BOXES

Shade in all the letters that appear in the word 'PEACE' to reveal a hidden bird.

B	R	C	H	R	S	V	F	I	T	E	A
O	H	A	T	C	E	P	S	G	W	C	B
F	I	C	O	P	B	A	O	Y	J	E	P
E	P	A	Y	A	C	E	V	H	R	C	T
C	F	E	J	R	S	X	R	T	X	A	P
A	C	P	X	J	I	C	Y	B	T	C	W
W	J	R	V	F	H	S	A	O	E	V	G
G	S	Y	T	J	Y	O	Y	P	X	S	O

ADD A LETTER

Add one letter to each word in capitals to create a new word that answers the clue. The orders of the letters does not need to be changed.

For example – 'I BET it's more superior' would be BEST.

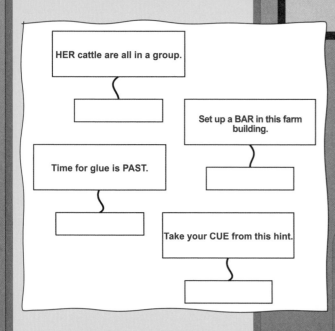

HER cattle are all in a group.

Set up a BAR in this farm building.

Time for glue is PAST.

Take your CUE from this hint.

TRUE OR FALSE WORDSEARCH

The grid contains 13 words meaning false hidden vertically, horizontally or diagonally. The unused letters spell out another connected word.

BAFFLE
BUNK
CHARADE
DISGUISE
DUPE
FAKE
FANTASY

FARCE
GARBLE
ILLUSION
MYTH
PRETENCE
PRETEXT

E	C	H	A	R	A	D	E
C	H	T	Y	M	E	A	S
N	O	I	S	U	L	L	I
E	C	R	A	F	B	E	U
T	X	E	T	E	R	P	G
E	B	U	N	K	A	U	S
R	C	T	A	A	G	D	I
P	B	A	F	F	L	E	D

HOLLYWOOD ANAGRAMS

Here are four anagrams on a movie related topic. The number and length of words to find is shown in brackets. The four anagram solutions are all linked in some way – can you find the link?

OUTRAN MAP (9)		
MONTGOMERY DEAL WRY (5, 7, 5)	THE LINK IS	
MARKED ROWS (10)		
ABUSIVE ANT (5, 5)		

QUICK QUIZ QUESTIONS

Can you get all of these quiz questions correct?

WHO WAS THE ARTIST?	
1. GUERNICA	
2. THE LAST SUPPER	
3. THE HAY WAIN	
4. THE SCREAM	
5. SUNFLOWERS	
6. MONARCH OF THE GLEN	

NINE NUMBERS

Try to fill in the missing numbers.
Use the numbers 1 to 9 to complete the equations. Each number is only used once. Each row and column is an equation with the totals given below and to the right.

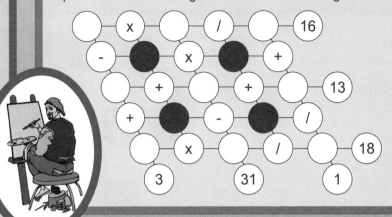

COUNTING CRITTERS

Can you find the number that is represented by each animal face? You will find the total of the numbers below each column and to the right of each row.

🐶	🕷	🕷	🐷	🕷	15
🐱	🐱	🕷	🐷	🐶	17
🦉	🐱	🐱	🐷	🕷	13
🕷	🦉	🐶	🐷	🐱	15
🐷	🐷	🐷	🐷	🐱	19
15	13	16	20	15	

🐶 =
🐱 =
🦉 =
🕷 =
🐷 =

CODED CROSSWORD

Each number in the grid represents a different letter of the alphabet. Can you fill in the grid using the given letters to get you started?

(coded crossword grid)

1	2	3	4 A	5	6	7 O	8	9	10	11	12	13
14 E	15	16 B	17	18 S	19 T	20	21	22	23	24	25	26

SUDOKU

To solve, fill in the grid so that every row, column and box contains the numbers 1 through 9.

1	3	7	9	8		6		2
		9	3	2				
2	8			4	7	5		3
		3		5	8			7
7	6	2		9				
			1		7		6	
		8						
							3	7
		2	4					

WORD WHEEL

For each of the circles, can you find two letters which, when placed in the middle, will form three six-letter words?

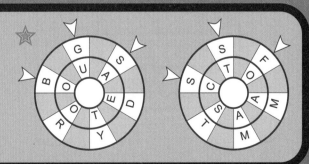

CROSSWORD

Across
1 Identification of disease (9)
6 Garden tool (5)
7 Fitting (3)
8 To eject (4)
10 Breather (4)
13 Overwhelming wonder (3)
14 Semi-precious stone (5)
16 One yard (5,4)

Down
1 Club for dancing (5)
2 Name of Miss Gardner, actress (3)
3 Require (4)
4 Aggitate (5)
5 Posed (3)
9 Bullock (5)
11 River in central England (5)
12 Wan (4)
13 At the stern (3)
15 To mimic (3)

STEP LADDER

Starting with the top word, change one letter at a time to make a new word at every step until you have reached the bottom word.

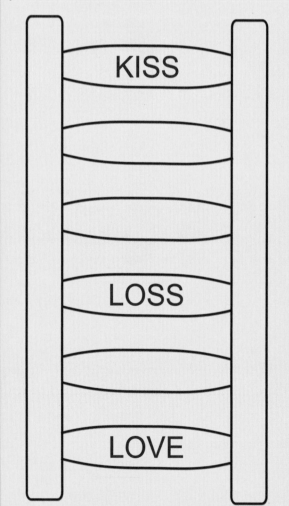

KISS

LOSS

LOVE

ZOO HUNT

An animal has escaped from the zoo and is hiding somewhere in the grid. If you cross out all the letters that appear more than twice, the remaining letters will spell out the missing creature.

THE MISSING CREATURE IS A

....

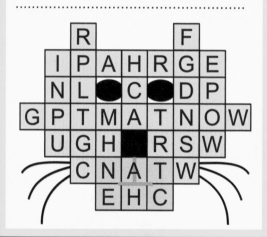

REBUS TOWER

Can you work out which common phrases are represented by each of the three diagrams in the tower below?

ESGG GGES
SEGG GSEG

WORDS

GNINRUTON

NINE NUMBERS

Try to fill in the missing numbers. Use the numbers 1 to 9 to complete the equations. Each number is only used once. Each row and column is an equation with the totals given below and to the right.

	/	4	-		1
-		x		x	
9	/	3	+		5
+		+		+	
	-		+		8
6		17		8	

ADD THREE TO THREE

Can you add three letters to the three words in red below to make another word which solves the clue? For example, by adding three letters to the clue 'BAN this fruit', you can make the word BANANA.

1. It's **SLY** to draw monthly pay.

2. **DAN** is in peril

3. Find a relative who's **NEW**.

PLACE THE PLACES

To solve the puzzle place the letters from the place in capitals into the empty spaces in the grid. Four everyday words should be formed reading across the grid and three everyday words reading down.

T E M P L E

KAKURO

In Kakuro the numbers in the black squares refer to the SUMS of the digits 1–9 which you are to fill into the empty spaces. The number ABOVE the diagonal line refers to the empty spaces directly to the RIGHT of that number. A number BELOW the diagonal line refers to the empty spaces directly BELOW that number. No zeros are used here and a digit can only appear once in any particular digit combination.

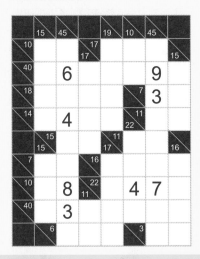

SKELETON CROSSWORD

Below is an incomplete quick crossword grid. Can you solve the puzzle by fitting the answers to the clues correctly into the grid, along with the remaining blocks and clue numbers? A few blocks have been shaded to give you a start. This grid has been rotated by 180 degrees.

Across
1 Classifies (5)
4 Board game (5)
7 Elegant woodland animal (3-4)
8 A vegetable (3)
9 A fool (3)
11 Design made on skin (6)
14 Performs like a ballerina (6)
17 Light afternoon meal (3)
19 Termite (3)
20 Small fragment (7)
22 Betting odds (5)
23 Wear away (5)

Down
1 A play presented in instalments (6)
2 Cereal crop (3)
3 Cover on the bed (5)
4 A measure of gold (5)
5 Take advantage of unethically (7)
6 Kill a fly (4)
10 To suddenly surprise (7)
12 Overwhelming wonder (3)
13 A fight (6)
15 Running expenses (5)
16 Malicious nastiness (5)
18 Fundamental part (4)
21 In favor of (3)

BITS AND PIECES

The tiles in the top grid are all jumbled up. Can you rearrange them in the grid below using only one tile from each column to reveal four related words and their theme?

CR	U	T	T	H
F	P	C	S	T
S	I	OR	BA	S
SQ	OO	A	KE	LL
T	E	N	NI	S

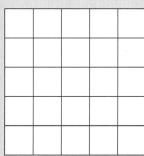

NOURISHING NINE

How many words of four letters or more can you track down in this game? At least one 'nourishing' word will contain all nine letters and all words must contain the central letter. Use each letter once only. No words with capital letters, foreign words, hyphens, or plurals and verb forms ending in -s are allowed.

UNDERDONE: 10 words
MEDIUM: 19 words
WELL DONE: 26 words

MOVIE HOUSE ★★★

Hidden in the grid are six Disney animated films. Can you find them all?

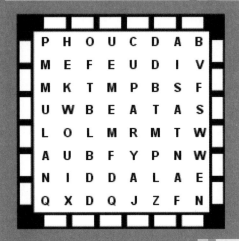

CHAIN REACTION ★★★

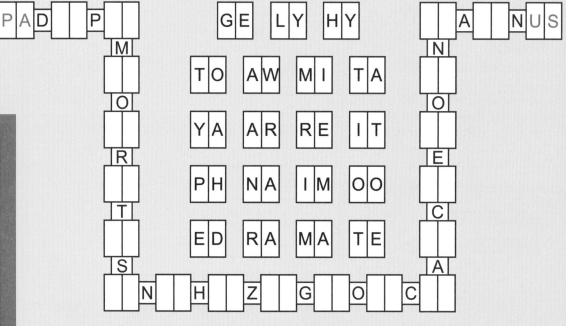

Solve this puzzle by creating a 'chain reaction' of 20 five-letter words that run left to right, beginning in the upper-left hand corner, using the 19 two-letter tiles in the middle. A two-letter tile that ends one begins the next. Each tile will only be used once. The single letters already entered are the middle letters of the words you are to form. Start by finishing the word that begins PAD_ _.

LITTLE TOUGHIE ★★★

Across

4 Look out for conflict in social insect (6)
5 Letter that causes a buzz? (3)
6 Meat is served in such a meal (3)
8 Mark on Edward makes you frightened (6)

Down

1 Go back about lines of poetry (7)
2 Bit of a sniff – a deadly craze (3)
3 Told a story with relevance (7)
7 Ice, night or hub (3)

HIDDEN COLORS ★

Shade in all the letters that appear in the word PUZZLES to reveal a hidden color.

J	B	N	F	P	L	Z	C	V	H	W	K
S	Z	L	I	S	T	E	R	U	J	B	V
U	O	L	Q	U	G	Z	M	E	T	I	H
E	U	Z	M	B	K	I	T	P	G	Q	P
Z	K	R	Z	O	C	R	F	Z	V	S	X
P	M	G	L	I	H	O	J	U	E	W	F
S	C	O	P	T	G	B	K	P	W	U	X
H	N	I	S	J	C	T	H	L	F	V	Z

WORD SPLITZ ★

① ECARAGNLEE

② FGOIONSCHE

③ QROUBIANIL

④ SSTWOIRFTK

Each row of ten letters can be split into two five-letter birds. These words read from left to right and are in order.

For example SMOKOSUENK can be split to reveal SKUNK and MOOSE.

CAGED ANIMALS

An animal has escaped from the zoo. To put him back in his cage answer the eight clues and put them in the grid starting from the outermost circle. When this is done the central circles starting clockwise from number nine will reveal the name of the animal who escaped.

1 Not shut (4)
2 Not straight (4)
3 Entice (4)
4 Fen (4)
5 Period of time (4)
6 Series of connected novels (4)
7 Portable light (4)
8 Against (4)

BLOCKBUSTERS

Complete the square by using each number and symbol provided in the top row ONCE only in every other row and column to equal the given answer. The first column and all the + signs have been put in to give you a start!

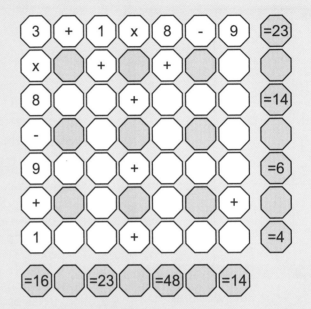

LETTER STEW

Use all the given letters in the stew to spell three words meaning big.

E G G G
E M I
S L E
E A U
E H M R N

PAIR WHEELS

Place each of the twelve pairs of letters into one of the circles in the grid, so that every line running through the central circle gives you a six-letter word with the middle letters ST.

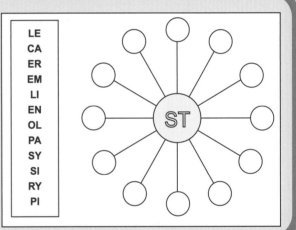

LE
CA
ER
EM
LI
EN
OL
PA
SY
SI
RY
PI

ARROWS

Put the following numbers in the arrows below:

1 1 2 3 3 4 4 4

Be careful though.
The total numbers in the 3 arrows pointing at each other must add up to 9.

The total numbers in the arrows which are back to back must add up to 5.

SWIMMING TRAINING

Tom is a swimmer who is training for his school sports day.
The trainer tells Tom that he has five days to swim 200 lengths of a pool. Tom starts slowly but picks up speed and manages to complete the task on the fifth day. In fact each day he swam 12 more lengths than on the previous training day.

How many lengths did Tom swim on the first day?

....

SUDOKU

To solve, fill in the grid so that every row, column and box contains the numbers 1 through 9.

7			2		5	8	9	
9			3	8	4		1	6
8	1	6			5	4	2	3
5		4		6	7		3	8
1		9		4	3	6	5	7
6	3	7	9		8			1
4	9	5	8		6			
2			3			6	5	
3	6		5	7		8		4

ZOO HUNT

An animal has escaped from the zoo and is hiding somewhere in the grid. If you cross out all the letters that appear more than twice, the remaining letters will spell out the missing creature.

THE MISSING CREATURE IS A

....

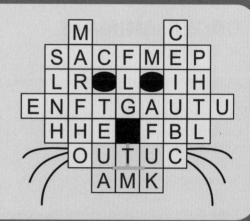

NOURISHING NINE

How many words of four letters or more can you track down in this game? At least one 'nourishing' word will contain all nine letters and all words must contain the central letter. Use each letter once only. No words with capital letters, foreign words, hyphens, or plurals and verb forms ending in -s are allowed.

UNDERDONE: 9 words
MEDIUM: 13 words
WELL DONE: 18 words

JIG GRID

Can you fit the blocks back into the grid to reveal, reading from left to right, six materials?

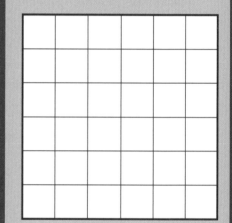

ROWING WORDSEARCH

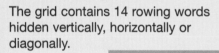

The grid contains 14 rowing words hidden vertically, horizontally or diagonally.

ADRIFT
ASTERN
BANKS
CLUB
COXLESS
CREW
EIGHT
GALLEY
HENLEY
OXFORD
PAIR
REGATTA
RIVER
STROKE

S	T	R	O	K	E	A	Z
K	S	H	P	S	G	S	D
N	R	E	G	A	T	T	A
A	I	N	L	I	I	E	D
B	V	L	W	X	E	R	R
D	E	E	R	R	O	N	I
Y	R	Y	B	U	L	C	F
C	D	R	O	F	X	O	T

HELLO NUMBER PIC

Can you create a picture from the grid on the right?

Each number represents a group of shaded squares, so for example means that on this row there is a group of 3 black squares to the left of a group of 2 black squares, with one or more white squares in between (there must be at least one white square in between the groups, or the 3 and 2 would join up to become a 5.) The numbers are always in order, so 4 2 means a group of 4 black squares to the left of a group of 2 black squares in that row, and 5/3 means a block of 5 black squares above a block of 3 black squares in that column.

ADDING GRIDS

Place any digits 0 to 9 into the empty circles. When complete each row should add up to the figures on the right and each column to the figures below. The shaded numbers are the total of the diagonal circles.

				26
	6			22
9		7		19
			0	15
9		5		26
27	22	24	9	12

A'MAZE'ING NUMBERS ⭐⭐⭐

Try to make your way through the maze. The number at the beginning of each row and column tells you exactly how many squares you will have to cross though in order to reach the finish. No diagonal moves are allowed.

SOLVING HINT: To begin, blacken any box that you determine will not be used, and place a dot in any box that you know must be used.

START

	1	1	5	3	7	1	1	1	1
5									
1									
1									
1									
1									
3									
1									
1									
7									

FINISH

CODED CROSSWORD ⭐⭐⭐

Each number in the grid represents a different letter of the alphabet. Can you fill in the grid using the given letters to get you started?

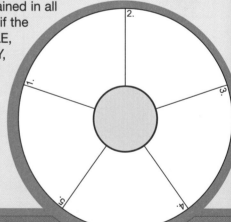

NATUREGRAMS ⭐⭐

Solve each clue, then rearrange the five letters in every answer to form a set of three reptiles.

CLUES:
1 Fearful anticipation
2 Move furtively
3 Chocolate substitute

COMMON WORDS ⭐⭐⭐

Your task here is to determine the answers to each set of tricky definitions below, as well as the word that is contained in all five of the set's answers. For example, if the five solutions were ERRAND, TERRIBLE, MERRY MEN, PREFERRED and PERRY, the word in the central circle would be ERR.

CLUES:
1 Write down
2 Friendly
3 Squeeze player
4 Piled pants
5 Juice grape

QUESTION NUMBER PIC

★★

Can you create a picture from the grid below?

Each number represents a group of shaded squares, so for example **3 2** means that on this row there is a group of 3 black squares to the left of a group of 2 black squares, with one or more white squares in between (there must be at least one white square in between the groups, or the 3 and 2 would join up to become a 5)

The numbers are always in order, so **4 2** means a group of 4 black squares to the left of a group of 2 black squares in that row, and **5 3** means a block of 5 black squares above a block of 3 black squares in that column.

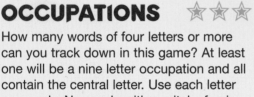

FLOWERY PHRASES

★★★

We have described a well-known saying using flowery language. Can you uncover the more familiar form? For example, 'An eruption in the cook pot' would be 'A Flash in the pan'.

In the event that an article that could resemble a brogue or a balmoral is discovered to be an appropriate length and width, it is recommended that the individual possessing this article direct it toward, and secure it on, its intended location.

CROSSWORD

★

Across

2 Actively occupied (4)
4 Lose color in the sun (4)
5 Odd or unusual (7)
6 Chair (4)
7 Small restaurant (4)

Down

1 Ice-cream flavor (7)
2 Since (7)
3 Scotsman's money pouch (7)

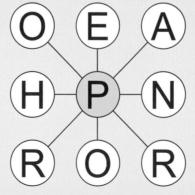

ON TARGET

★

Put the answers to the clues in the grid starting from the outside. Each answer has five letters and ends with the central letter S. When you've finished the outer ring will reveal the name of a UK soccer team (7).

1 Payments to workmen (5)
2 Chasm (5)
3 Changes course in sailing (5)
4 Expressions (5)
5 Fertile spot in the desert (5)
6 Horse events (5)
7 UK pub game (5)

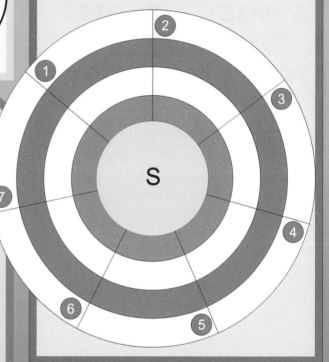

NAME THE DATE

★

Can you circle the correct date for these famous events?

1. World War II began in...		
193030	1940	1950

2. The battle of Hastings was in ...		
1242	1537	1066

3. The first modern Olympic Games was held in...		
1596	1996	1896

OCCUPATIONS

★★★

How many words of four letters or more can you track down in this game? At least one will be a nine letter occupation and all contain the central letter. Use each letter once only. No words with capitals, foreign words, hyphens, or plurals and verb forms ending in -s are allowed.

GOOD: 15 words VERY GOOD: 22 words
EXCELLENT: 29 words

O E A
H P N
R O R

CHAIN REACTION

Solve this puzzle by creating a 'chain reaction' of 20 five-letter words that run left to right, beginning in the upper-left hand corner, using the 19 two-letter tiles in the middle. A two-letter tile that ends one begins the next. Each tile will only be used once. The single letters already entered are the middle letters of the words you are to form. Start by finishing the word that begins CRU_ _.

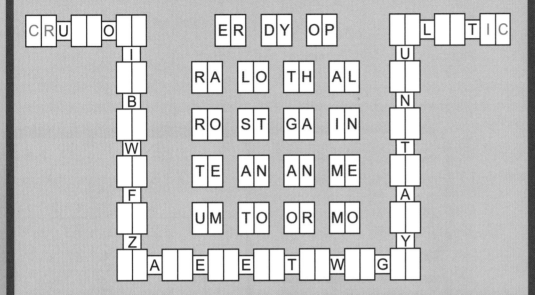

Chain grid letters:
- Top row: C R U | | O ... ER DY OP ... L | T I C
- Left column: I, B, W, F, Z
- Middle tiles rows:
  - RA LO TH AL
  - RO ST GA IN
  - TE AN AN ME
  - UM TO OR MO
- Right column: U, N, T, A, Y
- Bottom row: A E E T W G

NINE NUMBERS

Try to fill in the missing numbers. Use the numbers 1 to 9 to complete the equations. Each number is only used once. Each row and column is an equation with the totals given below and to the right.

3	x		+		11
x		-		-	
	+		+		19
+		x		+	
	-	7	+	8	2
13		-49		7	

UK TV SLEUTHS SQUIRCLE

Put vowels in the circles and consonants in the squares to make words in all the vertical columns. Definitions of these words are given. When this has been done, the first and fourth horizontal lines will make the names of three TV sleuths.

DEFINITIONS
1 A tropical fruit
2 In the lead
3 Sounds like a lion
4 Festive occasion
5 South American animal
6 Body joint
7 Prickle on plant
8 Bad language
9 Avarice

Grid columns numbered 1 2 3 4 5 6 7 8 9

ALPHABET SUDOKU

To solve, fill in the grid so that every row, column and box contains the letters a to i.

a			b	f				
g	d	e		i		b		f
c		h	e			d		
	b				a			
d		a	g	f			c	e
f			a	c			d	h
		f				i	d	
	e							a
	d		i	e	c			

FIVE SNEAKY SNAKES

Can you add five letters to each of the words in capitals in the snakes below, to make another word which solves the clue? For example, by adding five letters to the clue 'A revolt can make you REEL', you can make the word REBELLION. Each of the answers share a common theme.

1. Build CANE into an oblong or square.
2. PEN-portrait of US army headquarters.
3. Branch of maths MET at school.
4. RIG up something with three sides.
5. Line MET going across a circle.

ODD ONE OUT

Can you spot the odd one out in this sequence of British places?

MANCHESTER
Glasgow
LEEDS
London
BRISTOL
Oxford

ANAGRAM LADDER

Solve the anagrams on the right to reveal the names of seven vegetables. The shaded column in the middle will then reveal the name of another vegetable.

TOUSPR
TOPTOA
TORCAR
DISHRA
NASIPCH
ONNOI
REPEPP

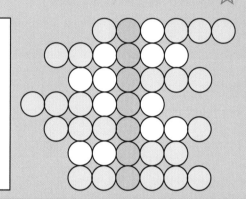

WORD WALL ★★

Make your way up the wall by changing one letter at a time until you reach the top word.

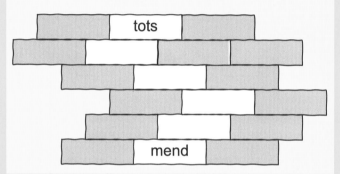

tots

mend

SUDOKU ★★★

To solve, fill in the grid so that every row, column and box contains the numbers 1 through 9.

		9	8	7				4
		7	5				9	6
	4		3			8	5	7
			2	3		7		
6		2			9	4	3	
	3			6	5		8	
	2		9		4			8
4				2	3			
9				8		2		3

WORD FIT ★★★

Can you fit all the Commonwealth members into the grid below?

4 letter word
Fiji

5 letter words
Ghana
India
Tonga

6 letter words
Brunei
Canada
Uganda

7 letter words
Antigua
Grenada
Lesotho
Nigeria

8 letter words
Dominica
Pitcairn
Tanzania

9 letter words
Australia
Swaziland

KAKURO ★★

In Kakuro the numbers in the black squares refer to the SUMS of the digits 1–9 which you are to fill into the empty spaces. The number ABOVE the diagonal line refers to the empty spaces directly to the RIGHT of that number. A number BELOW the diagonal line refers to the empty spaces directly BELOW that number. No zeros are used here and a digit can only appear once in any particular digit combination.

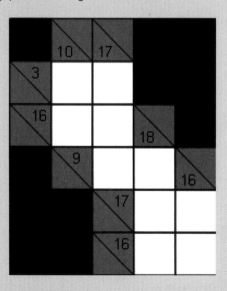

NINE NUMBERS ⭐⭐

Try to fill in the missing numbers. Use the numbers 1 to 9 to complete the equations. Each number is only used once. Each row and column is an equation with the totals given below and to the right.

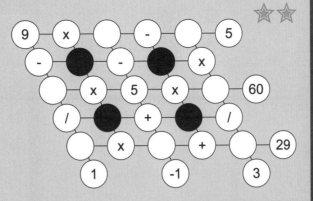

NATURAL NINE ⭐

Try and become king of the jungle in this natural puzzle.

How many words of four letters or more can you track down? At least one will use all nine letters and all contain the central letter N. Use each letter once only. No words with capitals, foreign words, hyphens, or plurals are allowed.

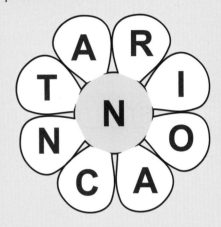

The nine letter word is

....

PUSSYCAT STANDARD: 8 words
PANTHER STANDARD: 13 words
LION STANDARD: 20 words

PAIR WHEELS ⭐⭐

Place each of the twelve pairs of letters into one of the circles in the grid, so that every line running through the central circle gives you a six-letter word with the middle letters RO.

AD
IC
AB
AC
EU
ST
NG
HE
PE
TH
AT
SS

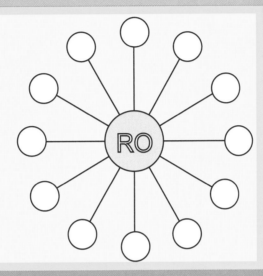

NUMBER HEX ⭐

Can you correctly enter six numbers into the Number Hex grid using the clues below? All are whole numbers below 10 and no two numbers are the same.

CLUES:
The numbers increase each time from A to F
A plus C equals D
All the numbers are odd excepts A and E
E is the number of sides on an octagon

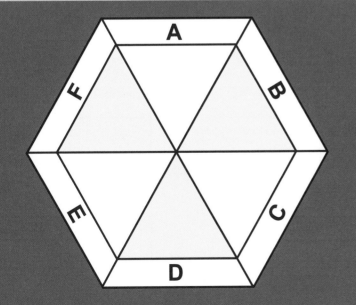

NAME THE DATE ⭐

Can you circle the correct date for these famous events?

1. The telephone was invented by Alexander Graham Bell in...		
1776	1976	1876

2. The ball-point pen was invented by Lazlo Biro in...		
1844	1944	1744

3. TV was invented by Vladimir Zworykin in...		
1923	1967	1823

WORD SPLITZ

Each row of ten letters can be split into two five-letter girls names. These words read from left to right and are in order.

For example SMOKOSUENK can be split to reveal SKUNK and MOOSE.

① N M A E N G C Y A N

② A W L E I N C E D Y

③ T S A U N S A Y A N

④ P P O E L G L G Y Y

CLOWN WORDSEARCH

The grid contains 15 clowning words hidden vertically, horizontally or diagonally. Can you find them all?

AMUSE
APPLAUD
BUCKET
CIRCUS
CLAP
COMIC
ENJOY
FUNNY

HAPPY
JOKER
KIDS
LAUGH
MESS
TRICK
WATER

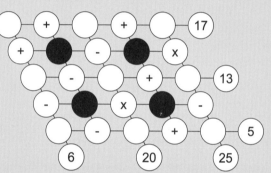

Y	M	Y	C	L	A	P	Q
N	T	E	Y	O	J	N	E
N	H	E	S	U	M	A	T
U	Y	G	K	S	D	I	K
F	P	S	U	C	R	I	C
A	P	P	L	A	U	D	I
W	A	T	E	R	L	B	R
V	H	R	E	K	O	J	T

NINE NUMBERS

Try to fill in the missing numbers. Use the numbers 1 to 9 to complete the equations. Each number is only used once. Each row and column is an equation with the totals given below and to the right.

BATTLESHIPS

There are seven ships hidden in the grid below. Look at the key to see which ships you have to find. The numbers on the grid tell you how many squares of each row or column part of a ship is found in. To get you started we've put a few parts of ships (in red) and a few squares with no ships (in black).

HINTS: Begin by shading in all the misses (all the columns which have a nought in them) as there are no ships here. When you have found a full ship you can shade all the blocks around that ship as misses because none of the ships are touching.

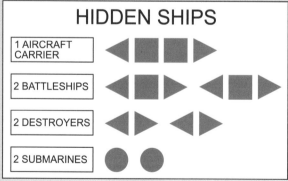

HIDDEN SHIPS

1 AIRCRAFT CARRIER	
2 BATTLESHIPS	
2 DESTROYERS	
2 SUBMARINES	

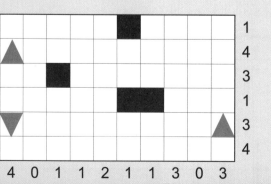

1
4
3
1
3
4

4 0 1 1 2 1 1 3 0 3

HOLLYWOOD ANAGRAMS

Below are four anagrams of films or film people. The number and length of words to find is shown in brackets. The four anagram solutions are all linked in some way – can you find the link?

FRANKLY REST ROY (5, 9)	
DISHIER FEED (5, 6)	THE LINK IS .....
ORCHARD BURN IT (7, 6)	
MICHIGAN ILL WED (7, 7)	

OCCUPATIONS

How many words of four letters or more can you track down in this game? At least one will be a nine letter occupation and all contain the central letter. Use each letter once only. No words with capitals, foreign words, hyphens, or plurals and verb forms ending in -s are allowed.

GOOD: 18 words,
VERY GOOD: 22 words,
EXCELLENT: 30 words

ADD A LETTER

Add one letter to each word in capitals to create a new word that answers the clue. The orders of the letters does not need to be changed. For example – 'I BET it's more superior' would be BEST.

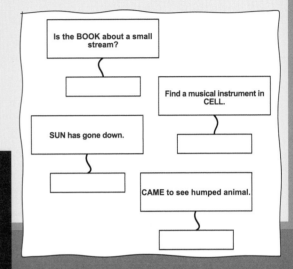

Is the BOOK about a small stream?

Find a musical instrument in CELL.

SUN has gone down.

CAME to see humped animal.

CODED CROSSWORD

Each number in the grid represents a different letter of the alphabet. Can you fill in the grid using the given letters to get you started?

1	2	3	4	5	6	7	8	9	10	11	12	13
					S		D	L			R	
14	15	16	17	18	19	20	21	22	23	24	25	26
	E			F								P

SUDOKU

To solve, fill in the grid so that every row, column and box contains the numbers 1 through 9.

2	4	7		1		5	3	
9			3					
5	3	6			7			
1						6		4
	8			6				
		2		5	8	1		
7						9	5	
6			7		2			1
8	9	1			5	2	7	6

COUNTING CRITTERS

Can you find the number that is represented by each animal face? You will find the total of the numbers below each column and to the right of each row.

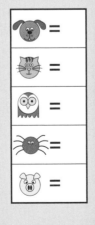

WORD WHEEL

For each of the circles, can you find two letters which, when placed in the middle, will form three six-letter words?

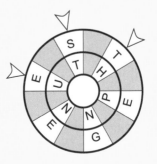

NATURAL NINE

Try and become king of the jungle in this natural puzzle. How many words of four letters or more can you track down? At least one will use all nine letters and all contain the central letter O. Use each letter once only. No words with capitals, foreign words, hyphens, or plurals are allowed.

The nine letter word is

....

PUSSYCAT STANDARD: 7 words,
PANTHER STANDARD: 11 words,
LION STANDARD: 16 words

ARROWS

Put the following numbers in the arrows on the right:

1 2 2 3 4 5 6 7

Be careful though.
The total numbers in the 3 arrows pointing at each other must add up to 11.

The total numbers in the arrows which are back to back must add up to 8.

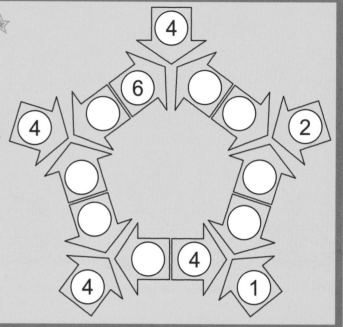

PAIR WHEELS ☆☆

Place each of the twelve pairs of letters into one of the circles in the grid, so that every line running through the central circle gives you a six-letter word with the middle letters EE.

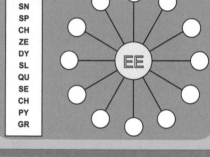

NS
SN
SP
CH
ZE
DY
SL
QU
SE
CH
PY
GR

SKELETON CROSSWORD ☆☆☆

Below is an incomplete quick crossword grid.Can you solve the puzzle by fitting the answers to the clues correctly into the grid, along with the remaining blocks and clue numbers? A few blocks have been shaded to give you a start. The puzzle has been rotated by 180 degrees.

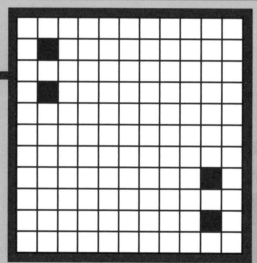

Across

1   Moved from one football club to another (11)
7   Jump when surprised (5)
8   Nonsensical talk (5)
9   Center of hurricane (3)
10 Shores of an ocean (5)
13 Garden flowers (5)
16 State of harmony (5)
19 Exhale audibly through the nose (5)
22 In the past (3)
23 Exhausted (5)
24 Intellect (5)
25 Industrious undertakings (11)

Down

1   Elongated elephant's teeth (5)
2   Once more (5)
3   Camping grounds (5)
4   Take part in competition (5)
5   Sudden short attacks (5)
6   Particles left from liquid (5)
11 Consumed (3)
12 Licensed medical practitioner (3)
14 Possess (3)
15 Spike of corn (3)
16 Group helping sheriff (5)
17 Watchful (5)
18 Consumer (5)
19 Plain and sedate (5)
20 Ellipses (5)
21 Pair of pincers (5)

BITS AND PIECES ☆☆☆

The tiles in the top grid are all jumbled up. Can you rearrange them in the grid below using only one tile from each column to reveal four related words and their theme?

DI	CA	E	HL	P
L	LE	GJ	U	N
J	S	V	AU	ON
PO	AV	T	LI	LT
DE	ON	C	UM	S

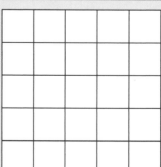

ADD THREE TO THREE ⭐⭐

Can you add three letters to the three words in red to make another word which solves the clue? For example, by adding three letters to the clue 'BAN this fruit', you can make the word BANANA.

1. You may receive such a package from a **PAL**.

2. **CAT** has got amongst the cows.

3. **BUN** found in this underground shelter.

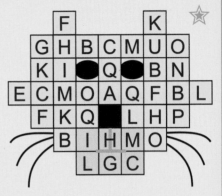

ZOO HUNT ⭐

An animal has escaped from the zoo and is hiding somewhere in the grid. If you cross out all the letters that appear more than twice, the remaining letters will spell out the missing creature.

THE MISSING CREATURE IS A ....

LITTLE TOUGHIE ⭐⭐⭐

Across

1 Polish in bus returned from outer part of city (6)

5 Be quick to turn with the fleet about (3)

6 Food that comes to nothing in the sky? (3)

7 It's boring breaking law (3)

8 Point in victory (3)

9 By the sound of it, I'll have to watch (3)

10 Most recent US city experiment (6)

Down

1 Scattered, Royal Navy's all at sea in west (6)

2 Old TV programme is great source of wealth (7)

3 Stuffed full of food, let peer off! (7)

4 Feel regret about 10 UK pence being damaged (6)

ANTIQUES WORDSEARCH ⭐⭐

The grid contains 14 antique words hidden vertically, horizontally or diagonally. The unused letters spell out another connected word.

AUCTION
BATE
BUYING
CASH
COPPER
GAME
OBJECT
PEWTER
PLATE
POTTERY
PRICE
TABLE
TEAPOT
VALUE

G	N	I	Y	U	B	N	A
A	H	P	R	R	O	P	R
M	S	R	E	I	E	E	T
E	A	I	T	W	P	L	O
U	C	C	T	P	E	B	P
L	U	E	O	T	T	A	A
A	R	C	P	L	A	T	E
V	T	C	E	J	B	O	T

QUITE

CRUSADERS
WARD

MOON

REBUS TOWER

Can you work out which common phrases are represented by each of the three diagrams in the tower below? ⭐⭐⭐

ADDING GRIDS ⭐

Place any digits 0 to 9 into the empty circles. When complete each row should add up to the figures on the right and each column to the figures below. The shaded numbers are the total of the diagonal circles.

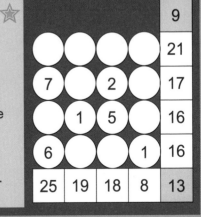

BIRD BOXES

☆

Shade in all the numbers that can be divided exactly by 25 to reveal a hidden bird.

70	15	350	60	170	45	140	110	175	155	120	170
225	175	140	125	135	150	210	100	285	65	20	165
100	115	30	180	25	205	325	195	10	235	130	310
25	200	130	40	110	165	15	160	120	125	375	400
66	300	5	70	155	50	300	175	65	275	230	75
150	175	160	20	60	200	190	375	145	200	220	125
110	45	135	60	240	350	100	250	40	170	115	370
10	165	30	185	120	150	215	175	160	5	145	70

NURSERY BLOCKS

☆

Rearrange each column of letters and write them in the grid to reveal the first two lines of a well-known nursery rhyme. Some of the letters have been put in to give you a head start.

	S							
S								
				F				.

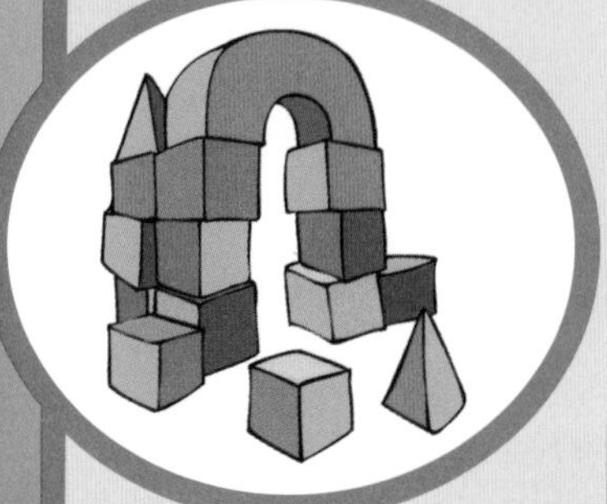

		P				A		
		I	N	E		T	O	
T	I	M	I	G	M	E	N	
A	O	I	O	N	L	I	E	
G	H	E	M	P	A	M	R	T

M O U R C U Y T U S B A S L R U T L

☆

LETTER STEW

Use all the given letters in the stew to spell three words meaning strong.

COMMON WORDS

☆☆☆

Your task here is to determine the answers to each set of tricky definitions below, as well as the word that is contained in all five of the set's answers. For example, if the five solutions were ERRAND, TERRIBLE, MERRY MEN, PREFERRED and PERRY, the word in the central circle would be ERR.

CLUES:
1 Thin
2 Tennis great
3 Jesting
4 Early class
5 Home Alone star

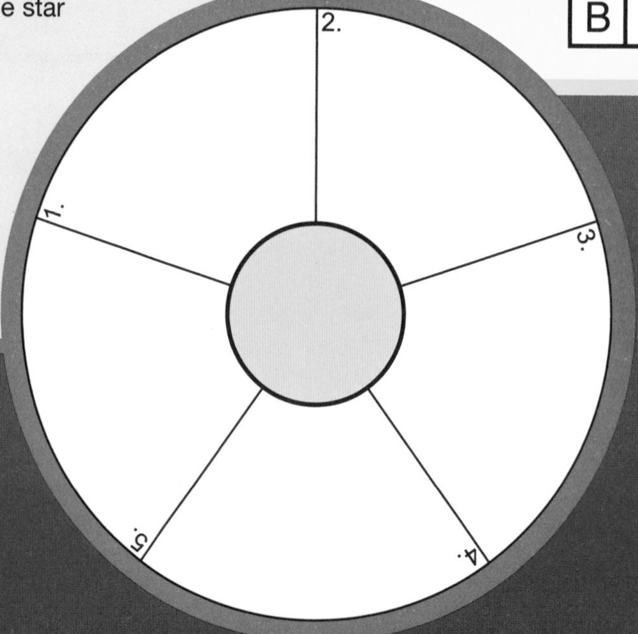

PLACE THE PLACES

☆☆

To solve the puzzle, place the letters from the place in capitals into the empty spaces in the grid. Four everyday words should be formed reading across the grid and three everyday words reading down.

G L A D E S

	P	A
	A	
A	R	
B		

BLOCKBUSTERS

☆☆☆

Complete the square by using each number and symbol provided in the top row ONCE only in every other row and column to equal the given answer. The first column and all the + signs have been put in to give you a start!

5	x	8	+	2	-	4	=38
+		+		+			
4			+				=50
-						+	
8			+				=42
x							
2			+				=24
=2		=46		=30		=14	

 Solutions start on page 189

ADD A LETTER ⭐

Add one letter to each word in capitals to create a new word that answers the clue. The orders of the letters does not need to be changed.

For example – 'I BET it's more superior' would be BEST.

EVE is not odd!

IRIS may come from Eire.

It may form the EDGE of garden.

Use teeth to get hold of a BIT.

TEABERRY WANT (6, 6)	
LANCASHIRE EMILY (7, 6)	THE LINK IS .....
CHESHIRE LANE (7, 5)	
EMOTIVE LIZ SEE (6, 7)	

HOLLYWOOD ANAGRAMS ⭐⭐⭐

Above are four anagrams of films or film people. The number and length of words to find is shown in brackets. The four anagram solutions are all linked in some way – can you find the link?

NOURISHING NINE ⭐⭐

How many words of four letters or more can you track down in this game? At least one 'nourishing' word will contain all nine letters and all words must contain the central letter. Use each letter once only. No words with capital letters, foreign words, hyphens, or plurals and verb forms ending in -s are allowed.

UNDERDONE: 13 words
MEDIUM: 20 words
WELL DONE: 27 words

CROSSWORD ⭐⭐

Across

2 Distorts (6)

5 Fast running mammal (4)

6 Old-fashioned or conventional (6)

7 Religious group (4)

8 Affirmative word (3)

11 Mislay (4)

13 Disorderly crowd (6)

14 Mountain summit (4)

15 To obtain by intimidation (6)

Down

1 Cook in the oven (4)

2 Touchy (5)

3 Mark of wound (4)

4 Person may bless you after this (6)

7 The point from which something originates (6)

9 Rested (5)

10 Assist in a crime (4)

12 False, fake (4)

ON TARGET ⭐

Put the answers to the clues in the grid starting from the outside. Each answer has five letters and ends with the central letter E. When you've finished the outer ring, it will reveal the name of a hobby (7)

1 Nimble (5)

2 Magnanimous (5)

3 Web-footed large birds (5)

4 Depart (5)

5 The personality presented to the public (5)

6 Din (5)

7 To fly without engine (5)

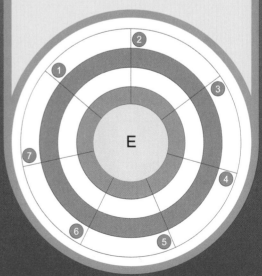

OCCUPATIONS

How many words of four letters or more can you track down in this game? At least one will be a nine letter occupation and all contain the central letter. Use each letter once only. No words with capitals, foreign words, hyphens, or plurals and verb forms ending in -s are allowed.

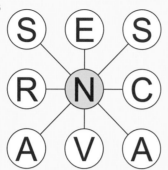

GOOD: 11 words, VERY GOOD: 14 words, EXCELLENT: 20 words

MONOPOLY WORDSEARCH ☆

The grid contains 13 Monopoly words hidden vertically, horizontally or diagonally. Can you find them all?

N	P	L	A	Y	E	R	O
B	A	N	K	E	R	O	J
P	R	O	P	E	R	T	Y
E	K	I	L	E	N	I	F
M	I	T	T	R	A	D	E
A	N	C	N	O	T	E	S
G	G	U	B	O	A	R	D
C	H	A	N	C	E	C	Y

AUCTION   CHANCE   LOAN   PROPERTY
BANKER   CREDITOR   NOTES   TRADE
BOARD   FINE   PARKING
    GAME   PLAYER

CONNECT THE DOTS

Join up the dots in the correct order starting from one. What does it reveal?

CODED CROSSWORD ★★★

Each number in the grid represents a different letter of the alphabet. Can you fill in the grid using the given letters to get you started?

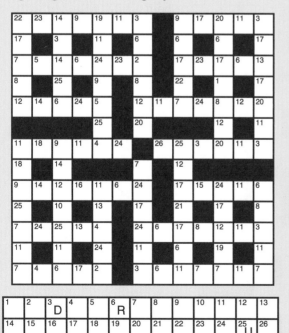

NATUREGRAMS ★★

Solve each clue, then rearrange the five letters in every answer to form a set of three mammals.

CLUES:
1 Planets composer
2 Crisped bread
3 Raised skin marking

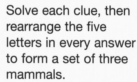

ODD ONE OUT ☆

Can you spot the odd one out in this sequence of numbers?

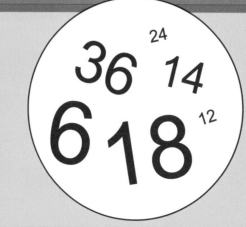

DIZZY DICTATION

Jeff's new secretary is having some trouble with dictation. Can you work out what he is trying to say in the following sentences?

1. AYE MUSSED CZECH ATE SEALINGS FOUR LEEKS.

2. WEAVE GROAN ROWS IS, TOO LIP SAND DAZE EASE.

3. EYES UP HOE SIDE LICHEN ICE STAY QUELL DUN, HANDSOME SAL ID.

NINE NUMBERS

Try to fill in the missing numbers.
Use the numbers 1 to 9 to complete the equations. Each number is only used once. Each row and column is an equation with the totals given below and to the right.

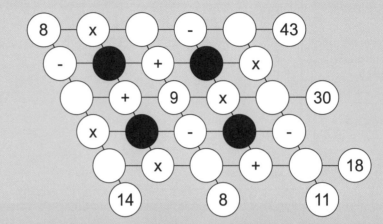

FORK AND KNIFE NUMBER PIC

Can you create a picture from the grid below?
Each number represents a group of shaded squares, so for example **3 2** means that on this row there is a group of 3 black squares to the left of a group of 2 black squares, with one or more white squares in between (there must be at least one white square in-between the groups, or the 3 and 2 would join up to become a 5). The numbers are always in order, so **4 2** means a group of 4 black squares to the left of a group of 2 black squares in that row, and **5/3** means a block of 5 black squares above a block of 3 black squares in that column.

CHAIN REACTION

Solve this puzzle by creating a 'chain reaction' of 20 five-letter words that run left to right, beginning in the upper-left hand corner, using the 19 two-letter tiles in the middle. A two-letter tile that ends one begins the next. Each tile will only be used once. The single letters already entered are the middle letters of the words you are to form. Start by finishing the word that begins GYP_ _.

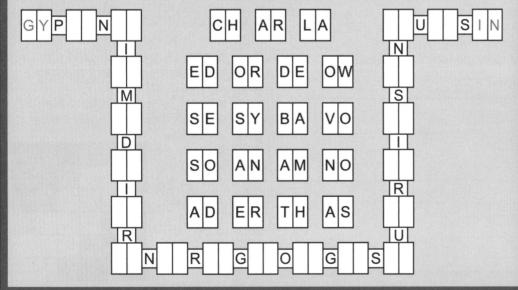

SUDOKU

To solve, fill in the grid so that every row, column and box contains the numbers 1 through 9.

9				8	7			
1	8				4	7		
			2	3				9
				2		9	7	
4	1		3			2		6
	9		4	7	6			
		3				5	2	
							9	7
	5		8			2	4	1

PAIR WHEELS ⭐⭐

Place each of the twelve pairs of letters into one of the circles in the grid, so that every line running through the central circle gives you a six-letter word with the middle letters OU.

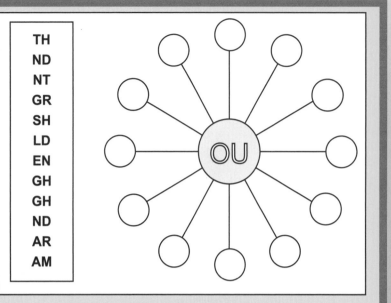

TH
ND
NT
GR
SH
LD
EN
GH
GH
ND
AR
AM

OU

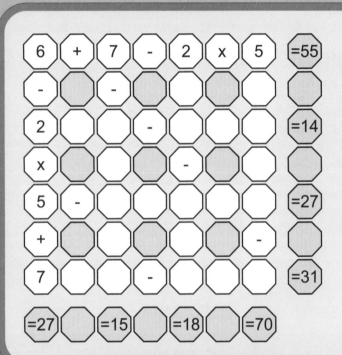

6	+	7	−	2	×	5	=55
−		−					
2				−			=14
×				−			
5		−					=27
+						−	
7			−				=31
=27		=15		=18		=70	

BLOCKBUSTERS ⭐⭐⭐

Complete the square by using each number and symbol provided in the top row ONCE only in every other row and column to equal the given answer. The first column and all the − signs have been put in to give you a start!

TRANSPORT SQUIRCLE ⭐

Put vowels in the circles and consonants in the squares to make words in all the vertical columns. Definitions of these words are given. When this has been done, the second and fifth horizontal lines will make the names of three modes of transport.

DEFINITIONS
1 Dependable
2 Slow a vehicle
3 Gambling money
4 Great merriment
5 Entice and trap
6 Japanese port
7 Rub hard
8 Works
9 Settle or understand

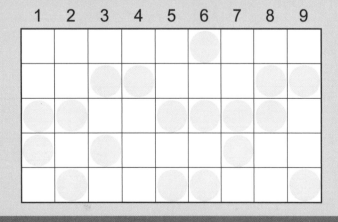

LITTLE TOUGHIE ⭐⭐⭐

Across
1 A note on string providing harmony (6)
5 Bit of brutal routine (3)
6 I'm cast amongst baddies! (3)
7 Determined group (3)
8 We will pursue eastern farm animal (3)
9 Hill dweller in Russian territory (3)
10 It's harsh, always, in South East (6)

Down
1 A vice was congenial (6)
2 Pets watch something in the road (4,3)
3 Record of socialist bureaucracy? (3-4)
4 Busy insect let off by winged type (6)

KAKURO ⭐⭐

In Kakuro, the numbers in the black squares refer to the SUMS of the digits 1–9 which you are to fill into the empty spaces. The number ABOVE the diagonal line refers to the empty spaces directly to the RIGHT of that number. A number BELOW the diagonal line refers to the empty spaces directly BELOW that number. No zeros are used here and a digit can only appear once in any one digit combo. Also bear in mind that all answers must be between 1 and 9.

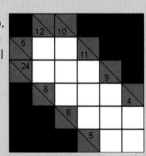

QUICK SPORTS QUIZ

1. Which English soccer player holds the record for scoring the most goals for his country; is it Gary Lineker or Bobby Charlton?

....

2. What surface is the tennis championships at Wimbledon played on?

....

3. What is the name of the darts player who has won the World Championships 13 times?

....

4. What is the name of the main baseball team from Arizona? Is it the Diamondbacks or the Goldbacks?

....

5. How many events are there in a decathlon?

....

SKELETON CROSSWORD

Below is an incomplete quick crossword grid. Can you solve the puzzle by fitting the answers to the clues correctly into the grid, along with the remaining blocks and clue numbers? A few blocks have been shaded to give you a start.

Across
3 Remove from office (6)
6 Sculptured figure (6)
7 On a ship (6)
8 Ooze (4)
11 Passage between seats (5)
12 Fly high in the air (4)
13 Border (4)
14 Was sick (5)
15 Letters meaning let it stand (4)
18 To slander or defame (6)
19 An angle (6)
20 Love unquestioningly (6)

Down
1 Enquires (4)
2 Hedge puzzle (4)
3 Complete lack of sound (4,7)
4 Profit from commercial transaction (8)
5 Throttle (8)
9 Make longer (8)
10 Animal that feeds off another (8)
16 Armored vehicle (4)
17 Open fruit pie (4)

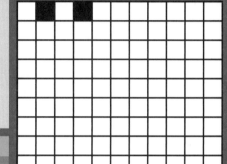

NATURAL NINE

Try and become king of the jungle in this natural puzzle. How many words of four letters or more can you track down? At least one will use all nine letters and all contain the central letter B. Use each letter once only. No words with capitals, foreign words, hyphens, or plurals are allowed.

The nine letter word is

....

PUSSYCAT STANDARD: 8 words
PANTHER STANDARD: 15 words
LION STANDARD: 23 words.

MATCH STICKS

Can you make seven squares by moving just four of the matches below?

PICTURE PHRASES

The images below represent three well known phrases. Look carefully and see if you can work out what they are.

1.

HO ROB OD

2.

M1Y L1I1F1E

3.

S K 8
| | | | |

CAGED ANIMALS

An animal has escaped from the zoo. To put him back in his cage, answer the eight clues and put them in the grid starting from the outermost circle. When this is done, the central circles starting clockwise from number nine will reveal the name of the animal that escaped.

1 A narrow zone (4)
2 Meat of a cow (4)
3 Period of time (4)
4 Country of the Incas (4)
5 Short skirt (4)
6 Domesticated mammal (4)
7 Arm or a leg (4)
8 Settee (4)

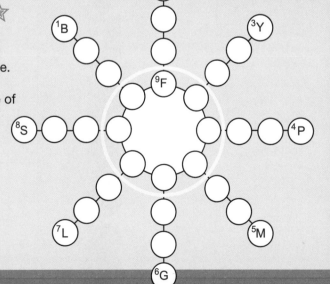

KAKURO

In Kakuro the numbers in the black squares refer to the SUMS of the digits 1-9 which you are to fill into the empty spaces. The number ABOVE the diagonal line refers to the empty spaces directly to the RIGHT of that number. A number BELOW the diagonal line refers to the empty spaces directly BELOW that number. No zeros are used here and a digit can only appear once in any particular digit combination

CLUB HOUSE

Hidden in the grid are six international golfers. Can you find them all?

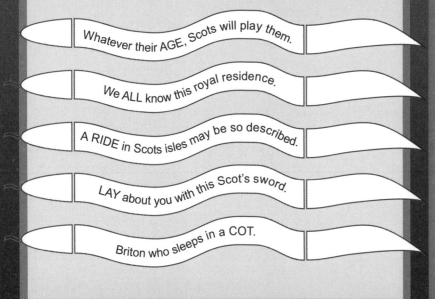

(circle word search grid)

```
V A Y C V U Z U
E S I N G H A C
W X I C J E L J
O G E K R A L C
O M Y M N A Z D
D I W G L A G S
S N E S O O G A
T R B S C V V W
```

NINE NUMBERS

Try to fill in the missing numbers. Use the numbers 1 to 9 to complete the equations. Each number is only used once. Each row and column is an equation with the totals given below and to the right.

4	-		x		-16
/		-		+	
	+	5	-		6
+		x		/	
7	-		/		4
9		-36		3	

NOURISHING NINE

How many words of four letters or more can you track down in this game? At least one 'nourishing' word will contain all nine letters and all words must contain the central letter. Use each letter once only. No words with capital letters, foreign words, hyphens, or plurals and verb forms ending in -s are allowed.

UNDERDONE: 13 words, MEDIUM: 20 words, WELL DONE: 27 words

```
  I  E  C
I     O
N  H
 N  A  C  L
   A  C  L
```

FIVE SNEAKY SNAKES

Can you add five letters to each of the words in capitals in the snakes below, to make another word which solves the clue? For example, by adding five letters to the clue 'A revolt can make you REEL', you can make the word REBELLION. Each of the answers share a Scottish theme.

Whatever their AGE, Scots will play them.

We ALL know this royal residence.

A RIDE in Scots isles may be so described.

LAY about you with this Scot's sword.

Briton who sleeps in a COT.

SUDOKU

To solve, fill in the grid so that every row, column and box contains the numbers 1 through 9.

	6	9	2	7	4	3	5	
3		7			9			4
		2	3	9	5		8	
		1	6		2	8	7	5
2	4			3	7		1	
	7		9	5	1	2	4	3
7	8	3			6		9	2
5			7	2		1	6	8
1	2	6	4	8	9	5		7

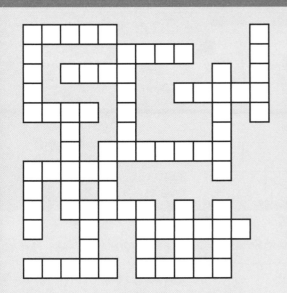

WORD FIT

Can you fit all the words linked with a pleasant country walk into the grid?

4 letter words
Bull
Farm
Hill
Lane
Path
Rain
Road
Sign
Tree

5 letter words
Birds
Boots
Field
Grass
Hedge
Horse
River
Sheep

6 letter words
Anorak
Flower
Gloves
Tavern

7 letter word
Tractor

JIG GRID ★ ★

Can you fit the blocks back into the grid to reveal, reading from left to right, seven girls names?

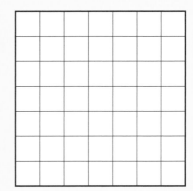

```
A B I      P A U    H A N
S A B      R A C    I N
V A L E R I  N I C

  E  G A I L
H A E L  R I N A E   S I O B L
H O L A      E          L
```

OPPOSITES ATTRACT ★

Place each of the tiles in the boxes below to form two words with opposite meaning.

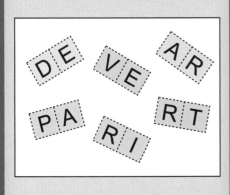

DE VE AR
PA RT
PA RI

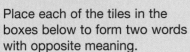

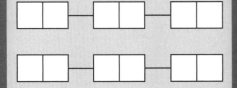

PYRAMID OF APPLES ★

Fill in the apples with numbers. Each one must equal the sum of the two apples below.

206
96
43
28
13 · 10
5

NUMBER HEX ★

Can you correctly enter six numbers into the Number Hex grid using the clues below? All are whole numbers below 10 and no two numbers are the same.

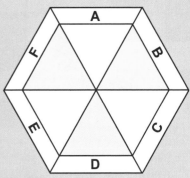

CLUES:
1 B is the number of days of the week containing the letter N
2 A multiplied by B equals F
3 E is the smallest number
4 C is the biggest number
5 F is twice B
6 C is an even number
7 D is A plus B

OCCUPATIONS

How many words of four letters or more can you track down in this game? At least one will be a nine letter occupation and all contain the central letter. Use each letter once only. No words with capitals, foreign words, hyphens, or plurals and verb forms ending in -s are allowed.

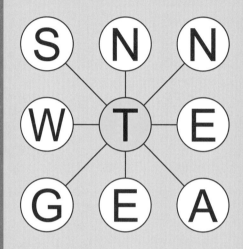

GOOD: 29 words
VERY GOOD: 34 words
EXCELLENT: 47 words

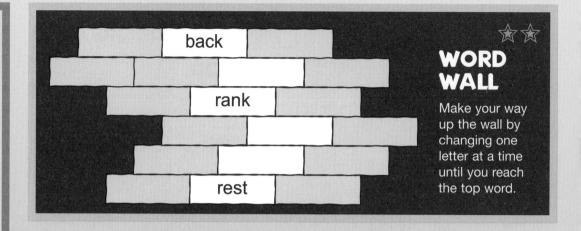

back

rank

rest

WORD WALL

Make your way up the wall by changing one letter at a time until you reach the top word.

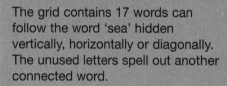

WHERE IN THE HUMAN BODY IS.......	
1. PITUITARY ?	
2. TRACHEA ?	
3. RADIUS BONE ?	
4. CORNEA ?	
5. PATELLA ?	
6. METATARSALS ?	

QUICK QUIZ QUESTIONS

Can you get all of these quiz questions correct?

CROSSWORD

Across
2 Symbol in Morse Code (4)
4 Walking with a limp (4)
5 Scheme (4)
6 Occasion for buying at reduced prices (4)
7 Program like Dynasty (4)
8 Sounds of a cat (4)

Down
1 Vegetable with leaves(7)
2 To lower in spirits (7)
3 Very strict or austere (7)

SEA WORDS WORDSEARCH

The grid contains 17 words can follow the word 'sea' hidden vertically, horizontally or diagonally. The unused letters spell out another connected word.

```
E A G L E R I F
Z W E E D S F B
E P O R T I O A
E C A G L R O S
R O H C N A D S
B H D E V I L A
O H O R S E O R
R S C O U T E G
```

ANCHOR   CHEST   FIRE   HORSE
BASS   CLIFF   FOOD   PORT
BOARD   DEVIL   GOING   SCOUT
BORNE   EAGLE   GRASS   WEED
BREEZE

BOOT MAZE

Can you find your way from top to bottom in the boot maze?

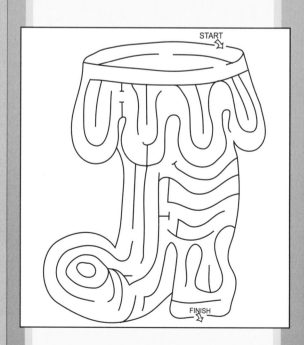

START

FINISH

NINE NUMBERS

Try to fill in the missing numbers. Use the numbers 1 to 9 to complete the equations. Each number is only used once. Each row and column is an equation with the totals given below and to the right.

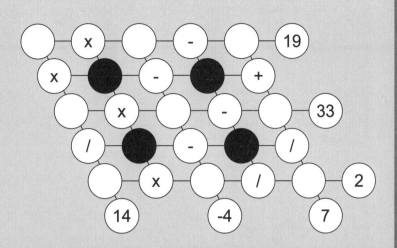

PLACE THE PLACES

To solve the puzzle place the letters from the place in capitals into the empty spaces in the grid. Four everyday words should be formed reading across the grid and 3 everyday words reading down.

D U R B A N

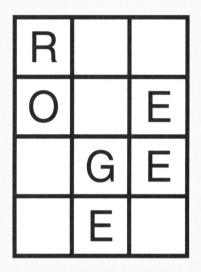

NAME THE DATE

Can you circle the correct date for these famous events?

1. The hot air balloon was invented in ...

1283	1783	1983

2. Chewing gum was invented in ...

1848	1948	1448

3. The compact disc was invented in ...

1872	1972	1772

ODD ONE OUT

Can you spot the odd one out in this sequence of words?

GEOGRAMS

Solve each clue, then rearrange the six letters in every answer to form a set of three cities.

CLUES:
1 Under narcotic influence
2 Flower pollen structure
3 Took illegally

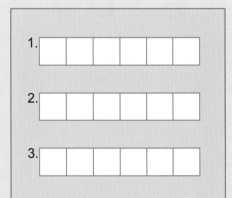

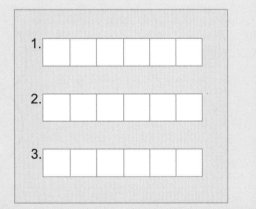

ADD A LETTER

Add one letter to each word in capitals to create a new word that answers the clue. The order of the letters does not need to be changed.

For example – 'I **BET** it's more superior' would be **BEST**.

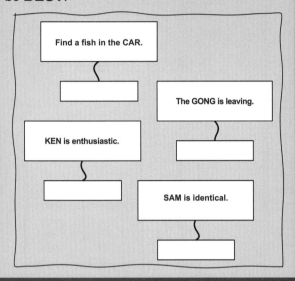

Find a fish in the CAR.

KEN is enthusiastic.

The GONG is leaving.

SAM is identical.

SUDOKU ⭐⭐

To solve, fill in the grid so that every row, column and box contains the numbers 1 through 9.

5	4							2
3		1	7	9		5		
	7		8		1	9		
9				7	4	6		
	8	2			9	4		3
6			3	4				
7			1	5			6	8
			9		6		5	

Solutions start on page 189

REBUS TOWER ⭐⭐⭐

Can you work out which common phrases are represented by each of the three diagrams in the tower below?

RELIEF

ERROR
ERROR

DAY DAY
DAY DAY

KAKURO ⭐⭐⭐

In Kakuro the numbers in the black squares refer to the SUMS of the digits 1-9 which you are to fill into the empty spaces. The number ABOVE the diagonal line refers to the empty spaces directly to the RIGHT of that number. A number BELOW the diagonal line refers to the empty spaces directly BELOW that number. No zeros are used here and a digit can only appear once in any particular digit combination.

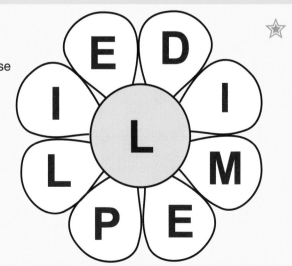

NATURAL NINE

Try and become king of the jungle in this natural puzzle.
How many words of four letters or more can you track down? At least one will use all nine letters and all contain the central letter L. Use each letter once only. No words with capitals, foreign words, hyphens, or plurals are allowed.

The nine letter word is

PUSSYCAT STANDARD: 7 words
PANTHER STANDARD: 11 words
LION STANDARD: 17 words

E D I
I L L
L M
P E

Solve this puzzle by creating a 'chain reaction' of 20 five-letter words that run left to right, beginning in the upper-left hand corner, using the 19 two-letter tiles in the middle. A two-letter tile that ends one begins the next. Each tile will only be used once. The single letters already entered are the middle letters of the words you are to form. Start by finishing the word that begins PRI_ _.

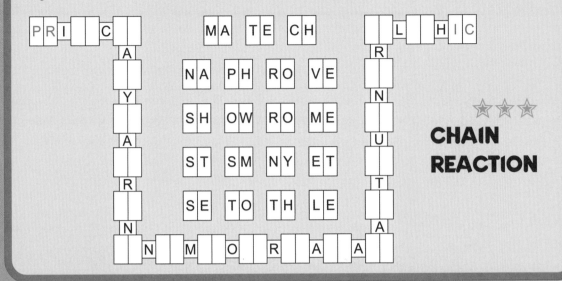

CHAIN REACTION

★ ★ ☆

BITS AND PIECES

★ ★ ☆

The tiles in the top grid are all jumbled up. Can you rearrange them in the grid below using only one tile from each column to reveal four related words and their theme?

P	A	AG	L	E
R	C	D	O	LI
LA	OO	S	O	A
N	S	VI	T	NI
MA	A	AR	N	E

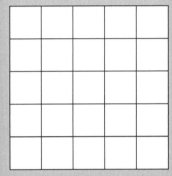

Can you solve the puzzle by fitting the answers to the clues correctly into the grid, along with the remaining blocks and clue numbers? A few blocks have been shaded to give you a start. This grid has been rotated by 180 degrees.

SKELETON CROSSWORD

★ ★ ☆

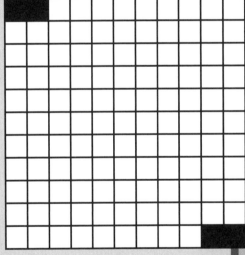

Across
1 Most imposing (8)
7 Accumulate (5)
8 Frighten (5)
9 Moves over ice (6)
10 Moray and conger, for instance (4)
12 Throw fishing line into water (4)
14 Refuse to accept (6)
17 Proverb (5)
18 Angry (5)
19 Driver's safety strap (4-4)

Down
1 Tropical fruit (5)
2 Solution to math-ematical problem (6)
3 Symbol in Morse Code (4)
4 Hackneyed like old joke (5)
5 Man's garment worn under jacket (9)
6 Large breed of dog (3,6)
11 Narrow gorge (6)
13 Stick driven into the ground (5)
15 Inappropriate (5)
16 Mark made in car body (4)

ADD THREE TO THREE

★ ★ ☆

Can you add three letters to the three words in red below to make another word which solves the clue? For example, by adding three letters to the clue 'BAN this fruit', you can make the word BANANA.

1. Is the **CAT** in the prickly plant?

2. It's no **SIN** to be unmarried.

3. The **BILL** is for a thousand million.

LITTLE TOUGHIE

★ ★ ☆

Across
2 Music that gives you the shakes? (4)
4 It's not wild, thanks to me (4)
5 Handing over sweets makes you self-satisfied (4)
6 It's light, for a start (4)
7 Men are bound to get it in the neck from them! (4)
8 Streams of liquid coming from planes (4)

Down
1 Luggage for slovenly woman (7)
2 Feels indignant about tenancy payments around South East (7)
3 State overthrow permitted in two lines (7)

BLOCKBUSTERS

Complete the square by using each number and symbol provided in the top row ONCE only in every other row and column to equal the given answer. The first column and all the - signs have been put in to give you a start!

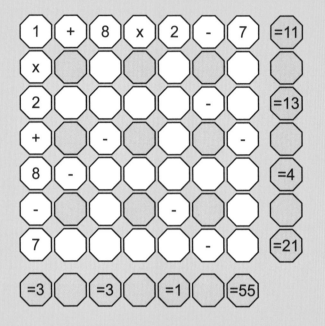

SPORTS QUIZ - RUGBY

1. Who won the Six Nations Championship in 2005?

....

2. What is the nickname of Sale rugby club?

....

3. England home internationals are played at which ground?

....

4. Which country does rugby star Keith Woods represent?

....

5. Which country were the last the join the six nations?

....

SUDOKU

To solve, fill in the grid so that every row, column and box contains the letters A through I.

	E	A		G	C			B
D	I	A	E	B	C	H		
C	B			H	D	E	F	A
		B		I	G	A	H	
B	A		D	H				
I				F		C		
	H	B	C		G			F
G	C		H			D	B	I
A	I	F	D		E	H	G	

LITTLE TOUGHIE

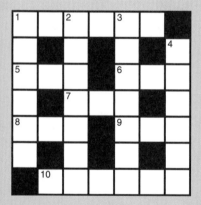

Across
1 One word for many learnt by actors (6)
5 Donkey as seen on front of sand (3)
6 Poem had something to give, we are told (3)
7 Small child has only small drink (3)
8 Preacher of sorts had to get flat (3)
9 Somehow make a living one way or the other (3)
10 Leave an uninhabited region (6)

Down
1 Vital food that gets a hammering? (6)
2 To make another shape, reel drunkenly round enclosure (7)
3 One with patron makes rope get entangled (7)
4 Failing which makes you leave country (6)

LETTER STEW

Use all the given letters in the stew to spell three words meaning enjoy.

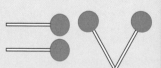

LOLLIPOPS

Can you put this lollipop sum right by moving just one lollipop?

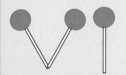

NOURISHING NINE

★★

How many words of four letters or more can you track down in this game? At least one 'nourishing' word will contain all nine letters and all words must contain the central letter. Use each letter once only. No words with capital letters, foreign words, hyphens, or plurals and verb forms ending in -s are allowed.

UNDERDONE: 13 words
MEDIUM: 20 words
WELL DONE: 27 words

KAKURO

★★

In Kakuro the numbers in the black squares refer to the SUMS of the digits 1-9 which you are to fill into the empty spaces. The number ABOVE the diagonal line refers to the empty spaces directly to the RIGHT of that number. A number BELOW the diagonal line refers to the empty spaces directly BELOW that number. No zeros are used here and a digit can only appear once in any particular digit combination.

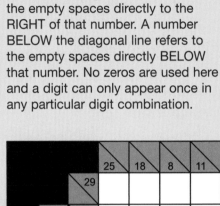

MOVIE HOUSE

★★★

Hidden in the grid are six Tom Hanks films. Can you find them all?

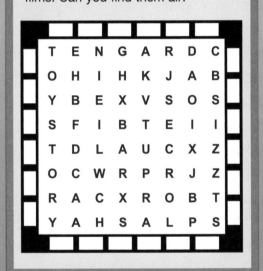

ANAGRAM LADDERS

★

Solve the anagrams below to reveal the names of seven birds. The shaded row in the middle will then reveal the name of another bird.

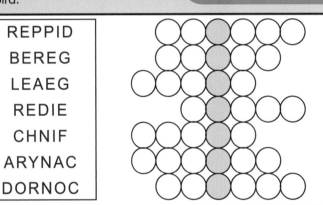

REPPID
BEREG
LEAEG
REDIE
CHNIF
ARYNAC
DORNOC

CAGED ANIMALS

An animal has escaped from the zoo. To put him back in his cage answer the eight clues and put them in the grid starting from the outermost circle. When this is done the central circle, starting clockwise from number nine, will reveal the name of the animal who escaped.

1 Tidings (4)
2 Amount of harvest (4)
3 Mr Coward, playwright (4)
4 A continent (4)
5 Encounter (4)
6 A theatre production (4)
7 Sea vessel (4)
8 Ballerina's skirt (4)

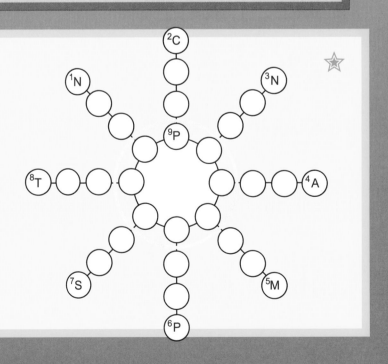

ON TARGET

Put the answers to the clues in the grid starting from the outside. Each answer has five letters and ends with the central letter L. When you've finished the outer ring will reveal the name of a UK soccer team (7)

1 Blacksmith's block (5)

2 Royal (5)

3 Bone of the head (5)

4 Bar from school (5)

5 Of the nose (5)

6 Cherub for instance (5)

7 Tag on garment (5)

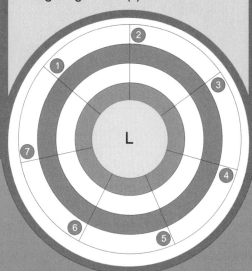

OCCUPATIONS

How many words of four letters or more can you track down in this game? At least one will be a nine letter occupation and all contain the central letter. Use each letter once only. No words with capitals, foreign words, hyphens, or plurals and verb forms ending in -s are allowed.

GOOD: 21 words
VERY GOOD: 25 words
EXCELLENT: 35 words

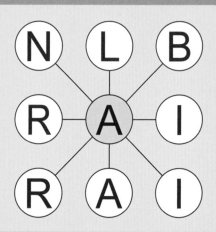

FLOWERY PHRASES

We have described a well-known saying using flowery language. Can you uncover the more familiar form? For example, 'An eruption in the cook pot' would be 'A Flash in the pan'.

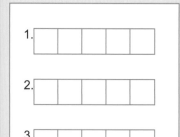

We are advised to discern with perspicacity the particular individual surface of a food staple made from flour, liquid, and a leavening agent upon which a congealed, yellowish emulsion churned from cream has been applied.

RIDDLE WORDS

Can you answer these word riddles with jobs?

Which job is also a book with lots of pictures?

Which job is also part of a book?

Which occupation also makes up part of the eye?

Which job is found at the top of the neck?

GEOGRAMS

Solve each clue, then rearrange the five letters in every answer to form a set of three capital cities.

CLUES:
1 Sets of two
2 Blood sucking insect
3 Building blocks

1.
2.
3.

1.
2.
3.

PICTURE PHRASES

The images below represent four well known phrases. Look carefully and see if you can work out what they are.

1. ME REPEAT

2. $\dfrac{111111111111}{\text{3 O'CLOCK}}$

3. 3S5A8F7E9T0Y7

4.

SHOP TEASE

Can you work out the answer to this teaser?

A shop has reduced the price of a toy car by 25% for a sale. By what percentage of the sales price must it be increased to put the toy car back up to its original price?

WORD WHEEL

For each of the circles, can you find two letters which, when placed in the middle, will form three six-letter words?

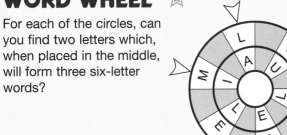

CROSSWORD

Across

2 Bunks in a ship (6)
5 Invoked upon (4)
6 Opposed, against (6)
7 Chair (4)
8 Pose for portrait (3)
11 Growth in number (4)
13 Raw army recruit (6)
14 Protected bird (4)
15 Garden clippers (6)

Down

1 Garden tool (4)
2 Rhythmic units in music (5)
3 Ripped (4)
4 Suddenly turn aside (6)
7 Gazes at fixedly (6)
9 Lock of hair (5)
10 To feel sorry for oneself (4)
12 Program like Dallas (4)

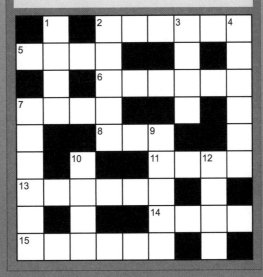

OPPOSITES ATTRACT

Place each of the tiles in the boxes below to form two words with opposite meaning.

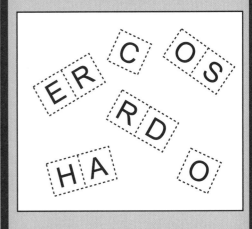

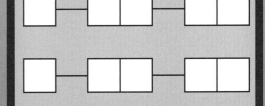

NATURE TRAIL

Find the plant that is growing inside the tree by removing all the letters that appear more than twice.

THE HIDDEN PLANT IS A

....

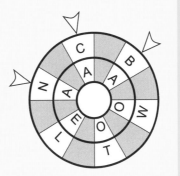

NATURAL NINE

Try and become king of the jungle in this natural puzzle.

How many words of four letters or more can you track down? At least one will use all nine letters and all contain the central letter G. Use each letter once only. No words with capitals, foreign words, hyphens, or plurals are allowed.

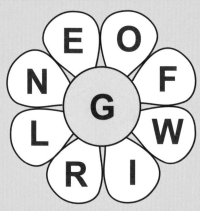

The nine letter word is

....

Pussycat standard: 12 words
Panther standard: 20 words
Lion standard: 28 words

COMMON WORDS

Your task here is to determine the answers to each set of tricky definitions below, as well as the word that is contained in all five of the set's answers. For example, if the five solutions were ERRAND, TERRIBLE, MERRY MEN, PREFERRED and PERRY, the word in the central circle would be ERR.

Clues:
1 Revolted
2 Hearth tools
3 Dixie cuties
4 Weights
5 Stomach

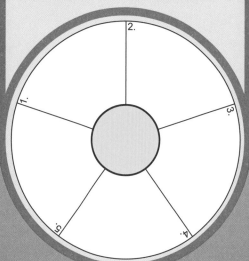

TV COMEDY SQUIRCLE

Put vowels in the circles and consonants in the squares to make words in all the vertical columns. Definitions of these words are given. When this has been done, the second and fourth horizontal lines will make three US comedies.

1	2	3	4	5	6	7	8	9

DEFINITIONS
1 Pungent
2 Large sea fish
3 Evil spirit
4 Wild animal
5 Excessive desire
6 Movie award
7 Unpleasant smell
8 Pass out
9 Be superior to

SUDOKU

To solve, fill in the grid so that every row, column and box contains the letters a to i.

c		f	b					
d	h			c	b			f
f	b			a	g	c	i	
a		d	b				i	g
h	i							d
	b		h					a
f		c	a	i	b	d	e	
d		a		c	f	i		

NINE NUMBERS

Try to fill in the missing numbers.

Use the numbers 1 to 9 to complete the equations. Each number is only used once. Each row and column is an equation with the totals given below and to the right.

1	+	8	−		3
−		+		+	
	+		+		18
×		+		−	
3	−		−		−6

−9	24	9

HOLLYWOOD ANAGRAMS

Below are four anagrams of films or film people. The number and length of words to find is shown in brackets. The four anagram solutions are all linked in some way – can you find the link?

VINDICATED ECHO (3, 2, 5, 4)

ASPIC RUSK JAR (8, 4)

STRONGHOLD FIRE (4, 2, 3, 5)

FATHER GATHER SWOP (3, 6, 2, 5)

THE LINK IS ......

....

ADD A LETTER

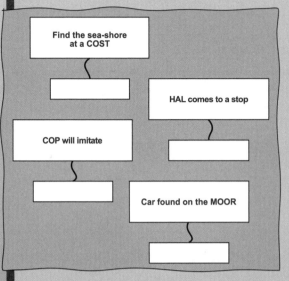

Find the sea-shore at a COST

HAL comes to a stop

COP will imitate

Car found on the MOOR

Add one letter to each word in capitals to create a new word that answers the clue. The order of the letters does not need to be changed.

For example – 'I BET it's more superior' would be BEST.

FIVE SNEAKY SNAKES

Can you add five letters to each of the words in capitals in the snakes below, to make another word which solves the clue? For example, by adding five letters to the clue 'A revolt can make you REEL', you can make the word REBELLION. Each of the answers share a common theme.

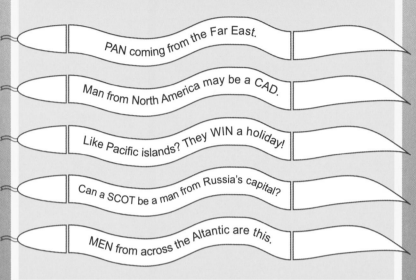

PAN coming from the Far East.

Man from North America may be a CAD.

Like Pacific islands? They WIN a holiday!

Can a SCOT be a man from Russia's capital?

MEN from across the Altantic are this.

PAIR WHEELS

Place each of the twelve pairs of letters into one of the circles in the grid, so that every line running through the central circle gives you a six-letter word with the middle letters EA.

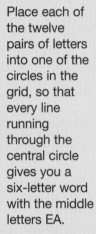

TH
DY
TR
SY
PL
GR
CR
ST
TE
SE
TY
BR

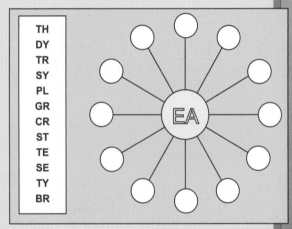

EA

SMILIE NUMBER PIC

Can you create a picture from the grid below?

Each number represents a group of shaded squares, so for example 3 2 means that on this row there is a group of 3 black squares to the left of a group of 2 black squares, with one or more white squares in between (there must be at least one white square in between the groups, or the 3 and 2 would join up to become a 5)
The numbers are always in order, so 4 2 means a group of 4 black squares to the left of a group of 2 black squares in that row, and 5/3 means a block of 5 black squares above a block of 3 black squares in that column.

CODED CROSS-WORD

Each number in the grid represents a different letter of the alphabet. Can you fill in the grid using the given letters to get you started?

1	2	3	4	5	6	7	8	9	10	11	12	13
L		E	A						P		T	
14	15	16	17	18	19	20	21	22	23	24	25	26

PICTURE TILES

Copy the contents of the tiles into the empty grid using the grid references to find the right places. What appears in the box?

	1	2	3	4
A				
B				
C				
D				
E				
F				

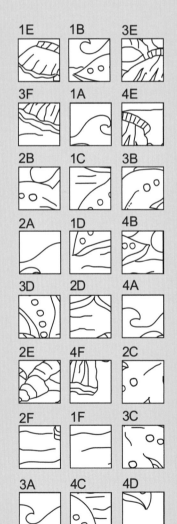

1E 1B 3E
3F 1A 4E
2B 1C 3B
2A 1D 4B
3D 2D 4A
2E 4F 2C
2F 1F 3C
3A 4C 4D

WORD FIT

Can you fit all the words linked with sales into the grid ?

Open
Rush
Shop
Till

5 letter words
Count
First
Goods
Label
Offer

3 letter words
Buy
Pay

4 letter words
Bill
Deal
Must

6 letter words
Change
Reduce
Return

7 letter words
Counter
Receipt

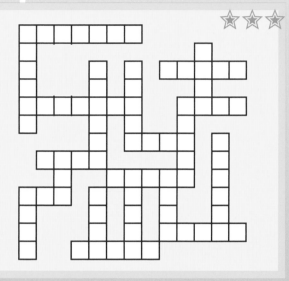

FAIRYTALE WORDSEARCH

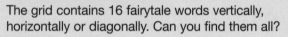

H	F	R	O	B	E	M	C
P	E	S	E	E	T	A	S
M	C	R	V	D	S	G	T
Y	A	I	O	T	A	I	E
N	L	I	L	I	E	C	E
E	A	E	D	M	B	R	D
A	P	P	L	E	G	N	A
D	R	A	G	O	N	S	D

The grid contains 16 fairytale words vertically, horizontally or diagonally. Can you find them all?

ANGEL · EVIL · NYMPH
APPLE · HERO · OGRE
BEAST · LOVE · PALACE
BEDTIME · MAGIC · ROBE
CASTLE · MAIDEN · STEED
DRAGON

NUMBER HEX

Can you correctly enter six numbers into the Number Hex grid using the clues below? All are whole numbers below 10 and no two numbers are the same.

CLUES
1 The bottom half of the grid adds up to 16
2 C is 9 times larger than E
3 The top half of the grid adds up to 20
4 F equals C minus E
5 A equals B plus E

NOURISHING NINE

How many words of four letters or more can you track down in this game? At least one 'nourishing' word will contain all nine letters and all words must contain the central letter. Use each letter once only. No words with capital letters, foreign words, hyphens, or plurals and verb forms ending in -s are allowed.

H B C
E O Y
O M N

UNDERDONE: 13 words
MEDIUM 22: words
WELL DONE: 33 words

KAKURO ⭐⭐

In Kakuro the numbers in the black squares refer to the SUMS of the digits 1-9 which you are to fill into the empty spaces. The number ABOVE the diagonal line refers to the empty spaces directly to the RIGHT of that number. A number BELOW the diagonal line refers to the empty spaces directly BELOW that number. No zeros are used here and a digit can only appear once in any particular digit combination.

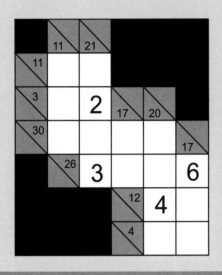

PYRAMID OF EGGS ⭐

Fill in the eggs with numbers, they must equal the sum of the two eggs below.

SUDOKU ⭐⭐⭐

To solve, fill in the grid so that every row, column and box contains the numbers 1 through 9.

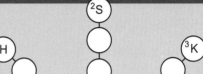

BLOCKBUSTERS ⭐⭐⭐

Complete the square by using each number and symbol provided in the top row ONCE only in every other row and column to equal the given answer. The first column and all the + signs have been put in to give you a start!

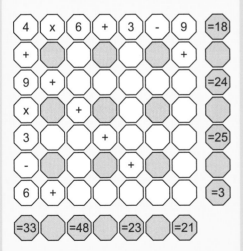

CAGED ANIMALS ⭐

An animal has escaped from the zoo. To put him back in his cage answer the eight clues and put them in the grid starting from the outermost circle. When this is done the central circles starting clockwise from number nine will reveal the name of the animal who escaped.

1 Strands on your head (4)
2 Fly high in the air (4)
3 Leg joint (4)
4 Indian woman's dress (4)
5 Eager or enthusiastic (4)
6 Unwanted plant (4)
7 Feature used to smell (4)
8 Woodwind instrument (4)

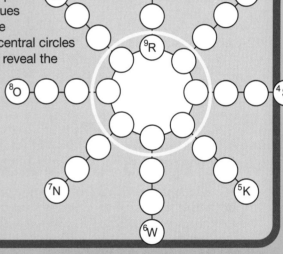

JIG GRID ⭐⭐⭐

Can you fit the blocks back into the grid to reveal, reading from left to right, seven flowers?

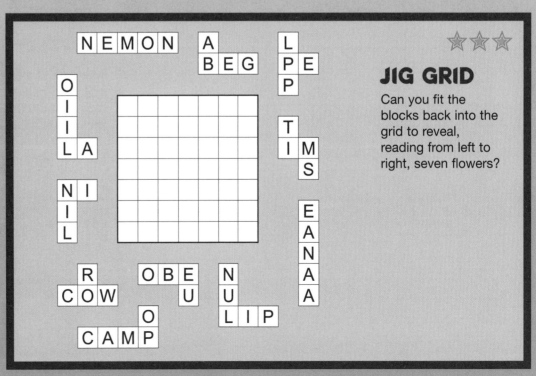

CROSSWORD

Across

1 Know someone's identity (9)

6 Tag on garment (5)

7 Fine curtain fabric (3)

8 Scream (4)

10 Neat and tidy (4)

13 Vegetable from a pod (3)

14 Obvious, plain (5)

16 Red Admiral for instance (9)

Down

1 Kind of team race (5)

2 Young lion (3)

3 Precious metal (4)

4 Inside (5)

5 Chew and swallow (3)

9 The smallest amount (5)

11 To wed (5)

12 Land measurement (4)

13 Inn (3)

15 Pixie (3)

NINE NUMBERS

Try to fill in the missing numbers. Use the numbers 1 to 9 to complete the equations. Each number is only used once. Each row and column is an equation with the totals given below and to the right.

6	x		+		38
-		x		/	
	x	3	+		25
x		+		+	
	x	1	-		-7
-2		16		11	

LETTER SWAP

Can you replace a letter from each word with a letter from the boxes below to reveal a well known saying? Each letter is used only once.

GO AT YOB WOUND
BY DINE MY

O E U S D L B

HOLLYWOOD ANAGRAMS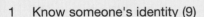

Below are four anagrams of films or film people. The number and length of words to find is shown in brackets. The four anagram solutions are all linked in some way – can you find the link?

HOLLANDAISE MUTE (6, 3, 6)	
FLITCH BUG (5,4)	THE LINK IS .....
EVELYN STEM WOK (6, 7)	
CONVENE EASEL (6, 6)	

COUNTING CRITTERS

Can you find the number that is represented by each animal face? You will find the total of the numbers below each column and to the right of each row.

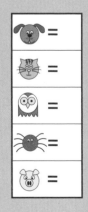

PAIR WHEELS ⭐⭐

Place each of the twelve pairs of letters into one of the circles in the grid, so that every line running through the central circle gives you a six-letter word with the middle letters NI.

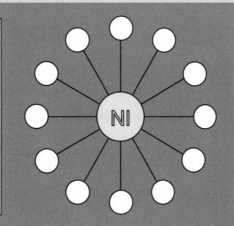

NG
TU
DE
ED
US
SH
PO
ES
OR
FI
JU
GE

EATING OUT WORDSEARCH ⭐⭐

The grid contains 14 words to do with eating out hidden vertically, horizontally or diagonally. The unused letters spell out another connected word.

BUFFET
CHEF
CHINESE
CREPE
DESSERT
ENTREE
GOURMET
ITALIAN
LUNCH
RICE
SAUCE
SERVICE
SPECIAL
TRAY

```
E N T R E E H G
L S R P O L O I
A T E F F U B T
I R S N R N S A
C A S M I C A L
E Y E T C H U I
P T D F E H C A
S E R V I C E N
```

OCCUPATIONS ⭐⭐⭐

How many words of four letters or more can you track down in this game? At least one will be a nine letter occupation and all contain the central letter. Use each letter once only. No words with capitals, foreign words, hyphens, or plurals and verb forms ending in -s are allowed.

GOOD: 22 words
VERY GOOD: 33 words
EXCELLENT: 47 words

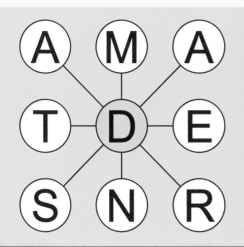

WHAT COMES FIRST? ⭐⭐

Can you work out which word commonly precedes the pairs of words below?

1. OLDIE / OPPORTUNITY

2. COACH / FRIGHT

3. FINGERS / CUP

4. DOLL / WEED

SUDOKU ⭐

To solve, fill in the grid so that every row, column and box contains the numbers 1 through 9.

5	3		1	8		7	6	2
	1			3	7	4	8	
	4		2	9	6		5	1
7	6	4			8	1		5
	5			1	3	9	4	
3		1		4		8		7
9	8		3	6	1		7	
1	7	3	4	5	2		9	
4		6		7	9	5		3

STEP LADDER ⭐⭐

Starting with the top word, change one letter at a time to make a new word at very step until you have reached the bottom word.

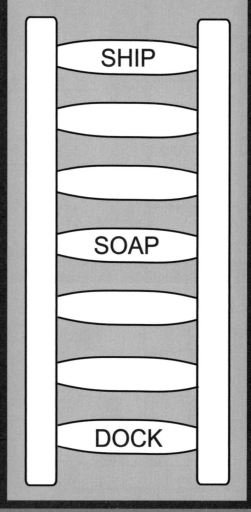

SHIP

SOAP

DOCK

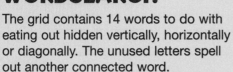

REBUS TOWER

★★★

Can you work out which common phrases are represented by each of the three diagrams in the tower below?

READING

JOKE
U

i i
BAG BAG

NOURISHING NINE

★★

How many words of four letters or more can you track down in this game? At least one 'nourishing' word will contain all nine letters and all words must contain the central letter. Use each letter once only. No words with capital letters, foreign words, hyphens, or plurals and verb forms ending in -s are allowed.

E N Y
R C I
L G E

UNDERDONE: 14 words
MEDIUM: 20 words
WELL DONE: 26 words

ADD A LETTER

★

Add one letter to each word in capitals to create a new word that answers the clue. The order of the letters does not need to be changed.

For example – 'I **BET** it's more superior' would be **BEST**.

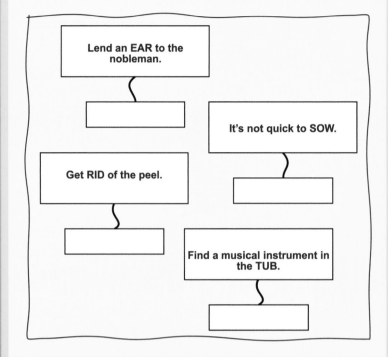

Lend an EAR to the nobleman.

It's not quick to SOW.

Get RID of the peel.

Find a musical instrument in the TUB.

SUDOKU

★★

To solve, fill in the grid so that every row, column and box contains the numbers 1 through 9.

		8	9	5		7		4
	7			8			3	5
	2		3		7			8
				4				
		7				8		
3	2	7	6	1				9
		5			9			
	4			2	9	8	1	6
		9	1			5		7

ON TARGET

★

Put the answers to the clues in the grid starting from the outside. Each answer has five letters and ends with the central letter E. When you've finished, the outer ring will reveal the name of a game (7)

1 Corn crop (5)
2 Love (5)
3 Distance gun will fire (5)
4 Emblem of office (5)
5 Soup spoon (5)
6 Dodge (5)
7 Tomato liquid for chips (5)

LITTLE TOUGHIE

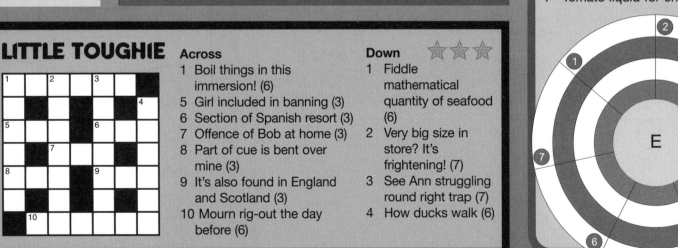

Across
1 Boil things in this immersion! (6)
5 Girl included in banning (3)
6 Section of Spanish resort (3)
7 Offence of Bob at home (3)
8 Part of cue is bent over mine (3)
9 It's also found in England and Scotland (3)
10 Mourn rig-out the day before (6)

Down
1 Fiddle mathematical quantity of seafood (6)
2 Very big size in store? It's frightening! (7)
3 See Ann struggling round right trap (7)
4 How ducks walk (6)

ADD THREE TO THREE

Can you add three letters to the three words in red below to make another word which solves the clue? For example, by adding three letters to the clue 'BAN this fruit', you can make the word BANANA.

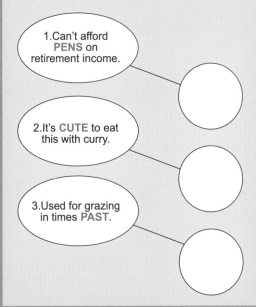

1. Can't afford **PENS** on retirement income.

2. It's **CUTE** to eat this with curry.

3. Used for grazing in times **PAST**.

BITS AND PIECES

Can you rearrange the tiles in the top grid are all jumbled up. Can you rearrange them in the grid below using only one tile from each column to reveal four related words and their theme?

C	WE	X	A	DO
OV	LO	CO	E	ER
T	ER	U	IN	G
S	U	A	T	RS
TR	O	TH	SE	T

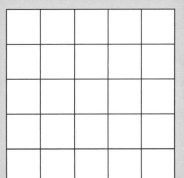

BIRD BOXES

Shade in all the numbers that can divide into 28 exactly to reveal a hidden bird.

14	4	2	15	6	13	3	2	6	9	5	14
7	5	12	8	10	5	15	14	3	7	8	4
2	6	11	3	15	12	10	4	11	4	15	2
14	4	7	13	9	3	13	7	14	2	4	7
3	8	15	2	14	10	6	8	10	12	3	8
10	9	11	4	13	7	2	14	3	5	11	9
6	12	3	7	5	14	11	7	8	13	9	5
3	5	13	10	6	4	7	2	11	6	3	11

BLOCKBUSTERS

Complete the square by using each number and symbol provided in the top row ONCE only in every other row and column to equal the given answer. The first column and all the x signs have been put in to give you a start!

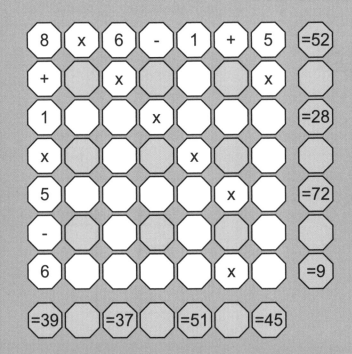

HEART NUMBER PIC

Can you create a picture from the grid below?

Each number represents a group of shaded squares, so for example 3 2 means that on this row there is a group of 3 red squares to the left of a group of 2 green squares. The numbers are always in order, so 4 2 means a group of 4 red squares to the left of a group of 2 green squares in that row, and 5 3 means a block of 5 green squares above a block of 3 red squares in that column.

NATURAL NINE

Try and become king of the jungle in this natural puzzle.

How many words of four letters or more can you track down? At least one will use all nine letters and all contain the central letter M. Use each letter once only. No words with capitals, foreign words, hyphens, or plurals are allowed.

The nine letter word is

....

PUSSYCAT STANDARD: 7 words
PANTHER STANDARD: 11 words
LION STANDARD: 15 words

MATCH STICKS ★★★

Can you make seven squares by moving only two matches?

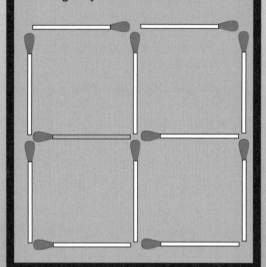

KAKURO ★★★

In Kakuro the numbers in the black squares refer to the SUMS of the digits 1-9 which you are to fill into the empty spaces. The number ABOVE the diagonal line refers to the empty spaces directly to the RIGHT of that number. A number BELOW the diagonal line refers to the empty spaces directly BELOW that number. No zeros are used here and a digit can only appear once in any particular digit combination.

NATURE TRAIL ★★

Find the plant that is growing inside the tree by removing all the letters that appear more than twice.

THE HIDDEN PLANT IS A

....

SUDOKU ★★★

To solve, fill in the grid so that every row, column and box contains the numbers 1 through 9.

PLACE THE PLACES ★★

To solve the puzzle place the letters from the place in capitals into the empty spaces in the grid. Four everyday words should be formed reading across the grid and three everyday words reading down.

S A H A R A

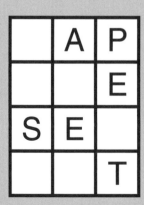

PAIR WHEELS

Place each of the twelve pairs of letters into one of the circles in the grid, so that every line running through the central circle gives you a six-letter word with the middle letters TI.

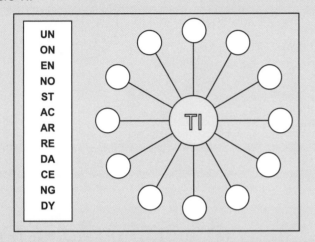

UN
ON
EN
NO
ST
AC
AR
RE
DA
CE
NG
DY

TI

HOLLYWOOD ANAGRAMS

Below are four anagrams of films or film people. The number and length of words to find is shown in brackets. The four anagram solutions are all linked in some way – can you find the link?

HEARTBURN HIKE PEN (9,7)		
FALSELY LID (5, 5)	THE LINK IS	
FORESIDE JOT (3,6)	------------	
ENGLAND JACK SO (6, 7)		

ANAGRAM LADDERS

Solve the anagrams on the left to reveal the names of seven rivers. The shaded row in the middle will then reveal the name of another river.

EED
SEMREY
RELOI
REAW
TNTRE
UBENAD
NETY

ADDING GRIDS

Place any digits 0 to 9 into the empty circles. When complete each row should add up to the figures on the right and each column to the figures below. The shaded numbers are the total of the diagonal circles.

			23
1		9	28
	6		21
2			10
2	0		8

22	11	18	16	16

SKELETON CROSSWORD

Below is an incomplete quick crossword grid. Can you solve the puzzle by fitting the answers to the clues correctly into the grid, along with the remaining blocks and clue numbers? A few blocks have been shaded to give you a start. This grid has been rotated by 180 degrees.

Across
1 One who brings a charge in court (10)
7 State of unconsciousness (4)
8 Routes (5)
9 Obese (3)
10 Definite article (3)
12 Support on car seat (4-4)
15 Loathed (8)
19 A can (3)
20 Sphere (3)
21 Kind of code (5)
22 Fit plates to horse's feet (4)
23 Greengrocer for instance (10)

Down
2 Disturbance by unruly mob (4)
3 Move over ice (5)
4 Restored to good health (5)
5 Business (5)
6 Take exam again (5)
7 Motive, reason (5)
11 Republic in Caribbean (5)
12 Garden implement (3)
13 Drive out, clear (3)
14 Gaze fixedly (5)
15 Tips (5)
16 Trunk of human body (5)
17 Slice of meat (5)
18 Follow in consequence (5)
20 Seep (4)

OCCUPATIONS ★★★

How many words of four letters or more can you track down in this game? At least one will be a nine letter occupation and all contain the central letter. Use each letter once only. No words with capitals, foreign words, hyphens, or plurals and verb forms ending in -s are allowed.

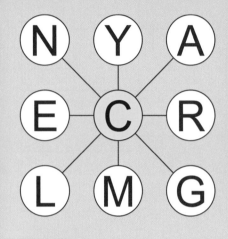

GOOD: 20 words
VERY GOOD: 28 words
EXCELLENT: 39 words

COMMON WORDS ★★★

Your task here is to determine the answers to each set of tricky definitions below, as well as the word that is contained in all five of the set's answers. For example, if the five solutions were ERRAND, TERRIBLE, MERRY MEN, PREFERRED and PERRY, the word in the central circle would be ERR.

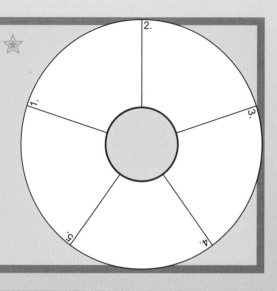

CLUES:
1 Xmas bird
2 Teen idol
3 Lively exercises
4 General Lee
5 Confirm

WORD SPLITZ ★

Each row of ten letters can be split into two five letter important people. These words read from left to right and are in order.

For example SMOKOSUENK can be split to reveal SKUNK and MOOSE.

1 B C A H R I O N E F
2 J M A U Y D O G E R
3 N Q U O E B E L E N
4 R V A I B C B I A R

CHAIN REACTION ★★★

Solve this puzzle by creating a 'chain reaction' of 20 five-letter words that run left to right, beginning in the upper-left hand corner, using the 19 two-letter tiles in the middle. A two-letter tile that ends one begins the next. Each tile will only be used once. The single letters already entered are the middle letters of the words you are to form. Start by finishing the word that begins FUN_ _.

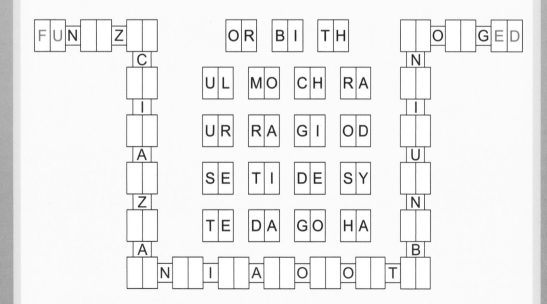

CROSSWORD ★

Across
2 Sit for photograph (4)
4 Ingredient of stuffing (4)
5 Growl of lion (4)
6 Enclosure of bars (4)
7 People who man aircraft (4)
8 Units of length (4)

Down
1 Parcel (7)
2 Flawless (7)
3 Hit with open hand (7)

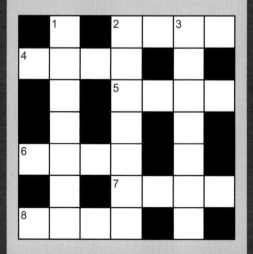

NAME THE DATE

Can you circle the correct date for these famous events?

1. Queen Elizabeth II came to the British throne in...		
1922	1853	1953

2. Queen Victoria died in...		
1901	1801	1701

3. Prince Charles married Diana in the year...		
1924	1981	1999

JIG GRID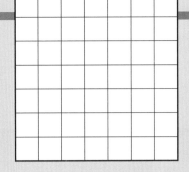

Can you fit the blocks back into the grid to reveal, reading from left to right, seven US states?

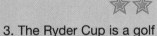

NINE NUMBERS

Try to fill in the missing numbers.
Use the numbers 1 to 9 to complete the equations. Each number is only used once. Each row and column is an equation with the totals given below and to the right.

4	x		+		33
x		+		-	
	+	9	/		5
-		+		-	
	+	8	/		10
22	24	1			

SPORTS QUIZ – GOLF

1. What is the name of the golf club usually used to escape from bunkers?

....

2. From which country does Colin Montgomerie hail from?

....

3. The Ryder Cup is a golf event between which two teams?

....

4. Which golfer is known as 'The Big Easy'?

....

5. How many shots under par does a player need to shoot to score an eagle?

....

NURSERY BLOCKS

Rearrange each column of letters and write them in the grid to reveal the first two lines of a well known nursery rhyme. Some of the letters have been put in to give you a head start.

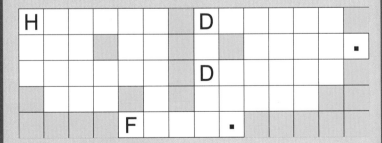

NATUREGRAMS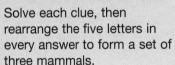

Solve each clue, then rearrange the five letters in every answer to form a set of three mammals.

CLUES:
1 Land next to water
2 Rich cake
3 Straw bundles

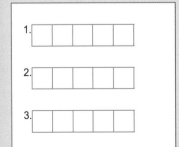

CODED CROSSWORD

Each number in the grid represents a different letter of the alphabet. Can you fill in the grid using the given letters to get you started?

22		15		19		1		21		16
19	9	1	1	24	1		16	1	22		8
	1		9		22		16		9		2
9	22	26	16		3	13	22	6	17		
		1		7		23		1		1	
16	1	22	16	12	6		16		26		8
	21			26		15			10		
16	20	12	7	8		16	7	11	3	1	1
	8		6		10		19		5		
10	12	6	25	5	9	12	9		9	5	26	16
	23		5		1		22		6		7
13	1	22	9	3		3	14	1	8	15	1
	18		1		3		1		18		1

1	2	3	4	5	6	7	8	9 R	10	11	12	13
14	15	16	17	18	19	20	21	22 A	23	24	25	26 G

FIVE SNEAKY SNAKES

Can you add five letters to each of the words in capitals in the snakes below, to make another word which solves the clue? For example, by adding five letters to the clue 'A revolt can make you REEL', you can make the word REBELLION. Each of the answers share a common theme.

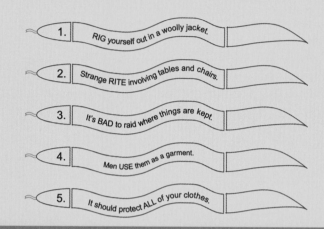

1. RIG yourself out in a woolly jacket.
2. Strange RITE involving tables and chairs.
3. It's BAD to raid where things are kept.
4. Men USE them as a garment.
5. It should protect ALL of your clothes.

LOLLIPOPS

By removing two of the lollipops below can you make four squares?

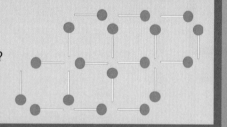

BIRD BOXES

Shade in all the letters that appear in the words 'NIGHT TIME' to reveal a hidden bird.

T	I	E	P	Y	O	W	K	S	H	F	C
G	X	N	L	B	V	J	U	F	N	X	O
M	I	H	W	W	F	Y	C	Z	E	U	K
B	P	W	C	K	W	Z	L	X	T	P	B
V	J	T	S	U	P	T	A	S	M	V	L
C	S	G	Y	E	X	I	J	Z	T	F	W
O	L	I	L	H	B	T	Y	V	G	W	O
F	U	N	G	I	M	E	K	W	C	S	J

TV PROGRAM TYPES SQUIRCLE

Put vowels in the circles and consonants in the squares to make words in all the vertical columns. Definitions of these words are given. When this has been done, the first and third horizontal lines will make the names of four kinds of TV program.

DEFINITIONS
1 Cinema entrance hall
2 Tube for bike tyre
3 Yorkshire city in the UK
4 Grasscutter
5 Indian class
6 Beginning
7 Elk
8 Precise
9 Storehouse

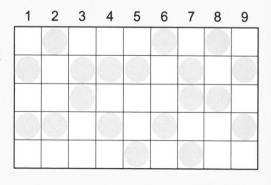

KAKURO

In Kakuro the numbers in the black squares refer to the SUMS of the digits 1-9 which you are to fill into the empty spaces. The number ABOVE the diagonal line refers to the empty spaces directly to the RIGHT of that number. A number BELOW the diagonal line refers to the empty spaces directly BELOW that number. No zeros are used here and a digit can only appear once in any particular digit combination.

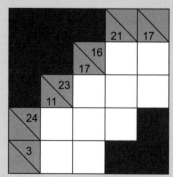

SUDOKU ⭐

To solve, fill in the grid so that every row, column and box contains the numbers 1 through 9.

1		8	7	6	2	4		5
	7	3	5	9	1		2	8
6		5			3	9	1	7
7	5	1		4		2	9	
3	6		2		5			4
	4			9	5	6	1	
5	3	6	1		8	7	4	
	8			3	4	1		6
9	1		6	5	7		8	2

ARROWS ⭐

Put the following numbers in the arrows below:

1 3 3 3 3 4 5 5

Be careful though.
The total numbers in the 3 arrows pointing at each other must add up to 10.

The total numbers in the arrows which are back to back must add up to 6.

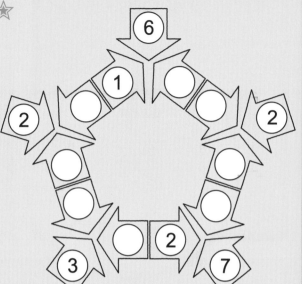

MOVIE HOUSE ⭐⭐⭐

Hidden in the grid are six Oscar nominated films from 2006. Can you find them all?

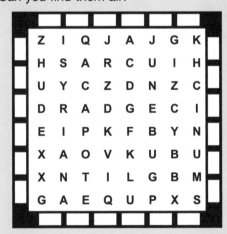

GEOGRAMS ⭐⭐

Solve each clue, then rearrange the six letters in every answer to form a set of three cities.

CLUES:
1. One of the Munsters
2. Speed up
3. West Indian island

1. ☐☐☐☐☐☐
2. ☐☐☐☐☐☐
3. ☐☐☐☐☐☐

1. ☐☐☐☐☐☐
2. ☐☐☐☐☐☐
3. ☐☐☐☐☐☐

SHIP NUMBER PIC ⭐⭐

Can you create a picture from the grid below?
Each number represents a group of shaded squares, so for example
 means that on this row there is a group of 3 black squares to the left of a group of 2 black squares, with one or more white squares in between (there must be at least one white square in between the groups, or the 3 and 2 would join up to become a 5).
The numbers are always in order, so means a group of 4 black squares to the left of a group of 2 black squares in that row, and 5 means a block 3 of 5 black squares above a block of 3 black squares in that column.

ODD ONE OUT

Can you spot the odd one out in this sequence of numbers?

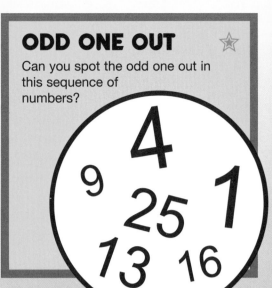

WORD WHEEL

For each of the circles, can you find two letters which, when placed in the middle, will form three six-letter words?

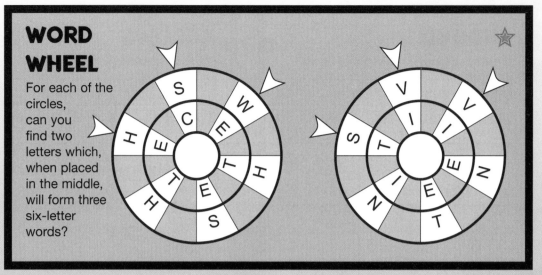

ALIENS WORDSEARCH

The grid contains 14 alien words hidden vertically, horizontally or diagonally. Can you find them all?

ABDUCT
BEAM
BRIGHT
CREATURE
EARTH
GALAXY
LIFT

LIGHT
NOISE
PLANET
SAUCER
SPIN
TRACK
TRAVEL

E	S	I	O	N	I	P	S
T	R	A	C	K	M	G	A
T	C	U	D	B	A	L	U
E	K	F	T	L	E	E	C
N	W	F	A	A	B	V	E
A	I	X	R	E	E	A	R
L	Y	T	H	G	I	R	B
P	H	L	I	G	H	T	C

PLACE THE PLACES

To solve the puzzle place the letters from the place in capitals into the empty spaces in the grid. Four everyday words should be formed reading across the grid and three everyday words reading down.

A L B E R T A

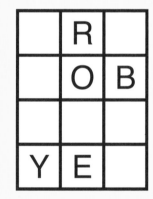

NUMBER HEX

Can you correctly enter six numbers into the Number Hex grid using the clues below? All are whole numbers below 10 and no two numbers are the same.

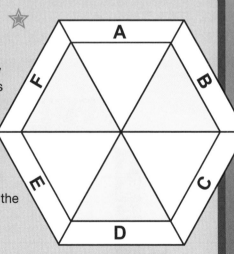

CLUES:
1 The top half of the grid adds up to 1 more than the bottom
2 B is twice F
3 E is 9 times bigger than D
4 B is the number of legs on 3 chickens

KAKURO

In Kakuro the numbers in the black squares refer to the SUMS of the digits 1-9 which you are to fill into the empty spaces. The number ABOVE the diagonal line refers to the empty spaces directly to the RIGHT of that number. A number BELOW the diagonal line refers to the empty spaces directly BELOW that number. No zeros are used here and a digit can only appear once in any particular digit combination.

NATURAL NINE

Try and become king of the jungle in this natural puzzle.

How many words of four letters or more can you track down? At least one will use all nine letters and all contain the central letter E. Use each letter once only. No words with capitals, foreign words, hyphens, or plurals are allowed.

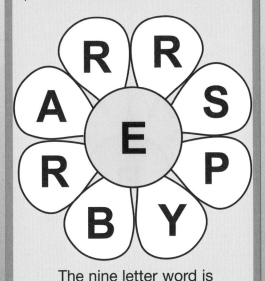

The nine letter word is

....

PUSSYCAT STANDARD: 8 words
PANTHER STANDARD: 14 words
LION STANDARD: 24 words

SUDOKU

To solve, fill in the grid so that every row, column and box contains the numbers 1 through 9.

4	8		7	5			3	
	6					1		7
3		9			4			
			3	9	7			
6				7				5
	5			6	8		9	1
	4				5		7	
8	3			4	6		1	2
9		5		2	7		8	

BLOCKBUSTERS

Complete the square by using each number and symbol provided in the top row ONCE only in every other row and column to equal the given answer. The first column and all the + signs have been put in to give you a start!

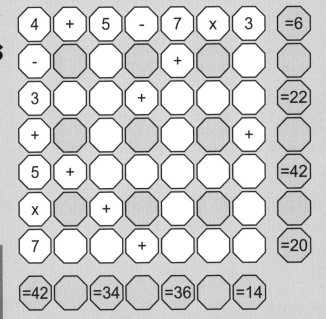

WORD FIT

Can you fit all the words linked with time into the grid below?

3 letter words
End
Eon
Era
Old

4 letter words
Ever
Gone
Hour
July
June
Then
Week
Year

5 letter words
April
Early
Until

6 letter words
Decade
During
Period
Thence
Timely

7 letter word
October

8 letter word
Outdated

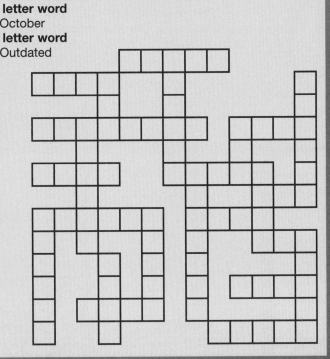

PYRAMID OF BRICKS

Fill in the bricks with numbers, they must equal the sum of the two bricks below.

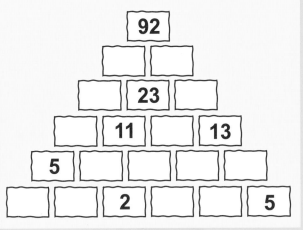

PAIR WHEELS

Place each of the twelve pairs of letters into one of the circles in the grid, so that every line running through the central circle gives you a six-letter word with the middle letters RT.

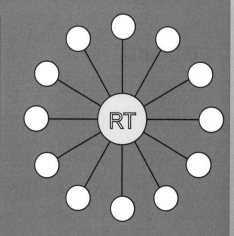

HS
EA
LE
TU
WO
LY
ED
PA
HY
DA
CA
ON

RT

NATURAL NINE

Try and become king of the jungle in this natural puzzle.
How many words of four letters or more can you track down? At least one will use all nine letters and all contain the central letter B. Use each letter once only. No words with capitals, foreign words, hyphens, or plurals are allowed.

The nine letter word is

....

PUSSYCAT STANDARD: 7 words
PANTHER STANDARD: 11 words
LION STANDARD: 16 words

PEACE WORDSEARCH

The grid contains 16 words to do with peace hidden vertically, horizontally or diagonally. When finished there should be no letters remaining.

ACCORD
CALM
CARE
COMFORT
CONTENT
EASE

EDEN
PEACE
PLACATE
PRAISE
READ
REPOSE

REST
SECURE
SHELTER
SLEEP

```
R E P O S E C S
P E E L S O H E
L R S M N E D C
A A A T L E R U
C C E T N A O R
A N E P E A C E
T R O F M O C A
E S I A R P A D
```

SKELETON CROSSWORD

Below is an incomplete quick crossword grid. Can you solve the puzzle by fitting the answers to the clues correctly into the grid, along with the remaining blocks and clue numbers? A few blocks have been shaded to give you a start. This grid has been rotated by 180 degrees.

Across
6   In an inconsistent and unpredictable way (11)
7   Diplomacy (4)
9   System of sound reproduction (6)
11 Against (4)
13 Frank, the English boxer (5)
14 Area of natural beauty in Cumbria (5)
16 Stalk (4)
18 Discarded waste (6)
20 Troubles (4)
22 Means of fighting off attacker (4-7)

Down
1   A direction (4)
2   Loose robe (6)
3   In front of all others (5)
4   Ceremonial staff of office (4)
5   Woodland flower (8)
8   Large passenger plane (8)
10 Roof slab (4)
12 Facial feature (4)
15 Astounded (6)
17 Person who perseveres (5)
19 Trifling argument (4)
21 Top tennis player (4)

HOLLYWOOD ANAGRAMS

Below are four anagrams of films or film people. The number and length of words to find is shown in brackets. The four anagram solutions are all linked in some way – can you find the link?

LAY DOWN LEO (5, 5)		
COARSENESS TRIM (6, 8)	THE LINK IS	
ORCHID CHECK FLAT (6, 9)		
BULKIEST CRANKY (7, 7)		

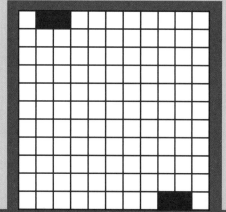

NINE NUMBERS

Try to fill in the missing numbers. Use the numbers 1 to 9 to complete the equations. Each number is only used once. Each row and column is an equation with the totals given below and to the right.

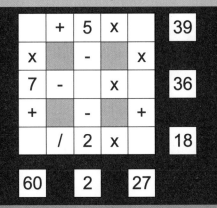

	+	5	x		39
x		-		x	
7	-		x		36
+		-		+	
	/	2	x		18
60		2		27	

BATTLESHIPS ★★

There are five ships hidden in the grid. Look at the key to see which ships you have to find. The numbers on the grid tell you how many squares of each row or column part of a ship is found in. To get you started we've put a few parts of ships (in red) and a few squares with no ships (in black).

HINTS: Begin by shading in all the misses (all the columns which have a nought in them) as there re no ships here. When you have found a full ship you can shade all the blocks around that ship as misses because none of the ships are touching.

HIDDEN SHIPS

1 AIRCRAFT CARRIER	
4 SUBMARINES	

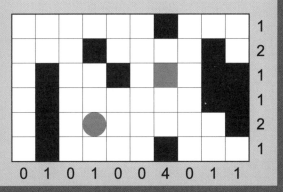

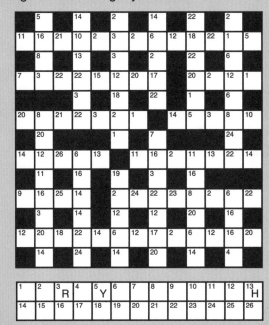

LITTLE TOUGHIE ★★★

Across

2 You'll get the bird for no score (4)

4 Note monkey having a yawn (4)

5 Victim of hunt at the party? (4)

6 Cover in mud from the bakery? (4)

7 Charge right over hazard at sea (4)

8 The man at athletics event (4)

Down

1 Competitive struggle in beastly heat (3,4)

2 Unusual red set's for last course (7)

3 Rough climb for learner in slope of road (7)

CODED CROSSWORD ★★★

Each number in the grid represents a different letter of the alphabet. Can you fill in the grid using the given letters to get you started?

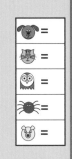

OPPOSITES ATTRACT

Place each of the tiles in the boxes below to form two words with opposite meaning.

LA ER RM FO TT ER

COUNTING CRITTERS ★

Can you find the number that is represented by each animal face? You will find the total of the numbers below each column and to the right of each row.

WORD SPLITZ

Each row of ten letters can be split into two five-letter boats. These words read from left to right and are in order.

For example SMOKOSUENK can be split to reveal SKUNK and MOOSE.

1. B C A A R N G E O E
2. F K E A R Y R A Y K
3. L C I R A N F E R T
4. Y S A C C H U T L L

KAKURO

In Kakuro the numbers in the black squares refer to the SUMS of the digits 1-9 which you are to fill into the empty spaces. The number ABOVE the diagonal line refers to the empty spaces directly to the RIGHT of that number. A number BELOW the diagonal line refers to the empty spaces directly BELOW that number. No zeros are used here and a digit can only appear once in any particular digit combination.

LITTLE TOUGHIE

Across

1 Crazy bird (6)

5 In the navy one made rapid progress (3)

6 Supporter in the cooler (3)

7 Vessel of war blows vehicle up (3)

8 English go for conceit (3)

9 Particular years are recalled here (3)

10 Place to have peg in living-room furniture (6)

Down

1 Trap is event on the soccer pitch (6)

2 Panel of switches has to provide comfort! (7)

3 Eccentric wandering copper will be here! (7)

4 Take on employees to start a fight (6)

REBUS TOWER

Can you work out which common phrases are represented by each of the three diagrams in the tower below?

rood

dynamite

A MOMENT

BIG FLOWER NUMBER PIC

Can you create a picture from the grid below?
Each number represents a group of shaded squares, so for example [3] [2] means that on this row there is a group of 3 red squares to the left of a group of 2 green squares. The [4] [2] numbers are always in order, so means a group of 4 red squares to the left of a group of 2 green squares in that row, and [5]/[3] means a block of

5 green squares above a block of 3 red squares in that column.

ADD A LETTER

Add one letter to each word in capitals to create a new word that answers the clue. The orders of the letters does not need to be changed.

For example – 'I BET it's more superior' would be BEST.

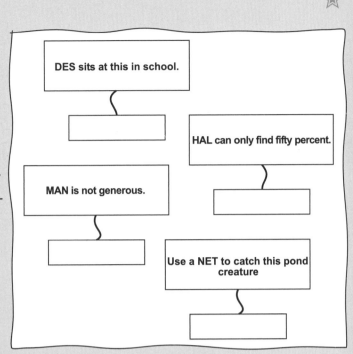

DES sits at this in school.

HAL can only find fifty percent.

MAN is not generous.

Use a NET to catch this pond creature

To solve, fill in the grid so that every row, column and box contains the numbers 1 through 9.

1		5		2		4	6	
8		3		7				1
9				1	5			
				9	6			5
				8	7	2		
7		6				9		
	4		5				3	
	3		9	8				
				3			7	

BLOCKBUSTERS ⭐⭐⭐

Complete the square by using each number and symbol provided in the top row ONCE only in every other row and column to equal the given answer. The first column and all the x signs have been put in to give you a start!

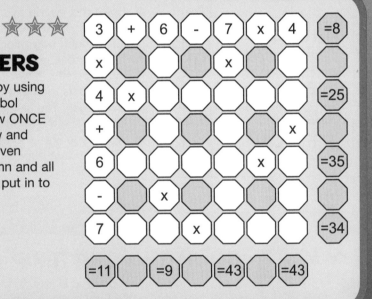

ADD THREE TO THREE ⭐⭐

Can you add three letters to the three words in red below to make another word which solves the clue? For example, by adding three letters to the clue 'BAN this fruit', you can make the word BANANA.

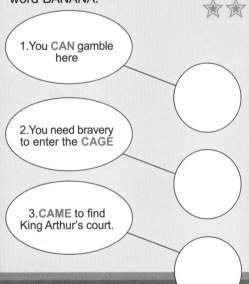

1. You **CAN** gamble here

2. You need bravery to enter the **CAGE**

3. **CAME** to find King Arthur's court.

NATURAL NINE ⭐

Try and become king of the jungle in this natural puzzle.
How many words of four letters or more can you track down? At least one will use all nine letters and all contain the central letter G. Use each letter once only. No words with capitals, foreign words, hyphens, or plurals are allowed.

The nine letter word is

....

PUSSYCAT STANDARD 9 words,
PANTHER STANDARD: 15 words, LION STANDARD: 23 words.

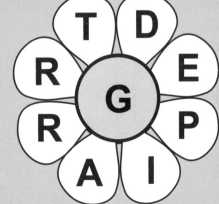

HIDDEN COLORS ⭐

Shade in all the numbers that can be divided exactly by 3 to reveal a hidden color.

26	10	32	34	38	17	25	5	6	37	23	28
1	16	11	40	28	1	13	19	24	4	8	17
41	15	20	2	31	19	15	9	18	32	11	20
16	9	13	22	1	37	6	29	6	21	36	30
23	30	14	15	21	36	27	12	27	24	34	2
12	27	4	3	2	9	8	29	22	18	15	6
10	38	25	33	3	18	20	7	26	33	35	5
14	4	17	12	35	21	19	31	7	3	15	21

A'MAZE'ING NUMBERS

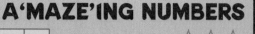

START

	1	1	8	1	1	1	8	8	2
5									
3									
3									
3									
3									
3									
3									
7									
1									

FINISH

Try to make your way through the maze. The number at the beginning of each row and column tells you exactly how many squares you will have to cross though in order to reach the finish. No diagonal moves are allowed.

Solving hint: To begin, blacken any box that you determine will not be used, and place a dot in any box that you know must be used.

SUDOKU

To solve, fill in the grid so that every row, column and box contains the numbers 1 through 9.

6	7	8	3		1		4	9
	4		9	8		6	7	2
2	9	5	4	6	7			
			8	9		1		4
4	2		5	7		3	9	8
5	8	9	1	4		2		
8				5		4		6
		4		3	8	7		
3	6	2	7		4		8	5

CHAIN REACTION

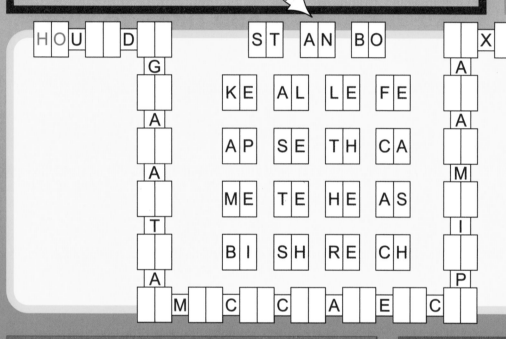

| HOU | D | | | ST | AN | BO | | | X | COT |

Tiles:
KE AL LE FE
AP SE TH CA
ME TE HE AS
BI SH RE CH
M C C A E C

Side letters (left): G A A T A
Side letters (right): A A M I P

Solve this puzzle by creating a 'chain reaction' of 20 five-letter words that run left to right, beginning in the upper-left hand corner, using the 19 two-letter tiles in the middle. A two-letter tile that ends one begins the next. Each tile will only be used once. The single letters already entered are the middle letters of the words you are to form. Start by finishing the word that begins HOU_ _.

COMMON WORDS

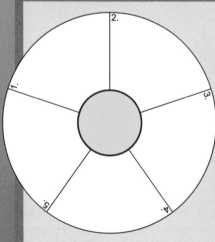

Your task here is to determine the answers to each set of tricky definitions below, as well as the word that is contained in all five of the set's answers. For example, if the five solutions were ERRAND, TERRIBLE, MERRY MEN, PREFERRED and PERRY, the word in the central circle would be ERR.

CLUES:
1 VCR button
2 Cheat
3 Shade adjunct
4 Decreasing
5 Chicago

COUNTING CRITTERS

Can you find the number that is represented by each animal face? You will find the total of the numbers below each column and to the right of each row.

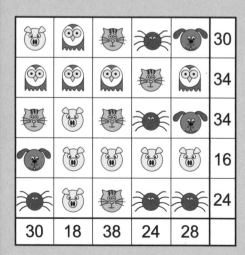

					30
					34
					34
					16
					24
30	18	38	24	28	

LETTER STEW

Use all the given letters in the stew to spell three words meaning good

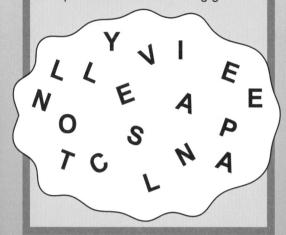

WORD WALL ★★

Make your way up the wall by changing one letter at a time until you reach the top word.

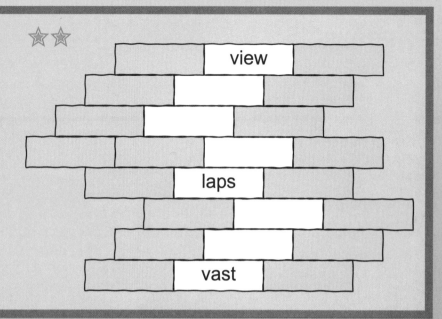

view

laps

vast

CROSSWORD ★

Across
2 Trial (4)
4 Chum (4)
5 Part of bird's plumage (7)
6 Oak for instance (4)
7 Fast running mammal (4)

Down
1 A dark purple-red (7)
2 Having left a valid will (7)
3 Plotter (7)

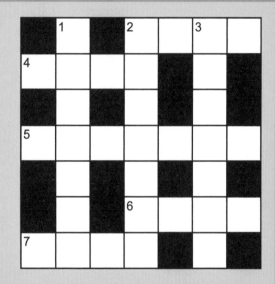

NOURISHING NINE ★★

How many words of four letters or more can you track down in this game? At least one 'nourishing' word will contain all nine letters and all words must contain the central letter. Use each letter once only. No words with capital letters, foreign words, hyphens, or plurals and verb forms ending in -s are allowed.

UNDERDONE: 10 words
MEDIUM: 16 words
WELL DONE: 22 words

PLACE THE PLACES ★★

To solve the puzzle place the letters from the place in capitals into the empty spaces in the grid. Four everyday words should be formed reading across the grid and three everyday words reading down.

D A L L A S

NINE NUMBERS ★

Try to fill in the missing numbers. Use the numbers 1 to 9 to complete the equations. Each number is only used once. Each row and column is an equation with the totals given below and to the right.

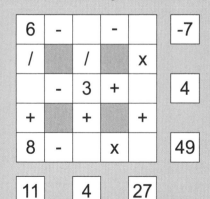

ARROWS

Put the following numbers in the arrows on the right:

1 1 2 3 5 5 6 6

Be careful though.
The total numbers in the 3 arrows pointing at each other must add up to 9.

The total numbers in the arrows which are back to back must add up to 7.

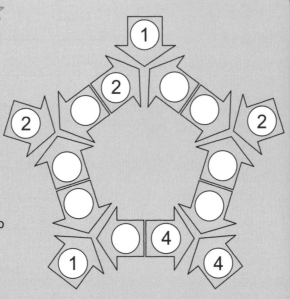

IN A... WORDSEARCH

The grid contains 12 words that can follow 'in a...' hidden vertically, horizontally or diagonally. The unused letters spell out another connected word.

CIRCLE	DRAUGHT	PICKLE
CLINCH	FASHION	STATE
CRISIS	MOOD	TANTRUM
DILEMMA	NUTSHELL	TRANCE

M	H	C	N	I	L	C	P
U	T	M	O	O	D	I	I
R	H	S	I	S	I	R	C
T	G	S	H	M	L	C	K
N	U	T	S	H	E	L	L
A	A	A	A	U	M	E	E
T	R	T	F	D	M	D	L
E	D	E	C	N	A	R	T

BIRD BOXES

Shade in all the numbers that appear exactly 3 times to reveal a hidden bird.

1	13	6	10	24	7	8	16	6	24	11	3
14	5	20	21	6	15	3	5	11	2	21	14
3	17	14	4	12	9	25	8	14	10	16	25
24	2	26	23	1	16	6	19	1	15	7	26
9	17	20	8	18	11	22	18	23	23	18	8
12	4	21	20	3	22	7	4	26	3	11	5
13	19	23	11	23	5	12	1	10	8	1	16
18	6	1	17	8	20	9	2	15	14	6	23

JIG GRID

Can you fit the blocks back into the grid to reveal, reading from left to right, seven items of clothing?

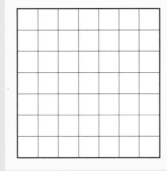

BRICK TEASE

Can you work out the answer to this teaser?

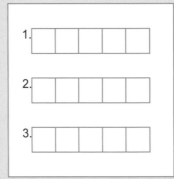

If the Smith brothers can build a wall 5 bricks long and 5 bricks high in 1 minute, how long will it take them to build a wall 10 bricks long and 10 bricks high?

The Smith brothers can build a wall 10 bricks high in.......... minutes.

NATUREGRAMS

Solve each clue, then rearrange the five letters in every answer to form a set of three flowers.

CLUES:
1 Solemn promises   2 Unruly oafs   3 Thoroughly unpleasant

1.

2.

3.

1.

2.

3.

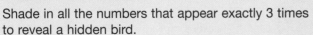

OCCUPATIONS

How many words of four letters or more can you track down in this game? At least one will be a nine letter occupation and all contain the central letter. Use each letter once only. No words with capitals, foreign words, hyphens, or plurals and verb forms ending in -s are allowed.

GOOD: 22 words

VERY GOOD: 33 words

EXCELLENT: 44 words

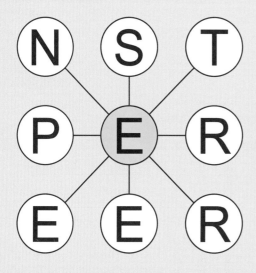

ON TARGET

Put the answers to the clues in the grid starting from the outside. Each answer has five letters and ends with the central letter R. When you've finished the outer ring will reveal the name of a game (7).

1 Supply food and drink (5)
2 Behind (5)
3 On no occasion (5)
4 Thespian (5)
5 Not as dangerous (5)
6 Private teacher (5)
7 Fossil resin (5)

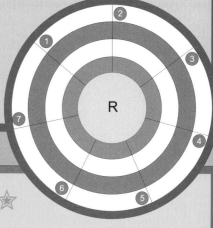

NINE NUMBERS

Try to fill in the missing numbers.
Use the numbers 1 to 9 to complete the equations. Each number is only used once. Each row and column is an equation with the totals given below and to the right.

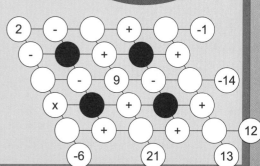

CROSSWORD

Across
1 Social worker's clients (4-4)
6 Time expected to arrive (3)
7 Kill someone like vigilantes (5)
9 Primary color (4)
11 Mediocre (2-2)
12 Large book (4)
14 Rotate (4)
16 Consent (5)
18 Matching collection of objects (3)
19 UK TV writer and funnyman (3,5)

Down
1 Pawn or knight, for instance (8)
2 Wounds with a knife (5)
3 Bubbly Scottish singer who likes to 'Shout' (4)
4 Girl's name (3)
5 To menace (8)
8 Abominable snowman (4)
10 Mislay (4)
13 Beginning (5)
15 Small dog (4)
17 Eggs of a fish (3)

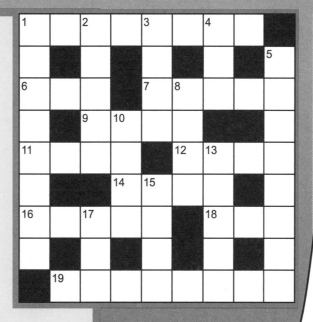

1. THEY'RE NAY BOARS GRATE DEIGN HOWELL'S AWL KNIGHT.

2. WHEAT RYE TOUPEE HOUR WREN TAUNT I'M, BUTTON AUK ASIA KNIT SLATE.

3. HEED PEDAL HISS WEARS BY THEE MAUL AWN SUNDAES.

DIZZY DICTATION

Jeff's new secretary is having some trouble with dictation. Can you work out what he is trying to say in the sentences above?

SUDOKU

To solve, fill in the grid so that every row, column and box contains the numbers 1 through 9.

8	4			5				2
	3						9	
	2	1	4	3				7
6		5	4					
2						4	3	
7	8	4			2	9		
		8		4	5		1	
1		9	6		2			3
	7		3		6	8	9	

FIVE SNEAKY SNAKES

Can you add five letters to each of the words in capitals in the snakes on the right, to make another word which solves the clue? For example, by adding five letters to the clue 'A revolt can make you REEL', you can make the word REBELLION. Each of the answers share a common theme.

1. Sweet cake can give you a pain in the GUT.

2. In the USA this Greek dish is popular.

3. LES likes this cabbage salad.

4. In stew you DIG into a ball of dough?

5. Quick meal found in KEW.

FLOWERY PHRASES

We have described a well-known saying using flowery language. Can you uncover the more familiar form? For example, 'An eruption in the cook pot' would be 'A Flash in the pan'.

The particular item or subject that ultimately occurs after all others in sequence or chronological order is not necessarily the item or subject that is to be assessed as the lowest in significance or the smallest in magnitude.

STEP LADDER

Starting with the top word, change one letter at a time to make a new word at every step until you have reached the bottom word.

HEAD

TELL

TAIL

NATURAL NINE

Try and become king of the jungle in this natural puzzle.
How many words of four letters or more can you track down? At least one will use all nine letters and all contain the central letter R. Use each letter once only. No words with capitals, foreign words, hyphens, or plurals are allowed.

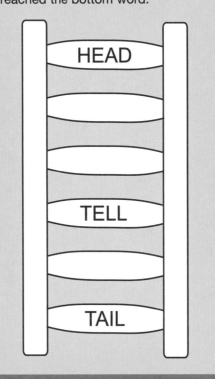

R V
B I
E R H
O E

The nine letter word is

....

PUSSYCAT STANDARD: 7 words
PANTHER STANDARD: 11 words
LION STANDARD: 18 words

QUICK NATURAL WORLD QUIZ

1. What is the young of a horse called?

....

2. Which mountain range separates France and Spain?

....

3. What country are the Eiger and Matterhorn mountains in?

....

4. On what tree does a koala bear mostly feed?

....

5. What is a Panda bear's favorite food?

....

EYE SQUIRCLE ⭐⭐

Put vowels in the circles and consonants in the squares to make words in all the vertical columns. Definitions of these words are given. When this has been done, the second and fourth horizontal lines will make four parts of the eye.

DEFINITIONS
1 Sharp smell
2 Feel sadness
3 Attribute
4 Grind teeth
5 Speed of music
6 Amount or quality
7 Underground chamber
8 Film
9 Pastoral

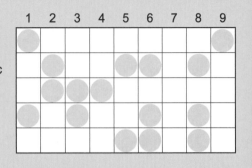

FISHY NUMBER PIC ⭐⭐

Can you create a picture from the grid below? Each number represents a group of shaded squares, so for example [3][2] means that on this row there is a group of 3 red squares to the left of a group of 2 green squares. The numbers are always in order, so [4][2] means a group of 4 red squares to the left of a group of 2 green squares in that row, and [5][3] means a block of 5 green squares above a block of 3 red squares in that column.

LETTER SWAP ⭐

Can you replace a letter from each word with a letter from the boxes below to reveal a well known saying? Each letter is used only once.

LACK IF AIL TRADER
MISTER ON BONE

N F O A J S L

CODED CROSSWORD ⭐⭐⭐

Each number in the grid represents a different letter of the alphabet. Can you fill in the grid using the given letters to get you started?

CAGED ANIMALS ⭐

An animal has escaped from the zoo. To put him back in his cage answer the eight clues and put them in the grid starting from the outermost circle. When this is done the central circles starting clockwise from number nine will reveal the name of the animal who escaped.

1 Armored vehicle (4)
2 A record (4)
3 A track (4)
4 Kind of house (4)
5 Soggy mass (4)
6 Space (4)
7 Member of African tribe (4)
8 Collapsed building (4)

ALPHABET SUDOKU

To solve, fill in the grid so that every row, column and box contains the letters A through I.

G	I		A		H	C	D	F
	H	G	D	C				
		A	F	E		G	H	B
D	E		I		B	H	G	
H	A	G	D		F		B	E
C	I	H		E		F		
	H	D	C	F	A		I	
	B		E		D	F		H
I		C	B		G	D	E	A

WHAT COMES FIRST?

Can you work out which word commonly precedes the pairs of words below?

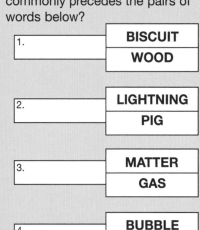

1. | **BISCUIT** |
   | **WOOD** |

2. | **LIGHTNING** |
   | **PIG** |

3. | **MATTER** |
   | **GAS** |

4. | **BUBBLE** |
   | **OPERA** |

NATURE TRAIL

★

Find the plant that is growing inside the tree by removing all the letters that appear more than twice.

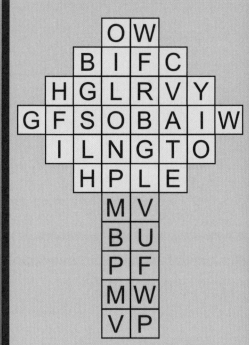

THE HIDDEN PLANT IS A

....

CHAIN REACTION

★ ★ ★

Solve this puzzle by creating a 'chain reaction' of 20 five-letter words that run left to right, beginning in the upper-left hand corner, using the 19 two-letter tiles in the middle. A two-letter tile that ends one begins the next. Each tile will only be used once. The single letters already entered are the middle letters of the words you are to form. Start by finishing the word that begins LYM_ _.

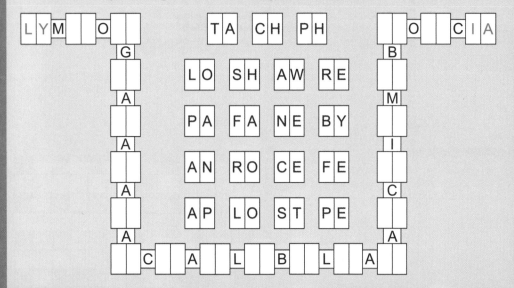

WORD WHEEL

★

For each of the circles, can you find two letters which when placed in the middle will form three six-letter words?

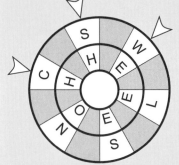

PYRAMID OF EGGS

★

Fill in the eggs with numbers, they must equal the sum of the two eggs below.

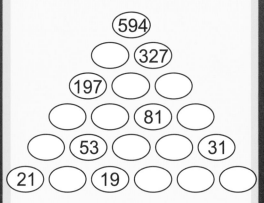

594
327
197 · ·
· · 81
· 53 · · 31
21 · 19 · ·

NUMBER HEX

Can you correctly enter six numbers into the Number Hex grid using the clues below? All are whole numbers below 10 and no two numbers are the same.

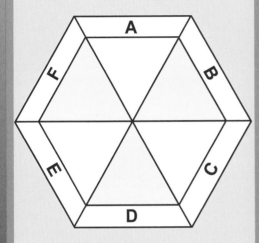

CLUES:
1. E is half a dozen
2. B and C add up to half a score
3. F times E equals B times D
4. A, B and F add up to D
5. B is half of E

NOURISHING NINE

How many words of four letters or more can you track down in this game? At least one 'nourishing' word will contain all nine letters and all words must contain the central letter. Use each letter once only. No words with capital letters, foreign words, hyphens, or plurals and verb forms ending in -s are allowed.

UNDERDONE: 17 words
MEDIUM: 25 words
WELL DONE: 37 words

CROSSWORD

Across
1. Spend money recklessly (6,3)
6. Give a speech (5)
7. Beer (3)
8. Mediocre (2-2)
10. Back of the neck (4)
13. Top card (3)
14. Tray (5)
16. Inflammation of the joints (9)

Down
1. Loses speed (5)
2. A meadow (3)
3. Toboggan (4)
4. Normandy landing beach (5)
5. Part of the foot (3)
9. Rested (5)
11. Betting odds (5)
12. Person who operates machine (4)
13. Woman's name (3)
15. Perform on stage (3)

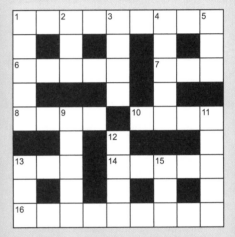

BLOCKBUSTERS

Complete the square by using each number and symbol provided in the top row ONCE only in every other row and column to equal the given answer. The first column and all the - signs have been put in to give you a start!

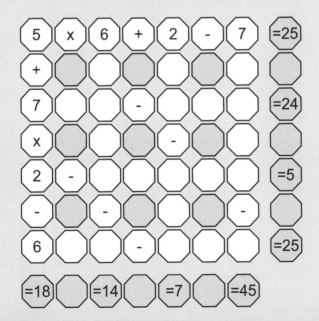

KAKURO

In Kakuro the numbers in the black squares refer to the SUMS of the digits 1-9 which you are to fill into the empty spaces. The number ABOVE the diagonal line refers to the empty spaces directly to the RIGHT of that number. A number BELOW the diagonal line refers to the empty spaces directly BELOW that number. No zeros are used here and a digit can only appear once in any particular digit combination.

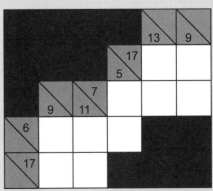

WEATHER

The grid contains 15 weather words vertically, horizontally or diagonally. Can you find them all?

BRIGHT	FLOOD	SLEET
CHILL	FOGGY	SLUSH
CLOUD	FREEZE	STORM
COLD	GUST	THAW
DAMP	MISTY	WARM

S	L	U	S	H	T	O	M
L	D	L	O	C	B	J	R
E	Z	E	E	R	F	C	O
E	C	H	I	L	L	F	T
T	T	G	P	O	O	W	S
B	H	M	U	G	O	A	U
T	A	D	G	V	D	R	G
D	W	Y	T	S	I	M	U

NINE NUMBERS

Try to fill in the missing numbers. Use the numbers 1 to 9 to complete the equations. Each number is only used once. Each row and column is an equation with the totals given below and to the right.

7	+		x	2	**24**
x		-		+	
	-	8	+		**-1**
+		+		+	
	-		+		**8**

10	**1**	**17**

FIVE SNEAKY SNAKES ⭐⭐⭐

Can you add five letters to each of the words in capitals, in the snakes below to make another word which solves the clue? For example, by adding five letters to the clue 'A revolt can make you REEL', you can make the word REBELLION. Each of the answers share a common theme.

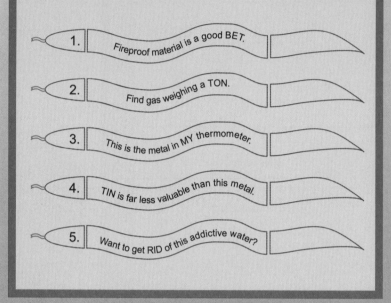

1. Fireproof material is a good BET.
2. Find gas weighing a TON.
3. This is the metal in MY thermometer.
4. TIN is far less valuable than this metal.
5. Want to get RID of this addictive water?

BITS AND PIECES ⭐⭐⭐

The tiles in the top grid are all jumbled up. Can you rearrange them in the grid below using only one tile from each column to reveal four related words and their theme?

W	A	EE	A	G
MO	G	R	N	E
G	H	ER	L	G
S	TO	I	IN	GE
EN	TE	R	IN	S

80s MUSIC QUIZ ⭐⭐⭐

1. Which singer released the album No Jacket Required?

....

2. Who topped the UK charts in 1983 with the song True?

....

3. Which UK singer attracted 400,000 people to his concert in New York's Central Park in 1980?

....

4. Which road were Talking Heads on in 1985?

....

5. Which year was the Live Aid concert aired?

....

COUNTING CRITTERS ⭐

Can you find the number that is represented by each animal face? You will find the total of the numbers below each column and to the right of each row.

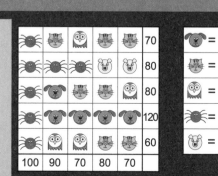

SUDOKU

To solve, fill in the grid so that every row, column and box contains the numbers 1 through 9.

	5						3	4
6			4					
			9	1	2			
		9		4		2	6	
7		8						
	4	6		3		8		5
1	6	7	3			5		8
	2				9	1		
		5	1	8	6		7	2

ADD THREE TO THREE

Can you add three letters to the three words in red below to make another word which solves the clue? For example, by adding three letters to the clue 'BAN this fruit', you can make the word BANANA.

1. It may be **FIT**, but it's so dirty.

2. It's hidden so you can't **SEE** it.

3. A **SET** of six.

SKELETON CROSSWORD ★★★

To the right is an incomplete quick crossword grid. Can you solve the puzzle by fitting the answers to the clues correctly into the grid, along with the remaining blocks and clue numbers? A few blocks have been shaded to give you a start. This grid has been rotated by 180 degrees.

Across
1 Bears the responsibility (9)
6 Large snake (3)
7 Take delivery of letter (7)
8 Small portable ladder (5)
11 Loathe (6)
14 To cross out (6)
17 Machines used for gambling (5)
20 Cardgame (7)
21 Large (3)
22 Not reasonable (9)

Down
1 Secure (4)
2 Paddles (4)
3 Money (5)
4 Banish from the country (5)
5 Cover on the bed (5)
6 Public transport vehicle (3)
9 Not fake (4)
10 Meat paste (4)
11 Female deer (3)
12 Divulge information (4)
13 Fat used for cooking (4)
14 Bobs one's head (5)
15 Russian leader (5)
16 Flavour (5)
17 Of sound mind (4)
18 Decorated spheres (4)
19 Droop (3)

LITTLE TOUGHIE ★★★

Across
4 Prepared in lab (6)
5 Long paces for street journeys (7)
8 Shout I've found in history (6)

Down
1 Special unit carrying guns initially droops (4)
2 In Seine, say, I'll have a holiday area (7)
3 Predicament that causes road hold-up (4)
6 On this you'll see budding relationships in a family (4)
7 Rolling gait is southern style (4)

WORD SPLITZ ★

Each row of ten letters can be split into two five letter fish. These words read from left to right and are in order.

For example SMOKOSUENK can be split to reveal SKUNK and MOOSE.

1. PSEHRACRHK
2. STEKNACTEH
3. TARONUTGEL
4. BPRRAEAMWN

ON TARGET

Put the answers to the clues in the grid starting from the outside. Each answer has five letters and ends with the central letter E. When you've finished the outer ring will reveal the name of a UK soccer team (7)

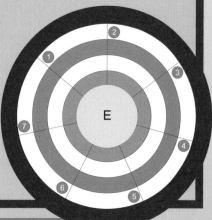

1 To fill with high spirits (5)

2 Imprecise,indistinct (5)

3 The pick of society (5)

4 To bring up (5)

5 Piece of furniture (5)

6 Unhealthily fat (5)

7 A relative (5)

GEOGRAMS

Solve each clue, then rearrange the six letters in every answer to form a set of three cities.

CLUES:
1 Seller   2 Lay bare   3 Retaliate

DUBLIN SQUIRCLE ★★

Put vowels in the circles and consonants in the squares to make words in all the vertical columns. Definitions of these words are given. When this has been done, the first and fourth horizontal lines will make three words associated with Dublin.

DEFINITIONS
1 Large cats
2 Senseless or silly
3 High temperature in illness
4 Artificial
5 Live
6 Alpine song
7 Magical servant
8 Prefix meaning extremely
9 Creek.

BLOCKBUSTERS ★★★

Complete the square by using each number and symbol provided in the top row ONCE only in every other row and column to equal the given answer. The first column and all the x signs have been put in to give you a start!

```
1  +  4  x  7  -  8  =27
+           x     
8  x        x        =59
x        x           
7           x        =11
-     x              
4     x              =31
=59   =3    =32   =26
```

DUBLIN SQUIRCLE grid

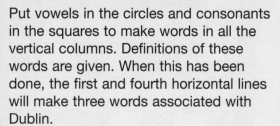

1	2	3	4	5	6	7	8	9

SUDOKU ★★★

To solve, fill in the grid so that every row, column and box contains the numbers 1 through 9.

3		6	7	1	2			
				5	9			3
		5					2	1
		2		3	6			
1	7			8		6	3	9
6	3		1	7		8	5	2
9	5		8				1	6
8	2	7	6				4	5
4			5		3	9	8	

SOCCER RIDDLES

Can you work out which soccer player the riddle is describing? Each line refers to a letter of his surname.

My first is seen in KENT but not in LONDON

My second occurs in IRELAND but is not seen in SCOTLAND

My next is found in APPLAUSE and in CLAP

My fourth is in NINE and also in TEN

My last is in HOUSE but not in PITCH

My whole is a new mover to CELTIC

The soccer player is: _____

WORD FIT

Can you fit all the words linked with a university into the grid?

3 letter words
- Art
- Job
- Sit

4 letter words
- Book
- Exam
- Fail
- Mark
- Pass
- Read
- Term

5 letter words
- Class
- Notes
- Paper
- Skill
- Tutor
- Write

6 letter words
- Campus
- Course
- Lesson

7 letter words
- Science
- Subject
- Teacher

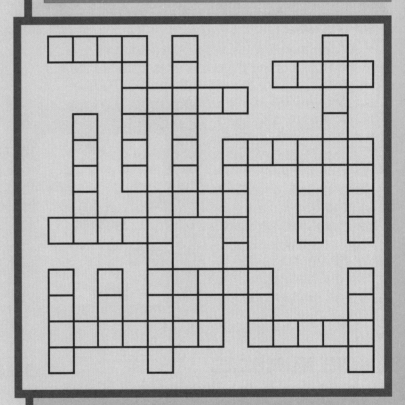

HIDDEN COLORS

Shade in all the numbers that be divided exactly by five to reveal a hidden color.

8	27	36	15	5	30	19	13	16	55	52	45
34	1	26	25	13	55	37	4	39	15	51	25
12	2	4	5	45	30	1	28	22	10	40	5
23	46	21	30	31	20	49	27	2	18	51	40
9	7	33	45	38	50	47	6	16	41	9	25
20	10	60	18	35	53	11	14	35	23	20	50
35	12	50	32	43	5	42	25	17	16	48	14
10	44	40	8	31	17	15	19	3	29	24	27

ALPHAFITS

One of each of the 26 letters of the alphabet has been removed from the crossword grid below. Can you replace them all to fill the crossword with everyday words?

A	B	C	D	E	F	G	H	I	J	K	L	M
N	O	P	Q	R	S	T	U	V	W	X	Y	Z

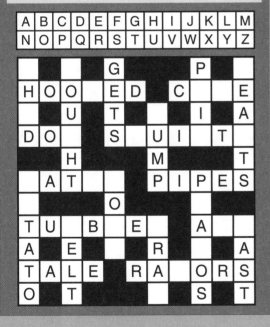

MOVIE HOUSE

Hidden in the grid are six Lord of the Rings characters. Can you find them all?

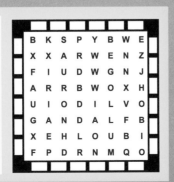

```
B K S P Y B W E
X X A R W E N Z
F I U D W G N J
A R R B W O X H
U I O D I L V O
G A N D A L F B
X E H L O U B I
F P D R N M Q O
```

WORD WALL

Make your way up the wall by changing one letter at a time until you reach the top word.

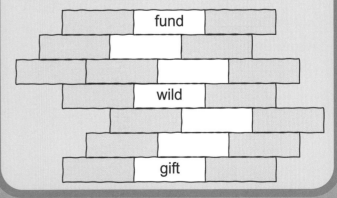

fund

wild

gift

CHAIN REACTION

Solve this puzzle by creating a 'chain reaction' of 20 five-letter words that run left to right, beginning in the upper-left hand corner, using the 19 two-letter tiles in the middle. A two-letter tile that ends one begins the next. Each tile will only be used once. The single letters already entered are the middle letters of the words you are to form. Start by finishing the word that begins WHE_ _.

★★★

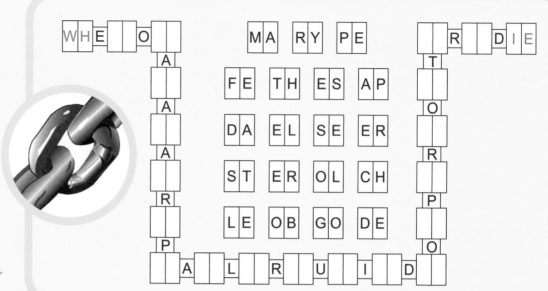

Tiles: MA RY PE / FE TH ES AP / DA EL SE ER / ST ER OL CH / LE OB GO DE / AL LR UI D

Grid letters: W H E [ ] O [ ] ... R [ ] D I E
Left column: A A A R P
Right column: T O R P O
Bottom row: A L R U I D

KAKURO

★★★

In Kakuro the numbers in the black squares refer to the SUMS of the digits 1-9 which you are to fill into the empty spaces. The number ABOVE the diagonal line refers to the empty spaces directly to the RIGHT of that number. A number BELOW the diagonal line refers to the empty spaces directly BELOW that number. No zeros are used here and a digit can only appear once in any particular digit combination.

Clues in grid: 10, 21, 10, 3, 5, 10, 6, 14, 28, 5, 7, 15, 4, 21, 6, 21, 3, 2, 6, 3, 9, 11, 16, 22, 9, 15, 2, 3, 5, 8, 28, 1, 4, 3, 6

JIG GRID

Can you fit the blocks back into the grid to reveal, reading from left to right, six countries?

★★

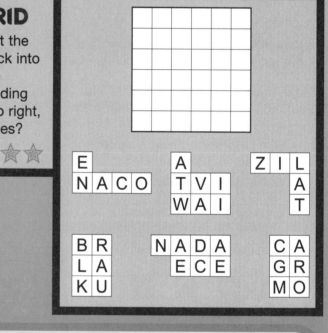

Blocks:
- E / N A C O
- A / T V I / W A I
- Z I L / A / T
- B R / L A / K U
- N A D A / E C E
- C A / G R / M O

NINE NUMBERS

★

Try to fill in the missing numbers. Use the numbers 1 to 9 to complete the equations. Each number is only used once. Each row and column is an equation with the totals given below and to the right.

5	x		-		11
+		+		x	
	+	2	-		5
-		-		-	
7	x		-		55
7		-3		23	

COMMON WORDS

★★★

Your task here is to determine the answers to each set of tricky definitions below, as well as the word that is contained in all five of the set's answers. For example, if the five solutions were ERRAND, TERRIBLE, MERRY MEN, PREFERRED and PERRY, the word in the central circle would be ERR.

Clues:
1 Wanted
2 Poe poem
3 Tourist
4 Serious
5 French composer

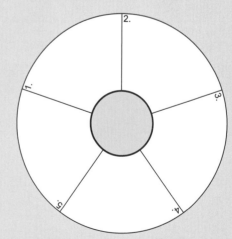

SUDOKU

To solve, fill in the grid so that every row, column and box contains the numbers 1 through 9.

7	1	9		5	6	8		2
3		4	1			5		
5	8		9	7	3	6	1	
2	7	6	8	3	5	4	9	
4	5		6	9	1	7		8
1	9			4		3		6
8		1	3		7	9		
	3		2		4		6	7
6	4		5	1			8	3

CROSSWORD

Across
1 Remained (6)
5 Make a mistake (3)
6 Espy (3)
7 Termite (3)
8 An age (3)
9 Long period of time (3)
10 Sewing implement (6)

Down
1 Cooked slowly by simmering (6)
2 Put into order (7)
3 London area featured in a soap (4,3)
4 Group of US politicians (6)

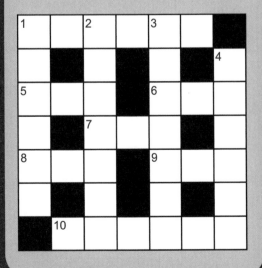

NOURISHING NINE

How many words of four letters or more can you track down in this game? At least one word will contain all nine letters and all words must contain the central letter. Use each letter once only. No words with capital letters, foreign words, hyphens, or plurals and verb forms ending in -s are allowed.

UNDERDONE: 10 words, MEDIUM: 17 words, WELL DONE: 24 words

SPORTS QUIZ – SNOOKER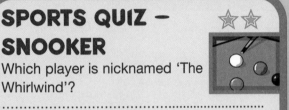

Which player is nicknamed 'The Whirlwind'?

....

How many points do you need to score a 'maximum break'?

....

Where is the World Championship annually held?

....

What is the value of the pink ball?

....

How many red balls are placed in the triangle at the start of each frame?

....

PLACE THE PLACES

To solve the puzzle place the letters from the place in capitals into the empty spaces in the grid. Four everyday words should be formed reading across the grid and three everyday words reading down.

L A R D E R

O	D	
	A	Y
	E	D

PLUG NUMBER PIC

Can you create a picture from the grid to the right?
Each number represents a group of shaded squares, so for example **3 2** means that on this row there is a group of 3 black squares to the left of a group of 2 black squares, with one or more white squares in between (there must be at least one white square in between the groups, or the 3 and 2 would join up to become a 5).
The numbers are always in order, so **4 2** means a group of 4 black squares to the left of a group of 2 black squares in that row, and **5** means a block of 5 black squares above a block of 3 black
3 squares in that column.

SUDOKU

To solve, fill in the grid so that every row, column and box contains the numbers 1 through 9.

★★

3		8		7	2			9
2			4				6	8
	4	9				7		2
					1			
6		1						
7		5		4	3		1	
	2			5	7			
1	7					8		
			4	3		2		1

CEREMONY WORDSEARCH ★★

The grid contains 12 words associated with ceremonies hidden vertically, horizontally or diagonally. The unused letters spell out another connected word.

R	E	W	O	L	F	B	Q
E	D	S	U	E	U	M	S
N	N	E	R	N	R	W	T
N	A	M	T	O	O	F	R
A	B	I	F	R	H	N	O
B	N	I	D	W	O	R	C
G	N	C	H	E	E	R	S
U	H	E	L	M	E	T	E

BAND
BANNER
BUNTING
CHEERS
CROWD
ESCORT
FLOWER
FOOTMAN
HELMET
HORSE
SWORD
UNIFORM

REBUS TOWER ★★★

Can you work out which common phrases are represented by each of the three diagrams in the tower?

blonde

HIS HAT

KAKURO ★★

In Kakuro the numbers in the black squares refer to the SUMS of the digits 1-9 which you are to fill into the empty spaces. The number ABOVE the diagonal line refers to the empty spaces directly to the RIGHT of that number. A number BELOW the diagonal line refers to the empty spaces directly BELOW that number. No zeros are used here and a digit can only appear once in any particular digit combination.

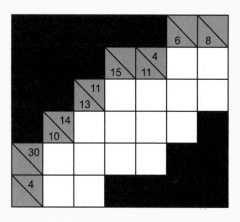

HOLLYWOOD ANAGRAMS ★★★

Below are four anagrams of films or film people. The number and length of words to find is shown in brackets. The four anagram solutions are all linked in some way – can you find the link?

	THE LINK IS	
SHALLOW JIM IN (4, 8)		
IVAN GELS (8)		
JON HEN LOT (5, 4)		
RONNIE MOON RICE (5, 9)		

NATURAL NINE

Try and become king of the jungle in this natural puzzle.

How many words of four letters or more can you track down? At least one will use all nine letters and all contain the central letter P. Use each letter once only. No words with capitals, foreign words, hyphens, or plurals are allowed.

The nine letter word is

....

PUSSYCAT STANDARD: 9 words, PANTHER STANDARD: 16 words, LION STANDARD: 26 words.

NINE NUMBERS

Try to fill in the missing numbers. Use the numbers 1 to 9 to complete the equations. Each number is only used once. Each row and column is an equation with the totals given below and to the right.

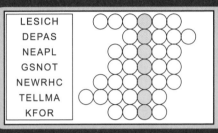

	-	7	-		-8
x			+		-
	+	8	x		126
+			-		x
4	x		+		9

| 16 | 14 | -30 |

ANAGRAM LADDERS

Solve the anagrams on the right to reveal the names of seven tools. The shaded row in the middle will then reveal the name of another tool.

LESICH
DEPAS
NEAPL
GSNOT
NEWRHC
TELLMA
KFOR

CODED CROSSWORD

Each number in the grid represents a different letter of the alphabet. Can you fill in the grid using the given letters to get you started?

R	S	T	U	V	W	X	Y	Z	RQ	RR	RS P	RT
RU	RV	RW	RX	RY	RZ	SQ R	SR	SS	ST	SU S	SV	SW

NAME THE DATE

Can you circle the correct date for these famous events?

1. Roger Bannister ran the 4 minute mile in...

1954	1924	1824

2. Ben Johnson was disqualified from the Olympics in...

1988	1978	1968

3. Jessie Owens won 4 gold medals at the Olympics in...

1946	1936	1906

WORD WHEEL

For each of the circles, can you find two letters which, when placed in the middle, will form three six-letter words?

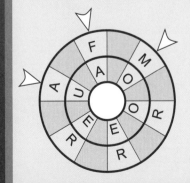

BLOCKBUSTERS ★★★

Complete the square by using each number and symbol provided in the top row ONCE only in every other row and column to equal the given answer. The first column and all the + signs have been put in to give you a start!

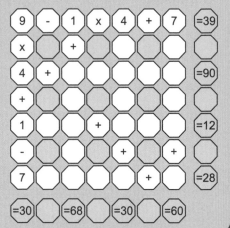

LITTLE TOUGHIE ★★★

Across
4 Strive to get to a top of a church (6)
5 They may be dire for group in dangerous waters (7)
8 It protects pupil from cane or otherwise (6)

Down
1 Food in a meat-safe (4)
2 Grotesque market in the east, you might almost say (7)
3 What follows ABC? Time to be clever! (4)
6 Rough coat for Mexican food (4)
7 Strike-breaker giving direction to taxi (4)

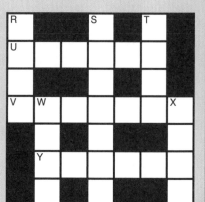

GEOGRAMS ★★

Solve each clue, then rearrange the five letters in every answer to form a set of three countries.

CLUES:
1 Causes anguish
2 Latin ballroom dance
3 Armed adversary

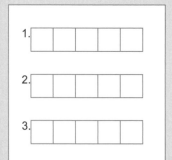
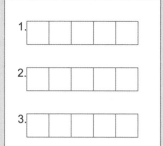

SKELETON CROSSWORD ★★★

Below is an incomplete quick crossword grid. Can you solve the puzzle by fitting the answers to the clues correctly into the grid, along with the remaining blocks and clue numbers? A few blocks have been shaded to give you a start. This grid has been rotated by 180 degrees.

Across
1 Unfounded panic (5,5)
8 Pleasant smell (5)
9 Retail stores (5)
10 Republic of Ireland (4)
12 Irritate (6)
14 Choose (6)
17 Utters aloud (4)
21 To fit pane of glass (5)
22 Normandy landing beach (5)
23 Gullible, full of naive wishes (6,4)

Down
2 Love affair (5)
3 Kill (4)
4 Passage between seats (5)
5 Up above (5)
6 Mean person (5)
7 Secure (4)
11 The day before (3)
12 Tap with the hand (3)
13 Distress signal (3)
14 Famous bridge in Venice (5)
15 S.American beast of burden (5)
16 Obvious, plain (5)
18 Conscious of (5)
19 Burglar's loot (4)
20 Blood and guts (4)

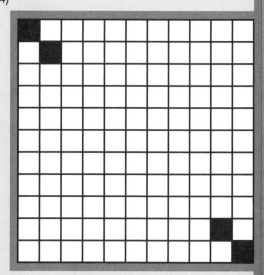

ADDING GRIDS ★

Place any digits 0 to 9 into the empty circles. When complete each row should add up to the figures on the right and each column to the figures below. The shaded numbers are the total of the diagonal circles.

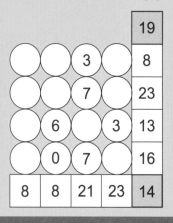

ARROWS

Put the following numbers in the arrows below:

2 2 3 3 4 5 5 6

Be careful though.
The total numbers in the 3 arrows pointing at each other must add up to 10.

The total numbers in the arrows which are back to back must add up to 7.

ODD ONE OUT

Can you spot the odd one out in this sequence of numbers?

$\frac{3}{4}$ THREE QUARTERS 0.75 $\frac{6}{12}$ $\frac{9}{12}$ 75%

ON TARGET

Put the answers to the clues in the grid starting from the outside. Each answer has five letters and ends with the central letter Y. When you've finished the outer ring will reveal the name of a game (7).

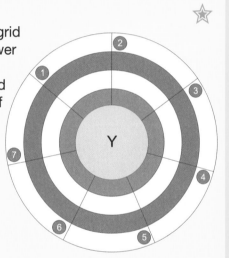

1 Sweets (5)
2 Exchange of shots in tennis (5)
3 Insinuate (5)
4 Mad (5)
5 Small child (5)
6 Before the expected time (5)
7 Worn out, shabby (5)

ALPHAFITS

One of each of the 26 letters of the alphabet has been removed from the crossword grid below. Can you replace them all to fill the crossword with everyday words?

			A		P		I		N	
	R		E		L		R			
O		L	L		S		A	T	E	
L		D		T		O				
	E	Y	E	D			E	T	S	
P				D						
E		P		R	U	S		I	A	
O		A						I		P
N	E			E		L	E		G	
E	G		L			T		E		R
D	E	N		I	S	T	S			

| A | B | C | D | E | F | G | H | I | J | K | L | M |
| N | O | P | Q | R | S | T | U | V | W | X | Y | Z |

SUDOKU

To solve, fill in the grid so that every row, column and box contains the numbers 1 through 9.

6		7			4		9	
5	4				6			2
		3		7	5	6		
7	5		1			3	2	8
	9			8			7	
		4			7		6	
2			4	3		9		
4	7	9	5	6				3
8			7		2		5	6

NOURISHING NINE

How many words of four letters or more can you track down in this game? At least one 'nourishing' word will contain all nine letters and all words must contain the central letter. Use each letter once only. No words with capital letters, foreign words, hyphens, or plurals and verb forms ending in -s are allowed.

UNDERDONE: 13 words
MEDIUM: 20 words
WELL DONE: 27 words

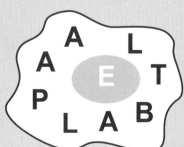

A A L T E P B L A

ANAGRAM RIDDLE

Each of the clues gives the anagram of four common words with the exception of one letter. Fill in the grid by solving the anagram and finding the missing letter.

A 10-letter word containing two Ss, two As, one I, one E, one M, one B, one L, and one other consonant.

An 11-letter word containing two Ns, two As, two Rs, one V, one Y, one S, one I and one other vowel.

A 12-letter word containing two Ms, two Cs, two Ls, one R, one A, one E, one I, one O, and one other consonant.

A 13-letter word containing three Is, two Cs, one A, one E, one O, one P, one T, one N, one S, and one other consonant.

1.

2.

3.

4.

HIDDEN COLORS

Shade in all the numbers that can be divided into 40 exactly to reveal a hidden color.

7	11	19	9	7	3	17	6	11	19	3	7
9	6	4	8	20	12	5	8	2	9	11	14
3	17	8	6	5	19	10	7	17	6	4	10
16	7	10	20	2	13	4	20	8	19	5	6
2	10	19	9	18	6	11	15	4	7	4	20
8	15	16	7	3	7	3	18	2	12	20	13
5	9	19	12	15	14	8	5	10	9	2	8
4	3	17	9	19	6	16	7	19	3	14	6

PLACE THE PLACES

To solve the puzzle place the letters from the place in capitals into the empty spaces in the grid. Four everyday words should be formed reading across the grid and three everyday words reading down.
S W E D E N

NUMBER HEX

Can you correctly enter six numbers into the Number Hex grid using the clues below? All are whole numbers below 10 and no two numbers are the same.

CLUES:
A multiplied by E equals C multiplied by F
E is the number of sides on a triangle
C is three times E
B plus D equals C
D is the number of legs on an elephant

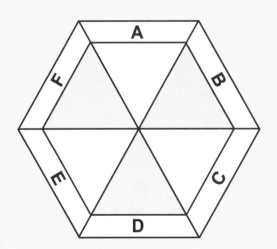

WORD SPLITZ

Each row of ten letters can be split into two five letter vehicles. These words read from left to right and are in order.

For example SMOKOSUENK can be split to reveal SKUNK and MOOSE.

① BCUOGAGYCH

② CLYOCLERRY

③ MWOAPGEDON

④ STERADANIN

CHAIN REACTION ★★★☆

Solve this puzzle by creating a 'chain reaction' of 20 five-letter words that run left to right, beginning in the upper-left hand corner, using the 19 two-letter tiles in the middle. A two-letter tile that ends one begins the next. Each tile will only be used once. The single letters already entered are the middle letters of the words you are to form. Start by finishing the word that begins FIR_ _.

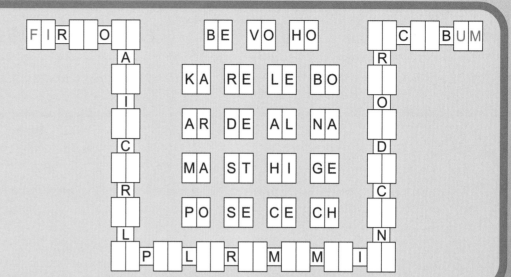

PLANE NUMBER PIC ★★

Can you create a picture from the grid below? Each number represents a group of shaded squares, so for example **3 2** means that on this row there is a group of 3 black squares to the left of a group of 2 black squares, with one or more white squares in between (there must be at least one white square in between the groups, or the 3 and 2 would join up to become a 5)

The numbers are always in order, so **4 2** means a group of 4 black squares to the left of a group of 2 black squares in that row, and **5 3** means

a block of 5 black squares above a block of 3 black squares in that column.

		2	3			3	2		
	1	2	1	1	10	10	1	1	2	1
2										
2										
2										
2										
4										
8										
10										
2										
2										
6										

ON TARGET ★

Put the answers to the clues in the grid starting from the outside. Each answer has five letters and ends with the central letter L. When you've finished the outer ring will reveal the name of a sport (7).

1 Get down to pray (5)
2 Spring month (5)
3 Regal (5)
4 The sum (5)
5 Best for the purpose (5)
6 Book of fiction (5)
7 To snarl (5)

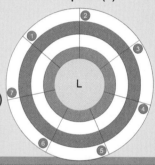

OPPOSITES ATTRACT ★

Place each of the tiles in the boxes below right to form two words with opposite meaning.

LOLLIPOPS ★

By moving six of the lollipops in the grid can you make a house?

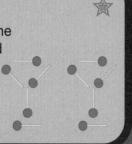

NINE NUMBERS ★★

Try to fill in the missing numbers. Use the numbers 1 to 9 to complete the equations. Each number is only used once. Each row and column is an equation with the totals given below and to the right.

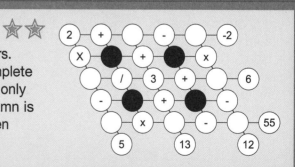

PAIR WHEELS

Place each of the twelve pairs of letters into one of the circles in the wheel, so that every line running through the central circle gives you a six-letter word with the middle letters RR.

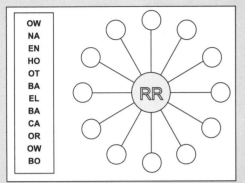

OW
NA
EN
HO
OT
BA
EL
BA
CA
OR
OW
BO

RR

COUNTING CRITTERS

Can you find the number that is represented by each animal face? You will find the total of the numbers below each column and to the right of each row.

cat	owl	dog	pig	cat	160
spider	spider	spider	cat	cat	70
pig	owl	pig	pig	cat	160
dog	dog	dog	dog	cat	180
cat	owl	spider	dog	owl	170
120	200	130	160	130	

dog =
cat =
owl =
spider =
pig =

PULLING WORDSEARCH

The grid contains 14 pulling words hidden vertically, horizontally or diagonally. Can you find them all?

ATTRACT
CRANK
DRAG
EFFORT
EXTRACT
HANDLE
HAUL
LURE
REMOVE
SNATCH
STRAIN
TOWS
TWITCH
UPROOT

J	K	L	U	A	H	E	T
H	S	N	Q	T	X	L	O
C	W	T	A	T	T	D	O
T	O	Y	R	R	R	N	R
I	T	A	O	A	C	A	P
W	C	F	G	C	I	H	U
T	F	H	C	T	A	N	S
E	V	O	M	E	R	U	L

KAKURO

In Kakuro the numbers in the black squares refer to the SUMS of the digits 1-9 which you are to fill into the empty spaces. The number ABOVE the diagonal line refers to the empty spaces directly to the RIGHT of that number. A number BELOW the diagonal line refers to the empty spaces directly BELOW that number. No zeros are used here and a digit can only appear once in any particular digit combination.

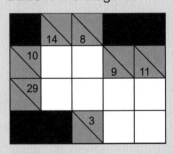

BLOCKBUSTERS

Complete the square by using each number and symbol provided in the top row ONCE only in every other row and column to equal the given answer. The first column and all the x signs have been put in to give you a start!

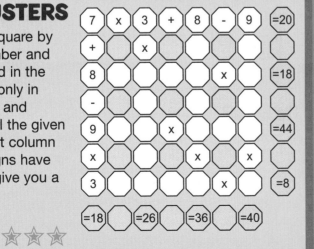

7 x 3 + 8 - 9 =20
+ x =18
8 x =18
-
9 x =44
x x x
3 x =8
=18 =26 =36 =40

SUDOKU ★★★

To solve, fill in the grid so that every row, column and box contains the numbers 1 through 9.

2	5		3	1				
6	1			5		8		9
	9			8			1	5
		2		3	1		6	
			5			9	8	
4		9		2		1	5	3
3			8			7		
9	7	6					3	8
8	4	1			3	5		

NATURAL NINE

Try and become king of the jungle in this natural puzzle. How many words of four letters or more can you track down? At least one will use all nine letters and all contain the central letter C. Use each letter once only. No words with capitals, foreign words, hyphens, or plurals are allowed.

The nine letter word is

....

PUSSYCAT STANDARD: 9 words,
PANTHER STANDARD: 14 words, LION STANDARD: 20 words

LITTLE TOUGHIE ⭐⭐⭐

Across
2 Look round in such cold water up north (4)
4 Departed in the long distant past! (4)
5 Shallow vessel for river in Scottish one (4)
6 Bob is sitting between Faith and Charity (4)
7 Drum for Scottish dancers? (4)
8 Novel point to put in media reports (4)

Down
1 Cave is terribly hot in cold part of planet (7)
2 Characters of landlords? (7)
3 It's marked on map made from the card (7)

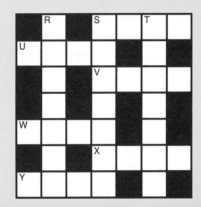

SKELETON CROSSWORD ⭐⭐⭐

Below is an incomplete quick crossword grid.Can you solve the puzzle by fitting the answers to the clues correctly into the grid, along with the remaining blocks and clue numbers? A few blocks have been shaded to give you a start. This puzzle has been rotated by 180 degrees.

Across
1 Divisions of an ocean (4)
3 Crockery service (3-3)
7 Conservative (4)
8 Conduct oneself properly (6)
10 Knocks down with a vehicle (4,4)
13 Place where old people live (4,4)
16 Rouse from sleep (6)
17 Job payment (4)
18 In a uniform way (6)
19 Immediately following (4)

Down
1 Wittily sarcastic entertainment (6)
2 Publicising (6)
4 Weather conditions (8)
5 Pierce with a knife (4)
6 Quaintly cute (4)
9 A fertiliser (8)
11 Find the whereabouts of (6)
12 Ingredient of concrete (6)
14 Gradual decline (4)
15 Magnetic recording strip (4)

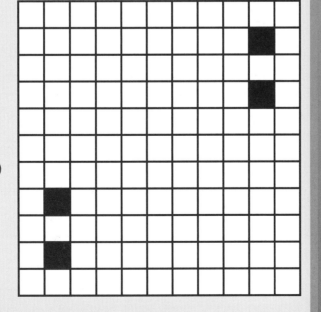

ADD THREE TO THREE ⭐⭐

Can you add three letters to the three words in red to make another word which solves the clue? For example, by adding three letters to the clue 'BAN this fruit', you can make the word BANANA.

1. Woodwind instrument is a **BOON**

2. Hats found in **HEDGE**

3. **RAT** gets an allowance of food.

QUICK SPORTS QUIZ ⭐

Which soccer club plays its home games at Elland Road in the UK?

....

Who won the Ashes in 2005?

....

Where were the 2004 Olympics held?

....

How many gold medals did UK athlete Kelly Holmes win at those Olympics, 1, 2 or 5?

....

Who won the 2005 Tour de France, was it Lance Armstrong or Lars Ulrich?

....

OCCUPATIONS

How many words of four letters or more can you track down in this game? At least one will be a nine letter occupation and all contain the central letter. Use each letter once only. No words with capitals, foreign words, hyphens, or plurals and verb forms ending in -s are allowed.

GOOD: 12 words
VERY GOOD: 18 words
EXCELLENT: 23 words

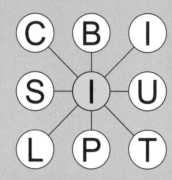

ZOO HUNT

An animal has escaped from the zoo and is hiding somewhere in the grid. If you cross out all the letters that appear more than twice, the remaining letters will spell out the missing creature.

THE MISSING CREATURE IS A

....

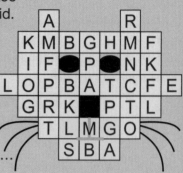

GREEK GODS SQUIRCLE

Put vowels in the circles and consonants in the squares to make words in all the vertical columns. Definitions of these words are given. When this has been done, the second and fifth horizontal lines will make three Greek Gods.

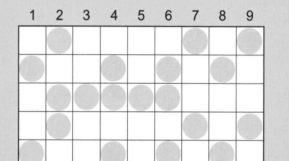

DEFINITIONS
1 Stringed instrument
2 Sign of the zodiac
3 Back of ship
4 Calm
5 Excessive compliments
6 Female relative
7 Burnt remains
8 Italian composer
9 Instinctive motives

BITS AND PIECES

The tiles in the top grid are all jumbled up. Can you rearrange them in the grid below using only one tile from each column to reveal four related words and their theme?

WI	OW	D	I	N
C	N	DW	IA	FF
S	L	B	E	Y
I	HE	R	O	T
SH	OO	T	OU	ST

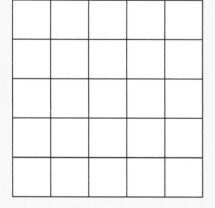

RIDDLE WORDS

Can you answer these word riddles with cricketing terms?

Which cricket term is a flying animal?

Which cricket term do you eat soup from?

Which cricket term is also a water bird?

Which cricket term also means ended?

WORD WHEEL

For each of the circles, can you find two letters which, when placed in the middle, will form three six-letter words?

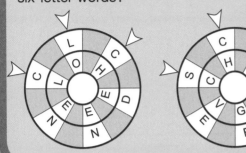

TELEPHONE NUMBER PIC

Can you create a picture from the grid below?
Each number represents a group of shaded squares, so for example **3 2** means that on this row there is a group of 3 black squares to the left of a group of 2 black squares, with one or more white squares in between (there must be at least one white square in between the groups, or the 3 and 2 would join up to become a 5).
The numbers are always in order, so **4 2** means a group of 4 black squares to the left of a group of 2 black squares in that row, and **5 3** means a block of 5 black square above a block of 3 black squares in that column.

MOVIE HOUSE

Hidden in the grid are six Best Film Oscar winners. Can you find them all?

CROSSWORD

Across
2 Remain (4)
4 Animal skin (4)
5 A runner perhaps (7)
6 Opening for coins (4)
7 Joke (4)

Down
1 Salad plant (7)
2 Hairdresser (7)
3 A sale in lots (7)

SUDOKU

To solve, fill in the grid so that every row, column and box contains the numbers 1 through 9.

	1	2		6	3	8	7	9
7	3	6		8	9			
5	8		2		4	3		1
1		3	9	4	8		5	
9		8		5	2	1		4
2	5	4		7		6	9	8
3	9	1	8	2	6	5		7
6	4	5	7	9		2		
	2		4	3		9		6

FIVE SNEAKY SNAKES

Can you add five letters to each of the words in capitals in the snakes below, to make another word which solves the clue? For example, by adding five letters to the clue 'A revolt can make you REEL', you can make the word REBELLION. Each of the answers share a common theme.

1. There'll be a ROW the morning after.

2. Do you carry a WAD in modern times?

3. It shows the year from beginning to END.

4. Not a weekday. TRY again.

5. MICE have got into this clock.

SUDOKU

To solve, fill in the grid so that every row, column and box contains the numbers 1 through 9.

	6	9	7	2	4	1		3
	1				6			
			1	8		7		
	5	3	9			4		8
6	7			5	9			2
	9	8		4				5
	8	7	4				2	6
5	4	6						
		1		5	9	8		

ANAGRAM LADDERS

Solve the anagrams on the right to reveal the names of seven computer words. The shaded column in the middle will then reveal the name of another computer word.

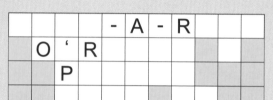

| TUPNI |
| ROSCUR |
| MEDOM |
| GINLO |
| RLLOSC |
| CASEPE |
| MATROF |

LETTER STEW

Use all the given letters in the stew to spell three words meaning clever.

NURSERY BLOCKS

Rearrange each column of letters and write them in the grid to reveal the first two lines of a well known nursery rhyme. Some of the letters have been put in to give you a head start.

COMMON WORDS

Your task here is to determine the answers to each set of tricky definitions below, as well as the word that is contained in all five of the set's answers. For example if the five solutions were ERRAND, TERRIBLE, MERRY MEN, PREFERRED and PERRY, the word in the central circle would be ERR.

CLUES:
1 Frighten
2 Chewy candy
3 The Lion King villain
4 Ford follower
5 Priest's home

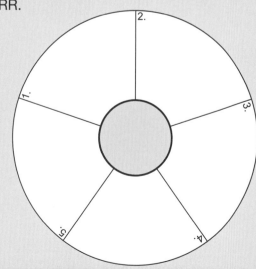

CROSSWORD

Across
2 Land suitable for crops (6)
5 Circuits of track (4)
6 Despot (6)
7 Small dog (4)
8 Rodent (3)
11 Flexible pipe (4)
13 Baby's cot (6)
14 Wander (4)
15 Toboggan (6)

Down
1 Of sound mind (4)
2 Showy flower (5)
3 Container for gravy (4)
4 Complete (6)
7 Sign of the zodiac (6)
9 In that place (5)
10 Ingredient of stuffing (4)
12 Close with a bang (4)

NOURISHING NINE

How many words of four letters or more can you track down in this game? At least one 'nourishing' word will contain all nine letters and all words must contain the central letter. Use each letter once only. No words with capital letters, foreign words, hyphens, or plurals and verb forms ending in -s are allowed.

UNDERDONE: 12 words
MEDIUM: 20 words
WELL DONE: 29 words

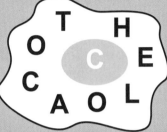

ON TARGET

Put the answers to the clues in the grid starting from the outside. Each answer has five letters and ends with the central letter T. When you've finished the outer ring will reveal the name of a sport (7).

1 Watchful (5)
2 Behave in response (5)
3 A measure of gold (5)
4 Custom (5)
5 To live (5)
6 Cook in fat in the oven (5)
7 It makes dough rise (5)

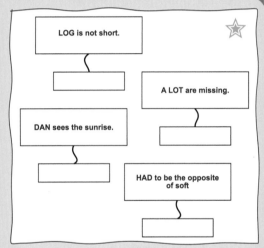

LETTER SWAP

Can you replace a letter from each word with a letter from the boxes below to reveal a well-known saying? Each letter is used only once.

| O | D | E | | S | H | A | L | L | O | W | | D | I | E | S |

| N | O | N | | M | I | K | E | | I | | H | U | M | M | E | R |

| S | A | T | O | W | N | A |

ADD A LETTER

Add one letter to each word in capitals to create a new word that answers the clue. The order of the letters does not need to be changed.

For example – I BET it's more superior would be BEST.

LOG is not short.

A LOT are missing.

DAN sees the sunrise.

HAD to be the opposite of soft

NINE NUMBERS

Try to fill in the missing numbers.
Use the numbers 1 to 9 to complete the equations. Each number is only used once. Each row and column is an equation with the totals given below and to the right.

9	x		+		59
/		/		-	
	-	2	-		-3
x		x		-	
1	+		+		16
3		24		-6	

PLACE THE PLACES

To solve the puzzle place the letters from the place in capitals into the empty spaces in the grid. Four everyday words should be formed reading across the grid and three everyday words reading down.

P E R S I A

G	A	
S		N
	A	T

LITTLE TOUGHIE

Across

4 Northerner may be seen in Prince's kimono? (6)
5 Put down bits of reed in laminar form (7)
8 A tart's built up in layers (6)

Down

1 It'll ring the changes! (4)
2 Gun reforms are embraced by company (7)
3 Prominent feature has information, we're told (4)
6 Recess, perhaps, even holds it (4)
7 Curse at having to chase doctor (4)

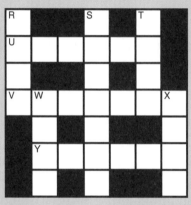

SHELLED CREATURES WORDSEARCH

The grid contains 10 shelled creatures hidden vertically, horizontally or diagonally. The unused letters spell out another creature with a shell.

BIVALVE   PIDDOCK
COCKLE   PRAWN
CRAWFISH   SHRIMP
CRAYFISH   SNAIL
MOLLUSC   TORTOISE

E	L	K	C	O	C	T	W
S	C	B	H	N	R	O	K
H	S	I	F	W	A	R	C
R	U	V	S	A	Y	T	O
I	L	A	N	R	F	O	D
M	L	L	A	P	I	I	D
P	O	V	I	E	S	S	I
L	M	E	L	K	H	E	P

ARROWS

Put the following numbers in the arrows below:

1 1 1 2 3 5 5 5

Be careful though. The total numbers in the 3 arrows pointing at each other must add up to 11.

The total numbers in the arrows which are back to back must add up to 6.

CAGED ANIMALS

An animal has escaped from the zoo. To put him back in his cage answer the eight clues and put them in the grid starting from the outermost circle. When this is done the central circles starting clockwise from number nine will reveal the name of the animal who escaped.

1 Leaf of book (4)
2 Slender (4)
3 Too (4)
4 Large village (4)
5 Small branch (4)
6 Brave man (4)
7 Capital of Norway (4)
8 Unmarried lady (4)

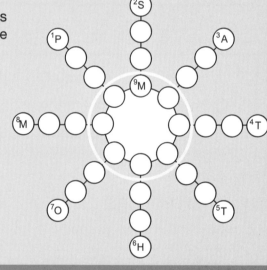

PICTURE PHRASES

The images below represent three well known phrases. Look carefully and see if you can work out what they are.

1.

2.

3.

KAKURO ⭐⭐

In Kakuro the numbers in the black squares refer to the SUMS of the digits 1–9 which you are to fill into the empty spaces. The number ABOVE the diagonal line refers to the empty spaces directly to the RIGHT of that number. A number BELOW the diagonal line refers to the empty spaces directly BELOW that number. No zeros are used here and a digit can only appear once in any particular digit combination.

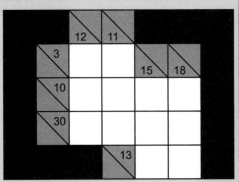

REBUS TOWER ⭐⭐⭐

Can you work out which common phrases are represented by each of the three diagrams in the tower below?

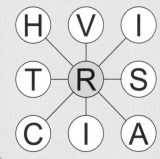

UCOGH

DUMP
DUMP GOOSE FEATHERS DUMP
DUMP

HAPPY HAPPY
HAPPY HAPPY
HAPPY HAPPY
HAPPY HAPPY
HAPPY HAPPY

OCCUPATIONS ⭐⭐⭐

How many words of four letters or more can you track down in this game? At least one will be a nine letter occupation and all contain the central letter. Use each letter once only. No words with capitals, foreign words, hyphens, or plurals and verb forms ending in -s are allowed.

GOOD: 10 words
VERY GOOD: 15 words
EXCELLENT: 22 words

ZOO HUNT ⭐

An animal has escaped from the zoo and is hiding somewhere in the grid. If you cross out all the letters that appear more than twice, the remaining letters will spell out the missing creature.

THE MISSING CREATURE IS A

....

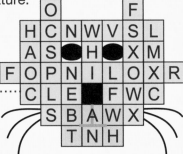

SUDOKU ⭐⭐⭐

To solve, fill in the grid so that every row, column and box contains the numbers 1 through 9.

5	1	2	8	4				6
		9	2	1			7	5
	3				2			4
7						1		9
	8	3		9	4		2	7
6								
2	7	6		5		3		
9				3				2
3	5			7		4		

SKELETON CROSSWORD ⭐⭐⭐

Below is an incomplete quick crossword grid. Can you solve the puzzle by fitting the answers to the clues correctly into the grid, along with the remaining blocks and clue numbers? A few blocks have been shaded to give you a start. This grid has been rotated by 180 degrees.

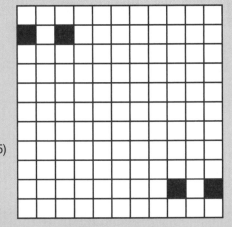

Across
1 Sprinkles with water (6)
5 Cummerbund (4)
7 A gag (4)
8 Diminished (6)
9 Ski slope (5)
12 Moving about (5)
13 Assistance (3)
14 Romantic assignation (5)
16 Loose stones on mountain side (5)
19 Spanish married woman (6)
20 Fly high in the air (4)
22 Tube (4)
23 Votes into office (6)

Down
2 Instruction to turn over (3)
3 Skilful (5)
4 Break in two (4)
5 Remains (5)
6 Barren (7)
10 Person from Jerusalem perhaps (7)
11 To dine (3)
12 Public promotions (3)
15 Part of bicycle wheel (5)
17 Hereditary Hindu class (5)
18 Entrance (4)
21 Perform on stage (3)

A'MAZE'ING NUMBERS

Try to make your way through the maze. The number at the beginning of each row and column tells you exactly how many squares you will have to cross though in order to reach the finish. No diagonal moves are allowed.

Solving hint: To begin, blacken any box that you determine will not be used, and place a dot in any box that you know must be used.

⭐⭐⭐

	1	1	1	5	1	3	1	7	1
4									
1									
4									
3									
4									
1									
1									
1									
2									

START →

FINISH →

BATTLESHIPS

⭐⭐

There are five ships hidden in the grid below. Look at the key to see which ships you have to find. The numbers on the grid tell you how many squares of each row or column part of a ship is found in. To get you started we've put a few parts of ships (in red) and a few squares with no ships (in black).

HINTS: Begin by shading in all the misses (all the columns which have a nought in them) as there re no ships here. When you have found a full ship you can shade all the blocks around that ship as misses because none of the ships are touching.

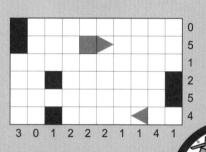

HIDDEN SHIPS

2 AIRCRAFT CARRIERS

3 BATTLESHIPS

Row numbers (top to bottom): 0, 5, 1, 2, 5, 4

Column numbers (left to right): 3 0 1 2 2 2 1 1 4 1

FLOWERY PHRASES

⭐⭐⭐

We have described a well-known saying using flowery language. Can you uncover the more familiar form? For example, 'An eruption in the cook pot' would be 'A Flash in the pan'.

The sound emanating from a male person, which is imitative of the noise made by members of the aquatic mammalian families of Phocidae and Otariidae, is judged considerably more harsh than that male's capacity to grip and grab with bonelike structures that are socketed in his jowls.

CROSSWORD

⭐⭐

Across

1   Shrub with fragrant flower (4-4)
6   U.S. heavyweight boxer (3)
7   Release without punishment (5)
9   Carry (4)
11 Perceived (4)
12 Oak for instance (4)
14 Miss Laine the jazz singer (4)
16 Bout of something (5)
18 Acquired (3)
19 Get or find back (8)

Down

1   Evaluate for a second time (8)
2   Inflict a heavy blow on (5)
3   Most suitable (4)
4   Ocean (3)
5   Move to new location (8)
8   Mr Waterman, the pop manager (4)
10 A single time (4)
13 'Rascal (5)
15 Sneering look (4)
17 Regret (3)

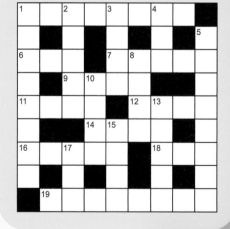

NATUREGRAMS

⭐⭐

Solve each clue, then rearrange the five letters in every answer to form a set of three trees and shrubs.
CLUES: 1 Fierce giants, 2 Fairly large, 3 Himalayan country

1. ☐☐☐☐☐   1. ☐☐☐☐☐

2. ☐☐☐☐☐   2. ☐☐☐☐☐

3. ☐☐☐☐☐   3. ☐☐☐☐☐

ALPHAFITS ⭐⭐

One of each of the 26 letters of the alphabet has been removed from the crossword grid below. Can you replace them all to fill the crossword with everyday words?

| A | B | C | D | E | F | G | H | I | J | K | L | M |
| N | O | P | Q | R | S | T | U | V | W | X | Y | Z |

NATURAL NINE ⭐

Try and become king of the jungle in this natural puzzle. How many words of four letters or more can you track down? At least one will use all nine letters and all contain the central letter F. Use each letter once only. No words with capitals, foreign words, hyphens, or plurals are allowed.

The nine letter word is

....

PUSSYCAT STANDARD: 9 words
PANTHER STANDARD: 18 words
LION STANDARD: 28 words

PAIR WHEELS ⭐⭐

Place each of the twelve pairs of letters into one of the circles in the wheel, so that every line running through the central circle gives you a six-letter word with the middle letters CK.

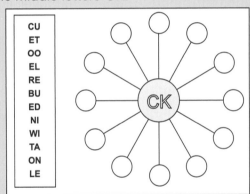

| CU |
| ET |
| OO |
| EL |
| RE |
| BU |
| ED |
| NI |
| WI |
| TA |
| ON |
| LE |

BUG TEASE ⭐

Can you work out the answer to this teaser?

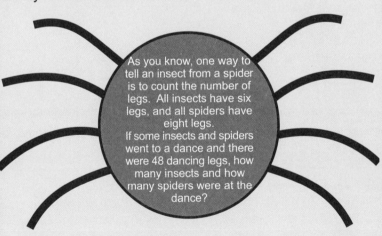

As you know, one way to tell an insect from a spider is to count the number of legs. All insects have six legs, and all spiders have eight legs. If some insects and spiders went to a dance and there were 48 dancing legs, how many insects and how many spiders were at the dance?

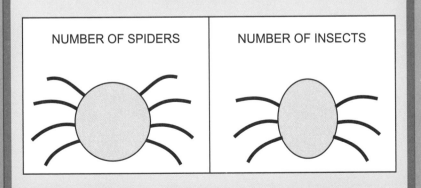

| NUMBER OF SPIDERS | NUMBER OF INSECTS |

UPSETTING WORDSEARCH ⭐

The grid contains 11 upsetting words, hidden vertically, horizontally or diagonally. Can you find them all?

AGITATE
CAPSIZE
CONFUSE
DERANGE
DISTURB
FLUSTER
INVERT
RUFFLE
TOPPLE
UPEND
UPTURN

A	G	I	T	A	T	E	R
E	L	P	P	O	T	Z	E
G	T	R	E	V	N	I	T
N	U	P	E	N	D	S	S
A	F	N	R	U	T	P	U
R	U	F	F	L	E	A	L
E	S	U	F	N	O	C	F
D	I	S	T	U	R	B	V

ODD ONE OUT

Can you spot the odd one out in this sequence of animals?

WORD WHEEL

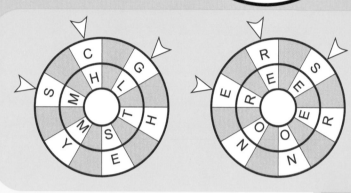

For each of the circles, can you find two letters which when placed in the centre will form three six-letter words?

OPPOSITES ATTRACT

Place each of the tiles in the boxes below to form two words with opposite meaning.

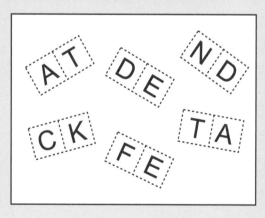

KAKURO

In Kakuro the numbers in the black squares refer to the SUMS of the digits 1–9 which you are to fill into the empty spaces. The number ABOVE the diagonal line refers to the empty spaces directly to the RIGHT of that number. A number BELOW the diagonal line refers to the empty spaces directly BELOW that number. No zeros are used here and a digit can only appear once in any particular digit combination.

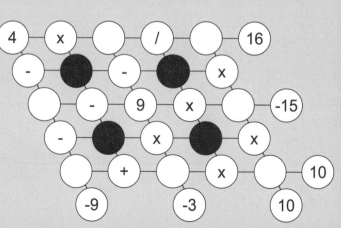

NUMBER HEX

Can you correctly enter six numbers into the Number Hex grid using the clues below? All are whole numbers below 10 and no two numbers are the same.

CLUES:
The grid has 3 odd and 3 even numbers
All numbers are less than 7
A is the lowest number and E the highest number
F times C equals B plus D
D is the number in a trio
C is greater than F

NINE NUMBERS

Try to fill in the missing numbers.
Use the numbers 1 to 9 to complete the equations. Each number is only used once. Each row and column is an equation with the totals given below and to the right.

THREE FOUR ALL

The object is to find three four-letter words using the letters given in each word without changing the order of the letters. For example, if the given word were PRICES, the first word might be PIES, the second might be RICE and the third would be ICES.

ARRANGED	_____	_____	_____
HOLSTER	_____	_____	_____

OCCUPATIONS

How many words of four letters or more can you track down in this game? At least one will be a nine letter occupation and all contain the central letter. Use each letter once only. No words with capitals, foreign words, hyphens, or plurals and verb forms ending in -s are allowed.

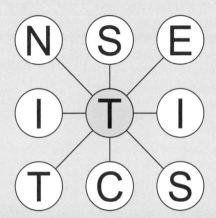

SUDOKU

To solve, fill in the grid so that every row, column and box contains the letters A through I.

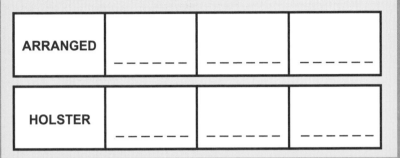

WORD FIT

Can you fit all the words linked with a telephone into the grid below?

3 letter word
Cut

4 letter words
Call
Chat
Code
Dead
Dial

Hear
Hold
Line
Ring
Slot
Talk
Text

5 letter words
Bands
Touch

6 letter words
Button
Listen
Number
Refund

Return

7 letter word
Engaged

8 letter word
Operator

PYRAMID OF EGGS

Fill in the eggs with numbers, they must equal the sum of the two eggs below.

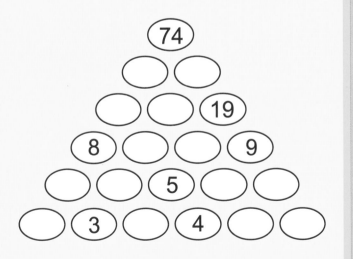

COUNTING CRITTERS

Can you find the number that is represented by each animal face? You will find the totals of the numbers below each column and to the right of each row.

⭐⭐⭐

NINE NUMBERS ⭐

Try to fill in the missing numbers. Use the numbers 1 to 9 to complete the equations. Each number is only used once. Each row and column is an equation with the totals given below and to the right.

8	+		+		19
x		x		+	
7	+		x		72
+		+		/	
	+		+	3	9
58		9		5	

SUDOKU ⭐⭐⭐

To solve, fill in the grid so that every row, column and box contains the numbers 1 through 9.

7	2	9	5		4			6
4	1		6			8		7
8		5			2			9
	5			6	7		8	3
	4			5	3		2	
9			2	1				
	8	4		9	6		3	5
3	9		8	4				
5	7		1	3			9	

WHAT CITIES ARE THESE AIRPORTS SITUATED IN?

1. O'HARE ?	
2. JFK ?	
3. JOHN LENNON ?	
4. ROBIN HOOD ?	
5. GATWICK ?	
6. SCHIPHOL ?	

STEP LADDER ⭐

Starting with the top word, change one letter at a time to make a new word at every step until you have reached the bottom word.

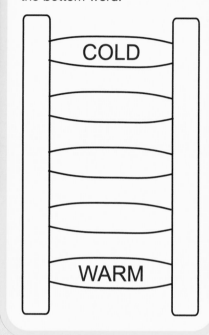

COLD

WARM

QUICK QUIZ QUESTIONS ⭐⭐

Can you get all of these quiz questions correct?

FIVE SNEAKY SNAKES ⭐⭐⭐

Can you add five letters to each of the words in capitals in the snakes below, to make another word which solves the clue? For example, by adding five letters to the clue 'A revolt can make you REEL', you can make the word REBELLION. Each of the answers shares a common theme.

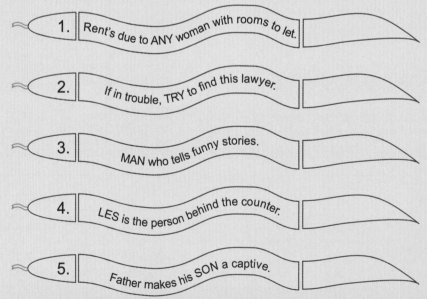

1. Rent's due to ANY woman with rooms to let.

2. If in trouble, TRY to find this lawyer.

3. MAN who tells funny stories.

4. LES is the person behind the counter.

5. Father makes his SON a captive.

ADD THREE TO THREE

Can you add three letters to the three words in red below to make another word which solves the clue? For example, by adding three letters to the clue 'BAN this fruit', you can make the word BANANA.

★ ★

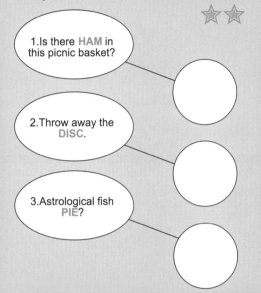

1. Is there **HAM** in this picnic basket?

2. Throw away the **DISC**.

3. Astrological fish **PIE**?

WORD SPLITZ

Each row of ten letters can be split into two five-letter boys names. These words read from left to right and are in order.

For example SMOKOSUENK can be split to reveal SKUNK and MOOSE.

① A B L A L R A N R Y
② B C R O I L A N I N
③ G J E A S O O F F N
④ N R A I L P G H E L

WORD WHEEL

★

For each of the circles, can you find two letters which when placed in the centre will form three six-letter words?

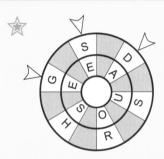
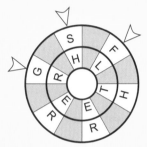

OPPOSITES ATTRACT

★ ★

Arrange the tiles below to create two pairs of four letter words. Each pair has words with opposite meanings.

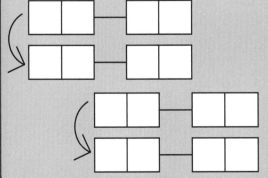

LITTLE TOUGHIE

★ ★ ★

Across

2. It's genuine and about a pound (4)
4. Manufactured for a girl (4)
5. Horse race accommodation (4)
6. Fan mostly wants me for notoriety (4)
7. Some terrific rewards in this company (4)
8. Bearing in plane is a joke (4)

Down

1. We will confine a deer for inefficient use (7)
2. Think you have to look in the mirror? (7)
3. A pad, done up by Ted and made suitable (7)

ADDING GRIDS

Place any digits 0 to 9 into the empty circles. When complete each row should add up to the figures on the right and each column to the figures below. The shaded numbers are the totals of the diagonal circles.

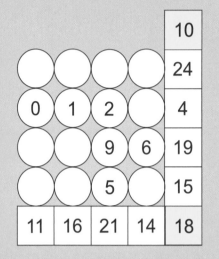

				10
				24
0	1	2		4
		9	6	19
		5		15
11	16	21	14	18

OCCUPATIONS

How many words of four letters or more can you track down in this game? At least one will be a nine letter occupation and all contain the central letter. Use each letter once only. No words with capitals, foreign words, hyphens, or plurals and verb forms ending in -s are allowed.

GOOD: 18 words
VERY GOOD: 24 words
EXCELLENT: 33 words

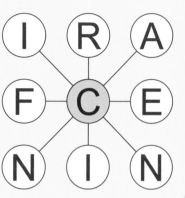

CASTLE MAZE ⭐

Can you find your way out of the castle and through the maze?

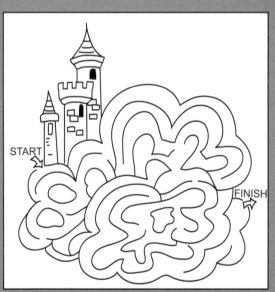

START

FINISH

JIG GRID ⭐⭐⭐

Can you fit the blocks back into the grid to reveal, reading from left to right, seven artists?

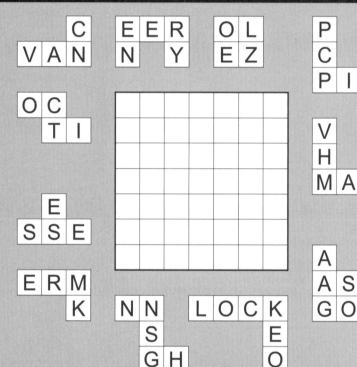

BIRD BOXES ⭐

Shade in all the numbers that can be divided exactly by seven to reveal a hidden bird.

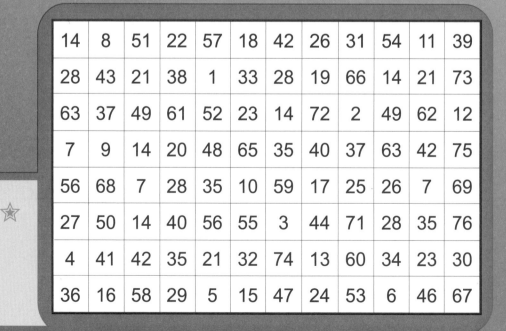

14	8	51	22	57	18	42	26	31	54	11	39
28	43	21	38	1	33	28	19	66	14	21	73
63	37	49	61	52	23	14	72	2	49	62	12
7	9	14	20	48	65	35	40	37	63	42	75
56	68	7	28	35	10	59	17	25	26	7	69
27	50	14	40	56	55	3	44	71	28	35	76
4	41	42	35	21	32	74	13	60	34	23	30
36	16	58	29	5	15	47	24	53	6	46	67

MOVIE HOUSE ⭐⭐

Hidden in the grid are six 90s sci-fi films. Can you find them all?

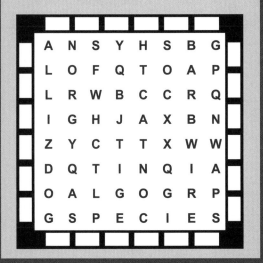

A	N	S	Y	H	S	B	G
L	O	F	Q	T	O	A	P
L	R	W	B	C	C	R	Q
I	G	H	J	A	X	B	N
Z	Y	C	T	T	X	W	W
D	Q	T	I	N	Q	I	A
O	A	L	G	O	G	R	P
G	S	P	E	C	I	E	S

PAIR WHEELS ⭐⭐

Place each of the twelve pairs of letters into one of the circles in the wheel, so that every line running through the central circle gives you a six-letter word with the middle letters UN.

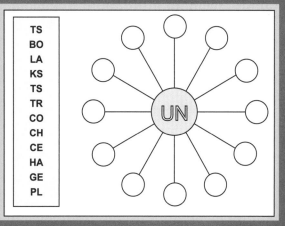

| TS |
| BO |
| LA |
| KS |
| TS |
| TR |
| CO |
| CH |
| CE |
| HA |
| GE |
| PL |

WINTER SPORTS SQUIRCLE ⭐⭐

Put vowels in the circles and consonants in the squares to make words in all the columns. Definitions of these words are given. When this has been done, the first and third rows will make the names of three winter sports.

DEFINITIONS
1 Lodging place
2 Additional
3 Stringed instrument
4 Small booth
5 Premium bond computer
6 Shouts loudly
7 Lacking sharpness
8 Block of metal
9 In front

TEA POT NUMBER PIC ⭐⭐

Can you create a picture from the grid below?

Each number represents a group of shaded squares, so for example means that on this row there is a group of 3 black squares to the left of a group of 2 black squares, with one or more white squares in between (there must be at least one white square in between the groups, or the 3 and 2 would join up to become a 5).

The numbers are always in order, so **4 2** means a group of 4 black squares to the left of a group of 2 black squares in that row, and **5** means a block of 5 black squares **3** above a block of 3 black squares in that column.

	1									
4	2	7	8	8	7	4	2	2	
2									
4 1									
9									
1 6									
1 5									
7									
5									
4									

CROSSWORD ⭐

Across
2 Sharp intake of breath (4)
4 Of sound mind (4)
5 Rip (4)
6 Identical (4)
7 Fibs (4)
8 Handle (4)

Down
1 A flourish of trumpets (7)
2 Card for sick person (3,4)
3 Hors d'oeuvre (7)

BITS AND PIECES

The tiles in the top grid are all jumbled up. Can you rearrange them in the grid below using only one tile from each column to reveal four related words and their theme?

C	AN	T	E	O
T	A	I	R	N
FO	W	N	S	S
D	X	C	G	T
T	A	NC	A	OT

⭐⭐⭐

LETTER STEW

Use all the letters in the stew to spell three words meaning laugh.

I F A E T L
O R R G W
G E C H
G G F L U

PICTURE TILES

Copy the contents of the tiles into the empty grid using the grid references to find the right places. What appears in the box?

	1	2	3	4
A				
B				
C				
D				
E				
F				

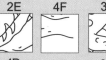
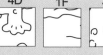
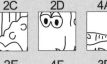

1E 1B 3F
3E 1A 4E
2B 1D 3B
2A 1C 4B
2C 2D 4A
2E 4F 3D
4D 1F 3C
3A 4C 2F

PICTURE PHRASES ★★

The images below represent four well known phrases. Look carefully and see if you can work out what they are.

1. WARDWALKROBE

2. KNEE / LIGHTS

3. TIME / AB DEFG

4. UWIN 3+7=10 / ULOSE 3+9=12

SUDOKU ★★★

To solve, fill in the grid so that every row, column and box contains the numbers 1 through 9.

6	4				7			
	7				5		4	
					8	6		
				8	1			
	4	9						6
7				9		3		
	8		1		2			
	9	2	4	3			7	
	5				9			

COMMON WORDS ★★★

Your task here is to determine the answers to the tricky definitions below, as well as the word that is contained in all five answers. For example if the five solutions were ERRAND, TERRIBLE, MERRY MEN, PREFERRED and PERRY, the word in the central circle would be ERR.

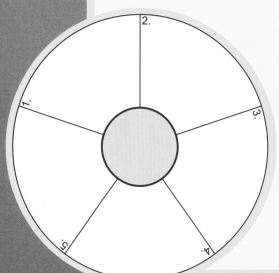

CLUES:
Sell
Said
Dim
Diamond
Southern state

SITTING WORDSEARCH ★

The grid contains 13 sitting words hidden vertically, horizontally or diagonally. Can you find them all?

BASKET
BATH
BENCH
COUCH
CUSHION
DINING
EASY
HAMMOCK
PILLION
ROCKING
SOFA
SWING

B	E	N	C	H	N	N	L
A	H	A	M	M	O	C	K
S	T	F	S	I	I	S	C
K	A	O	H	Y	L	W	X
E	B	S	P	T	L	I	T
T	U	D	I	N	I	N	G
C	O	U	C	H	P	G	G
R	O	C	K	I	N	G	I

80S SCIENCE QUIZ

What is the name of the company which manufactured the Stealth Bomber?

....

Which record was broken by the Antonov An-124 in 1985?

....

What planet was Magellan's destination in 1989?

....

What handheld computer system was launched in 1989?

....

What was the Cray-1?

....

ARROWS

Put the following numbers in the arrows below:

3 3 4 4 5 6 6 7

Be careful though.
The total numbers in the 3 arrows pointing at each other must add up to 12.

The total numbers in the arrows which are back to back must add up to 9.

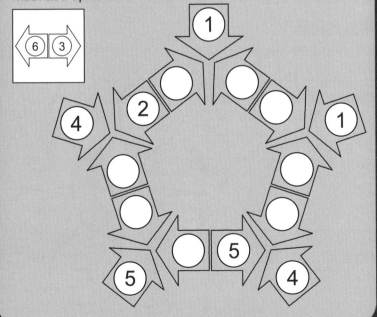

LOLLIPOPS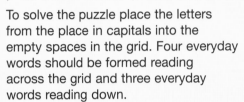

By moving two of the lollipops on the right can you move the ball outside of the glass?

PLACE THE PLACES

To solve the puzzle place the letters from the place in capitals into the empty spaces in the grid. Four everyday words should be formed reading across the grid and three everyday words reading down.

L A H O R E

SKELETON CROSSWORD

Below is an incomplete quick crossword grid. Can you solve the puzzle by fitting the answers to the clues correctly into the grid, along with the remaining blocks and clue numbers? A few blocks have been shaded to give you a start. This grid has been rotated by 180 degrees.

Across
1 Delivers a blow to (5)
4 Garden tool (5)
7 Bye in cricket for instance (3)
8 Throw about like seeds (7)
9 Wan (4)
10 Christen (4)
13 Groove from wheel (3)
15 Do as one's told (4)
16 Uncommon (4)
19 To clap (7)
21 Expected to arrive (3)
22 A sharp point (5)
23 Heat ore to extract metal (5)

Down
1 Mass of floating ice (4)
2 Ancestry (7)
3 Senior nurse (6)
4 Pierce with a knife (4)
5 Knack (3)
6 Worked for (6)
11 Shorten written material (7)
12 Members of the Queen's family (6)
14 Does business (6)
17 Charge for journey (4)
18 Units of length (4)
20 Unit of pressure (3)

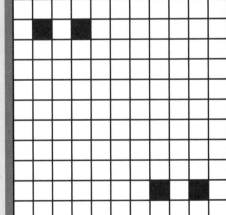

CHAIN REACTION

Solve this puzzle by creating a 'chain reaction' of 20 five-letter words that run left to right, beginning in the upper-left hand corner, using the 19 two-letter tiles in the middle. A two-letter tile that ends one begins the next. Each tile will only be used once. The single letters already entered are the middle letters of the words you are to form. Start by finishing the word that begins WEL_ _.

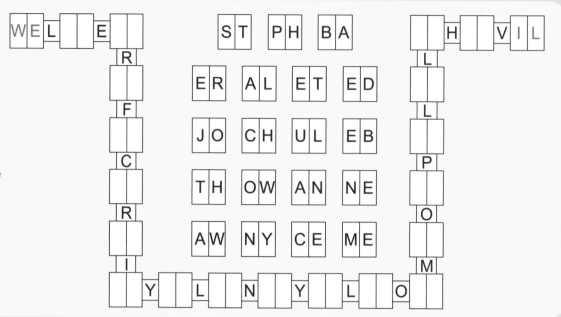

Chain grid letters:
WEL | E ... E | ... | H | VIL

Middle tiles:
ST PH BA
ER AL ET ED
JO CH UL EB
TH OW AN NE
AW NY CE ME

Left column: R F C R I ... Y
Right column: L L P O M
Bottom row: Y L N Y L O

GEOGRAMS ★★

Solve each clue, then rearrange the six letters in every answer to form a set of three rivers.

CLUES:
1 Peril
2 Control of your emotions
3 Baby's bed

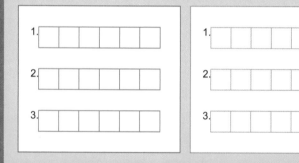

1.
2.
3.

1.
2.
3.

HOLLYWOOD ANAGRAMS ★★★

Below are four anagrams of films or film people. The number and length of words to find is shown in brackets. The four anagram solutions are all linked in some way – can you find the link?

FORGIVE NUN (10)

CHILLNESS DIRTS (10, 4)

THE LINK IS .....

PERFORMS GUT (7, 4)

INSTIGATE HELP THEN (3, 7, 7)

SUDOKU ★★

To solve, fill in the grid so that every row, column and box contains the numbers 1 through 9.

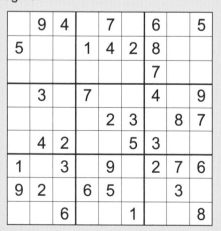

	9	4		7		6		5
5			1	4	2	8		
					7			
	3		7			4		9
			2	3			8	7
	4	2				5	3	
1		3		9		2	7	6
9	2		6	5				3
		6			1			8

NATURAL NINE ★

Try and become king of the jungle in this natural puzzle.

How many words of four letters or more can you track down? At least one will use all nine letters and all contain the central letter V. Use each letter once only. No words with capitals, foreign words, hyphens, or plurals are allowed.

The nine letter word is

....

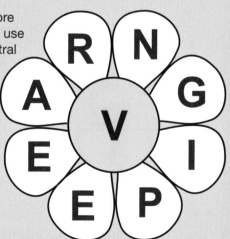

PUSSYCAT STANDARD: 9 words
PANTHER STANDARD: 15 words
LION STANDARD: 23 words

ANAGRAM LADDERS COUNTRIES ⭐

Solve the anagrams to reveal the names of seven countries. The shaded colomn in the middle will then reveal the name of another country.

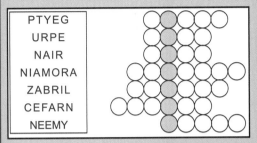

PTYEG
URPE
NAIR
NIAMORA
ZABRIL
CEFARN
NEEMY

CODED CROSSWORD ⭐⭐⭐

Each number in the grid represents a different letter of the alphabet. Can you fill in the grid using the given letters to get you started?

1	2	3 H	4	5	6 O	7	8	9	10	11	12	13
14	15	16 P	17	18	19 N	20	21	22	23	24	25	26

CHILDREN IN NEED WORDSEARCH ⭐⭐

The grid contains 14 words connected with the UK charity Children In Need hidden vertically, horizontally or diagonally. The unused letters spell out another connected word.

AMOUNT
APPEAL
ASSIST
BEAR
BENEFIT

BIDS
CARE
CASH
CHARITY
GENEROUS

GOOD
POVERTY
SHOW
SPONSOR

Y	A	S	S	I	S	T	S
A	T	D	Y	W	F	U	P
M	I	I	T	E	O	U	O
O	F	B	R	R	N	H	N
U	E	B	E	A	R	S	S
N	N	N	V	C	H	A	O
T	E	G	O	O	D	C	R
G	B	A	P	P	E	A	L

NATURE TRAIL ⭐

Find the plant that is growing inside the tree by removing all the letters that appear more than twice.

THE HIDDEN PLANT IS A

....

	J	H		
O	A	L	P	
M	F	P	R	F	M
S	B	I	E	A	I	C	W
P	H	L	E	B	J
	J	S	W	W	
	M	T		
	N	F		
	B	U		
	A	I		
	T	L		

KAKURO ⭐⭐

In Kakuro the numbers in the black squares refer to the SUMS of the digits 1–9 which you are to fill into the empty spaces. The number ABOVE the diagonal line refers to the empty spaces directly to the RIGHT of that number. A number BELOW the diagonal line refers to the empty spaces directly BELOW that number. No zeros are used here and a digit can only appear once in any particular digit combination.

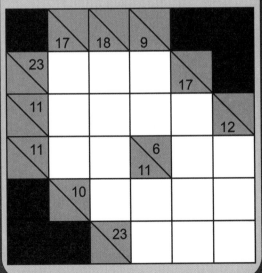

DIZZY DICTATION ⭐⭐

Jeff's new secretary is having some trouble with dictation. Can you work out what he is trying to say in the following sentences?

1. WEE MIST YEW WEN EWER AWEIGH IN GREASE.

2. WATTS YORE ANTS BILL DING CLOTHES TWO?

3. SIOUX WAR ADRESS BEAK OZ MERRY BAR ODE HIRSUITE.

HOLLYWOOD ANAGRAMS

Below are four anagrams of films or film people. The number and length of words to find is shown in brackets. The four anagram solutions are all linked in some way – can you find the link?

BATT DRIP (4, 4)	
WILBUR SLICE (5, 6)	THE LINK IS .....
ROMEO DIME (4, 5)	
JANET NEON FIR SIN (8, 7)	

ANAGRAM RIDDLE ⭐⭐⭐

Each of the clues gives the anagram of four common words with the exception of one letter. Fill in the grid by solving the anagram and finding the missing letter.

A six-letter word containing two Os, one G, one B, one N, and one other consonant.
A seven-letter word containing two Es, one T, one S, one N, one G, and one other consonant.
An eight-letter word containing two Cs, one P, one T, one I, one A, one E, and one other consonant.
A nine-letter word containing three Ls, one Y, one T, one A, one E, one I, and one other.

1.							
2.							
3.							
4.							

NINE NUMBERS ⭐

Try to fill in the missing numbers.
Use the numbers 1 to 9 to complete the equations. Each number is only used once. Each row and column is an equation with the totals given below and to the right.

	-	1	-	1
-		+	x	
9	-		+	13
x		-	-	
	x	3	-	4
-8		0		22

ALPHAFITS ⭐⭐

One of each of the 26 letters of the alphabet has been removed from the crossword grid below. Can you replace them all to fill the crossword with everyday words?

L	A				O		F	E		
O	■					O				T
	O	O	L			R	A		S	E
E		R		R			T			M
S		U	E			E	D			
		S				R		F		S
			E	A	L		U	S		
S		G		A		Y		T		M
U			B	L	E		B		L	
N		M		E				R		O
	R	E	E		Y		S	E	A	

A	B	C	D	E	F	G	H	I	J	K	L	M
N	O	P	Q	R	S	T	U	V	W	X	Y	Z

REBUS TOWER ⭐⭐⭐

Can you work out which common phrases are represented by each of the three diagrams in the tower below?

BED
FA ST

NO
ROAD

JUST

WORD WALL

Make your way up the wall by changing one letter at a time until you reach the top word.

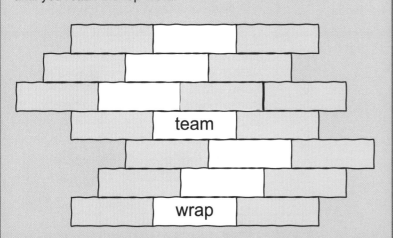

team

wrap

JIG GRID

Can you fit the blocks back into the grid to reveal, reading from left to right, six rocks and minerals?

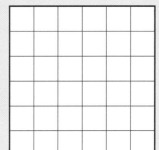

| U | A | R |
| Y | P | S | U | M |

| B | A |
| C | O |

A	L	T
		R
		R
		Z

| S |
| P | P | E |

| N | E |
| V | E | T |

G	A	R
S	I	L
Q	G
G

NATUREGRAMS

Solve each clue, then rearrange the five letters in every answer to form a set of three fruits and vegetables.

CLUES:
1 Light thin fabric
2 Low in price
3 Unwanted plants

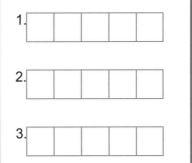

1.

2.

3.

1.

2.

3.

SUDOKU

To solve, fill in the grid so that every row, column and box contains the numbers 1 through 9.

7	4	6		2		3	9	8
8	9		6		7	4		5
3	1			8	9	2	6	7
9	8			4		5		
2	3			9	6		4	1
	6	4	8	1	2	7		
	5	3		7	1	6	8	
	2	9	3	5			7	
1	7	8	2	6	4		5	3

CROSSWORD

Across
1 Treat improperly (6)
5 Common girl's name (3)
6 Female pronoun (3)
7 Ignited (3)
8 Knack (3)
9 U.S. heavyweight boxer (3)
10 A farm (6)

Down
1 Unlucky accident (6)
2 Protection from bad weather (7)
3 To maintain, withstand (7)
4 Small and dainty (6)

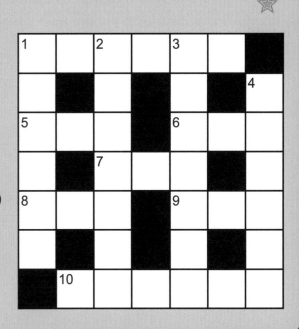

NINE NUMBERS

Try to fill in the missing numbers.
Use the numbers 1 to 9 to complete the equations. Each number is only used once. Each row and column is an equation with the totals given below and to the right.

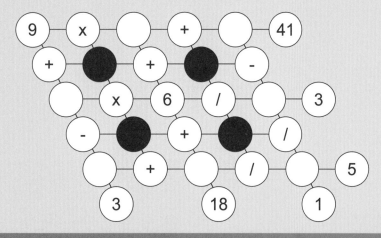

HIDDEN COLORS

Shade in all the vowels to reveal a hidden color.

W	H	J	Q	W	Z	G	B	C	V	H	B
O	I	E	D	H	A	L	E	S	N	L	K
I	X	O	X	T	I	M	I	F	C	J	Y
A	O	U	R	J	U	E	O	P	G	Q	M
E	S	V	E	N	Y	R	A	U	I	A	O
I	C	Y	U	F	K	L	E	T	E	F	U
B	G	V	I	S	Q	N	O	R	A	B	I
Z	P	K	A	P	M	W	E	Z	O	T	E

KAKURO

In Kakuro the numbers in the black squares refer to the SUMS of the digits 1–9 which you are to fill into the empty spaces. The number ABOVE the diagonal line refers to the empty spaces directly to the RIGHT of that number. A number BELOW the diagonal line refers to the empty spaces directly BELOW that number. No zeros are used here and a digit can only appear once in any particular digit combination.

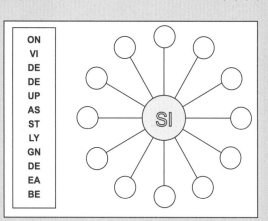

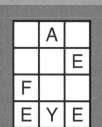

PLACE THE PLACES

To solve the puzzle place the letters from the place in capitals into the empty spaces in the grid. Four everyday words should be formed reading across the grid and three everyday words reading down.

W A R S A W

PYRAMID OF APPLES

Fill in the apples with numbers, they must equal the sum of the two apples below.

PAIR WHEELS

Place each of the twelve pairs of letters into one of the circles in the wheel, so that every line running through the central circle gives you a six-letter word with the middle letters SI.

ON
VI
DE
DE
UP
AS
ST
LY
GN
DE
EA
BE

ON TARGET

Put the answers to the clues in the grid starting from the outside. Each answer has five letters and ends with the central letter S. When you've finished the outer ring will reveal the name of a UK soccer team (7).

1 Country in the United Kingdom (5)
2 Brings up (5)
3 British peers (5)
4 Medical scans (1-4)
5 Manual workers (5)
6 Assumed name (5)
7 School subject (5)

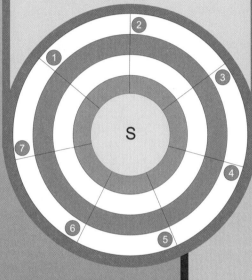

WORD FIT

Can you fit all the natural features into the grid?

3 letter words
Col
Sea

4 letter words
Cave
Dune
Lake
Pond
Scar
Tarn

5 letter words
Delta
Oasis
Ocean
Scree
Shore

6 letter words
Canyon
Desert
Island
Planet
Stream

7 letter words
Boulder
Drumlin

8 letter word
Mountain

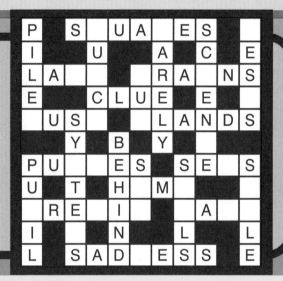

ALPHAFITS

One of each of the 26 letters of the alphabet has been removed from the crossword grid. Can you replace them all to fill the crossword with everyday words?

A	B	C	D	E	F	G	H	I	J	K	L	M
N	O	P	Q	R	S	T	U	V	W	X	Y	Z

JIG GRID

Can you fit the blocks back into the grid to reveal, reading from left to right, seven authors?

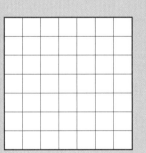

KIPL
GRI

STO
RROL

SHAM
KIEN
Y
L

TOL
TOL
CA

CER
ING
ING

CHAU
ROWL

ADD A LETTER

Add one letter to each word in capitals to create a new word that answers the clue. The order of the letters does not need to be changed.

For example – 'I BET it's more superior' would be BEST.

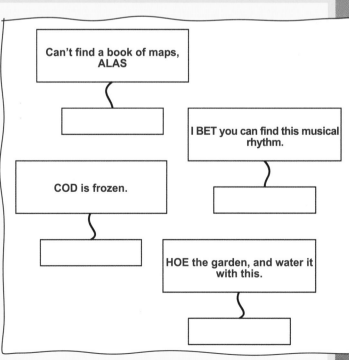

Can't find a book of maps, ALAS

I BET you can find this musical rhythm.

COD is frozen.

HOE the garden, and water it with this.

ADD THREE TO THREE ⭐⭐

Can you add three letters to the three words in red to make another word which solves the clue? For example, by adding three letters to the clue 'BAN this fruit', you can make the word BANANA.

1. The seeds you may **SEE** on bread.

2. **SAL** likes to drink here.

3. Use **ART** to discover a blood vessel

NATURAL NINE ⭐

Try and become king of the jungle in this natural puzzle. How many words of four letters or more can you track down? At least one will use all nine letters and all contain the central letter R. Use each letter once only. No words with capitals, foreign words, hyphens, or plurals are allowed.

The nine letter word is

....

PUSSYCAT STANDARD: 9 words
PANTHER STANDARD: 15 words
LION STANDARD: 22 words

I E L C R C O D O

STEP LADDER ⭐

Starting with the top word, change one letter at a time to make a new word at every step until you have reached the bottom word.

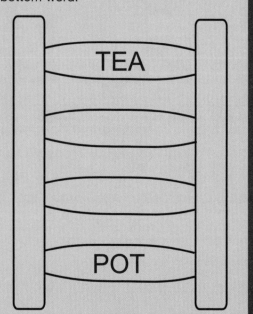

TEA

POT

⭐⭐⭐ BLOCKBUSTERS

Complete the square by using each number and symbol provided in the top row ONCE only in every other row and column to equal the given answer. The first column and all the + signs have been put in to give you a start!

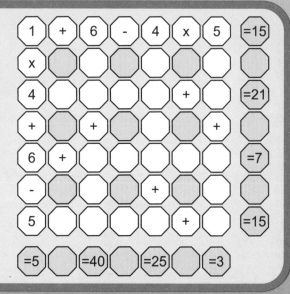

1	+	6	−	4	x	5	=15
x							
4					+		=21
+		+				+	
6	+						=7
−				+			
5					+		=15
=5		=40		=25		=3	

CLUB HOUSE ⭐⭐⭐

Hidden in the grid are six current male tennis stars. Can you find them all?

T M I I L G R H
R D U C Z O R E
E O F R D O B N
F J K D R T L M
E M I S S A G A
I C C P D I Y N
K G E A W Q L G
L L N H L H K Q

COUNTING CRITTERS ⭐

Can you find the number that is represented by each animal face? You will find the total of the numbers below each column and to the right of each row.

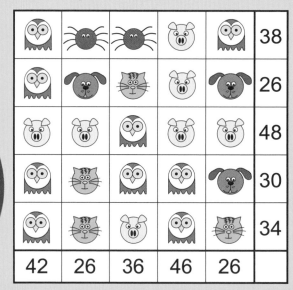

owl	spider	spider	pig	owl	38
owl	dog	cat	pig	dog	26
pig	pig	owl	pig	pig	48
owl	cat	owl	owl	dog	30
owl	cat	pig	owl	cat	34
42	26	36	46	26	

dog =
cat =
owl =
spider =
pig =

COMMON WORDS

Your task here is to determine the answers to each set of tricky definitions below, as well as the word that is contained in all five of the set's answers. For example, if the five solutions were ERRAND, TERRIBLE, MERRY MEN, PREFERRED and PERRY, the word in the central circle would be ERR.

CLUES:
1 Slip
2 Into pieces
3 Washer wonderland
4 Extremely awed
5 Pillaged

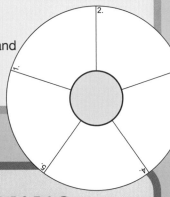

CROSSWORD

Across
1 Flight of steps (8)
6 In the manner of (1,2)
7 An abrasion (5)
9 Oak for instance (4)
11 Quaintly cute (4)
12 Plant with fleshy leaves (4)
14 Competent (4)
16 Allotted portion (5)
18 Name of Miss Gardner, actress (3)
19 Arrive at one's destination (3,5)

Down
1 Quickly, promptly (8)
2 To become less in intensity (5)
3 Intense anger (4)
4 Woman's name (3)
5 Rebel, traitor (8)
8 Actual (4)
10 Bring up (4)
13 Tenants contract (5)
15 Thrash (4)
17 Top card (3)

CAGED ANIMALS

An animal has escaped from the zoo. To put him back in his cage answer the eight clues and put them in the grid starting from the outermost circle. When this is done the central circle, starting clockwise from number nine, will reveal the name of the animal who escaped.

1 Primitive boat (4)
2 Kind of public transport vehicle (4)
3 Monetary unit of Italy (4)
4 Wild hog (4)
5 Stalk (4)
6 Reflection of sound (4)
7 Sound of snake (4)
8 Not working (4)

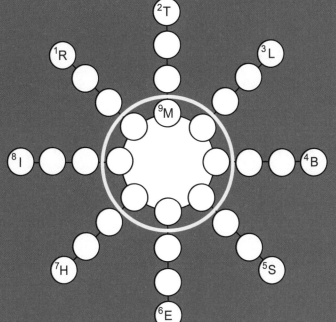

SPORTS QUIZ BOXING

The famous 'Rumble in the Jungle' contest was held between which two boxers?

....

Who is known for his catchphrase 'Know what I mean 'arry!'?

....

What are the trademark colors used for the boxers corners in the ring?

....

Which boxer is nicknamed 'The Prince'?

....

From which country does boxer Oscar De La Hoya hail?

....

FIVE SNEAKY SNAKES ★★★

Can you add five letters to each of the words in capitals in the snakes below, to make another word which solves the clue? For example, by adding five letters to the clue 'A revolt can make you REEL', you can make the word REBELLION. Each of the answers shares a common theme.

1. RON goes for a long run.

2. He hs a boat with paddles, NOT oars.

3. This gambling wheel may get stuck in a RUT.

4. Sports ACE plays this game with stick.

5. Part of the KIT for tenpin bowling.

OCCUPATIONS ★★★

How many words of four letters or more can you track down in this game? At least one will be a nine letter occupation and all contain the central letter. Use each letter once only. No words with capitals, foreign words, hyphens, or plurals and verb forms ending in -s are allowed.

GOOD: 18 words
VERY GOOD: 22 words
EXCELLENT: 30 words

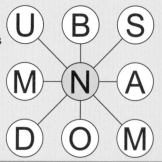

RACING NUMBER PIC ★★

Can you create a picture from the grid below? Each number represents a group of shaded squares, so for example `3` `2` means that on this row there is a group of 3 red squares to the left of a group of 2 green squares. The numbers are always in order, so `4` `2` means a group of 4 red squares to the left of a group of 2 green squares in that row, and `5` means a block of 5 green squares above a block of 3 red `3` squares in that column.

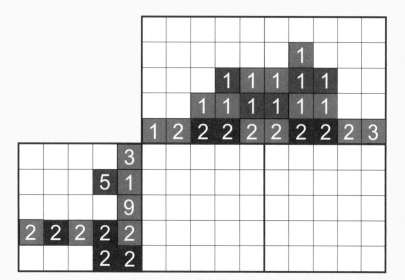

BRITISH MAMMALS SQUIRCLE ★★

Put vowels in the circles and consonants in the squares to make words in all the columns. Definitions of these words are given. When this has been done, the second and fourth rows will make the names of four British mammals.

DEFINITIONS
1 Pastime
2 Take illegally
3 Look at closely
4 Edge of road
5 Belief
6 Love greatly
7 Like a tree
8 Large fruit
9 Voter for another

SUDOKU ★★

To solve, fill in the grid so that every row, column and box contains the numbers 1 through 9.

BITS AND PIECES ★★★

The tiles in the top grid are all jumbled up. Can you rearrange them in the grid below using only one tile from each column to reveal four related words and their theme?

EA	E	SS	GO	N
S	A	N	ER	R
D	TI	RT	I	UT
WA	TA	T	E	T
N	I	PK	E	R

(empty grid below)

HOLLYWOOD ANAGRAMS ★★★

Here are four anagrams of films or film people. The number and length of words to find are shown in brackets. The four anagram solutions are all linked in some way – can you find the link?

STARLIGHT HOW (4, 4, 4)

GARISHNESS HAIR UP (8, 8)

RADIATED HONEY (3, 7, 3)

SWEATY PAW (5, 4)

THE LINK IS .....

WORD FIT ★★★

Can you fit all the words linked with a bicycle into the grid on the right?

4 letter words
Park
Path
Road
Tyre

5 letter words
Brake
Crash
Cycle
Gears
Rider
Speed
Spoke

Sport
Steer
Wheel

6 letter words
Enamel
Helmet
Saddle
Travel

7 letter words
Cyclist
Padlock

8 letter word
Puncture

CONTAINERS WORDSEARCH ★

The grid contains 17 containers hidden vertically, horizontally or diagonally. Can you find them all?

BARREL   CLOSET   RACK
BASIN   CONE   SALVER
BASKET   DISH   SILO
CASK   NETS   TRUNK
CELL   PAIL   TUREEN
CHEST   PLATE

C	L	O	S	E	T	R	Q
S	T	E	N	U	E	N	D
K	C	A	R	V	K	I	K
C	H	E	L	R	S	S	I
O	E	A	U	H	A	A	S
N	S	L	G	C	B	B	I
E	T	A	L	P	A	I	L
K	N	U	R	T	H	U	O

OPPOSITES ATTRACT ★

Place each of the tiles in the boxes below to form two words with opposite meanings.

WORD SPLITZ ★

Each row of ten letters can be split into two five-letter art words. These words read from left to right and are in order.

For example SMOKOSUENK can be split to reveal SKUNK and MOOSE.

1. BERAUSESHL
2. BCOHAALRDK
3. FGLRAAZMEE
4. MOPAUINTNT

A'MAZE'ING NUMBERS ⭐⭐⭐

Try to make your way through the maze. The number at the beginning of each row and column tells you exactly how many squares you will have to cross through in order to reach the finish. No diagonal moves are allowed.

Solving hint: To begin, blacken any box that you determine will not be used, and place a dot in any box that you know must be used.

	1	9	1	1	8	1	1	8	1
2									
5									
3									
3									
3									
3									
3									
3									
6									

ODD ONE OUT ⭐

Can you spot the odd one out in this selection of birds?

PAIR WHEELS ⭐⭐

Place each of the twelve pairs of letters into one of the circles in the wheel, so that every line running through the central circle gives you a six-letter word with the middle letters AN.

PE
CH
PL
CH
BR
UT
OR
GE
CE
ET
GR
NY

AN

CROSSWORD ⭐

Across
1   Physical movements for fitness (9)
6   Condition of something (5)
7   Knack (3)
8   Lean to one side (4)
10 Observes with the eye (4)
13 Plot for flowers (3)
14 Conscious of (5)
16 Moved downwards (9)

Down
1   Blackboard support (5)
2   A period of time (3)
3   Break up food in the mouth (4)
4   Drudge (5)
5   Pose for portrait (3)
9   Teams (5)
11 Travel too fast (5)
12 Rescue (4)
13 Make offer at auction (3)
15 Tot up (3)

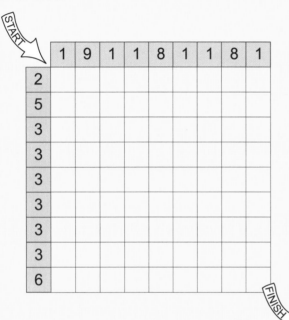

NURSERY BLOCKS ⭐

Rearrange each column of letters and write them in the grid to reveal the first two lines of a well known nursery rhyme. Some of the letters have been put in to give you a head start.

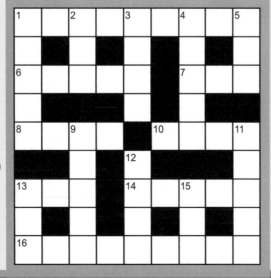

		S						
	S							
S								A
		R			.			

		N				
	P	L			T	
X	O	E	N	C	A	
O	I	G	K	O	E	
F	P	N	Y	G	O	F
I	U	L	C	E	E	F

LETTER SWAP

Can you replace a letter from each word with a letter from the boxes below to reveal a well known saying? Each letter is used only once.

TILE ANT TIME WANT

FIR DO MAP

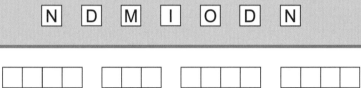

N D M I O D N

ON TARGET

Put the answers to the clues in the grid starting from the outside. Each answer has five letters and ends with the central letter N. When you've finished, the outer ring will reveal the name of a UK soccer team (7).

1 Meat from a pig (5)
2 Trade association (5)
3 Black bird (5)
4 Synthetic fibre (5)
5 Carrying cargo (5)
6 Dined (5)
7 To long (5)

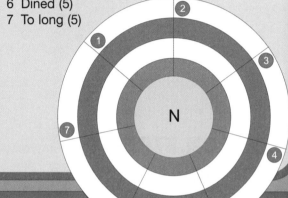

NOURISHING NINE

How many words of four letters or more can you track down in this game? At least one 'nourishing' word will contain all nine letters and all words must contain the central letter. Use each letter once only. No words with capital letters, foreign words, hyphens, or plurals and verb forms ending in -s are allowed.

UNDERDONE: 10 words, MEDIUM: 16 words, WELL DONE: 24 words

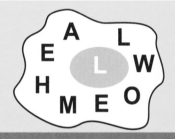

PLACE THE PLACES

To solve the puzzle place the letters from the place in capitals into the empty spaces in the grid. Four everyday words should be formed reading across the grid and three everyday words reading down.

THEATER

LETTER STEW

Use all the given letters in the stew to spell three words meaning hot.

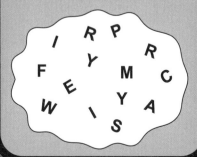

QUICK QUIZ QUESTIONS

Can you get all of these quiz questions correct?

WHAT DO THESE ACRONYMS AND INITIALS STAND FOR?	
1. NATO	
2. IBM	
3. BBC	
4. WHO	
5. WWW	
6. IOC	

SUDOKU

To solve, fill in the grid so that every row, column and box contains the letters A through I.

F	E			G				H
	I	G	D	E		C		A
B	A	C	F		H		G	D
	C		G			B	A	
	B			F	E	G		
		I	B	C		H	D	F
C				B	D			
			E			D	C	
G	D	B		H	C	F	E	I

CAGED ANIMALS

An animal has escaped from the zoo. To put him back in his cage answer the eight clues and put them in the grid starting from the outermost circle. When this is done the central circle, starting clockwise from number nine, will reveal the name of the animal who escaped.

1 Japanese unarmed combat (4)
2 Paperback for instance (4)
3 Roman cloak (4)
4 African wildcat (4)
5 Insect's instrument of flight (4)
6 Not any (4)
7 Sound from contented cat (4)
8 Board game (4)

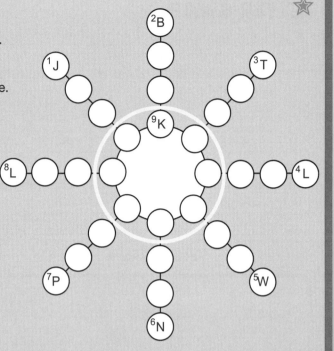

LONDON STREETS WORDSEARCH ⭐⭐

The grid contains 16 London street names hidden vertically, horizontally or diagonally. The unused letters spell out another street.

ARCHER
BAKER
CANNON
DEAN
EAGLE
ELDON
EUSTON
FLEET
OXFORD
PARK
REGENT
RUGBY
SOHO
STAND
WEST

D	P	T	E	E	L	F	B
N	A	D	N	O	B	D	B
A	R	C	H	E	R	O	A
R	K	O	A	O	G	Y	K
T	S	G	F	N	B	E	E
S	L	X	A	G	N	W	R
E	O	E	U	S	T	O	N
W	D	R	E	L	D	O	N

KAKURO ⭐⭐

In Kakuro the numbers in the black squares refer to the SUMS of the digits 1-9 which you are to fill into the empty spaces. The number ABOVE the diagonal line refers to the empty spaces directly to the RIGHT of that number. A number BELOW the diagonal line refers to the empty spaces directly BELOW that number. No zeros are used here and a digit can only appear once in any particular digit combination.

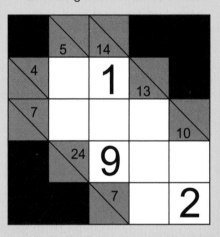

OCCUPATIONS ⭐⭐⭐

How many words of four letters or more can you track down in this game? At least one will be a nine letter occupation and all contain the central letter. Use each letter once only. No words with capitals, foreign words, hyphens, or plurals and verb forms ending in -s are allowed.

GOOD: 40 words, VERY GOOD: 46 words, EXCELLENT: 65 words

LITTLE TOUGHIE ⭐⭐⭐

Across
4 Indiana with attempt to produce blue dye (6)
5 Sea's old wreck held by rope (7)
8 It can paralyze an oarsman (6)

Down
1 A miss, but could be a hit with a boy (4)
2 Crack is sure to appear under top of funnel (7)
3 Betters use it to carry something (4)
6 A learner's like this as well (4)
7 River softly going to the ocean (4)

BATTLESHIPS

There are five ships hidden in the grid below. Look at the key to see which ships you have to find. The numbers on the grid tell you how many squares of each row or column part of a ship is found in. To get you started we've put a few parts of ships (in red) and a few squares with no ships (in black).

HINTS: Begin by shading in all the misses (all the columns which have a zero in them) as there are no ships here. When you have found a full ship you can shade all the blocks around that ship as misses because none of the ships are touching.

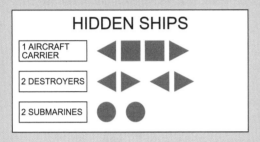

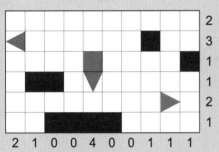

ALPHAFITS

One of each of the 26 letters of the alphabet has been removed from the crossword grid below. Can you replace them all to fill the crossword with everyday words?

NINE NUMBERS

Try to fill in the missing numbers. Use the numbers 1 to 9 to complete the equations. Each number is only used once. Each row and column is an equation with the totals given below and to the right.

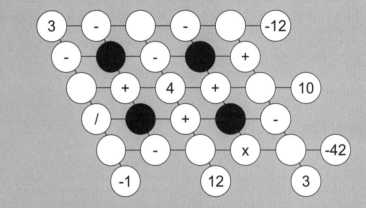

QUICK MUSIC QUIZ

1. Which 90s UK boy band comprised Gary, Robbie, Mark, Jason and Howard?

....

2. Which country do ABBA, Roxette and The Cardigans come from?

....

3. Which Spice Girl is married to soccer superstar David Beckham?

....

4. Who is Eminem's biggest fan?

....

5. Who was the first UK Pop Idol winner?

....

JIG GRID

Can you fit the blocks back into the grid to reveal six fish, reading from left to right?

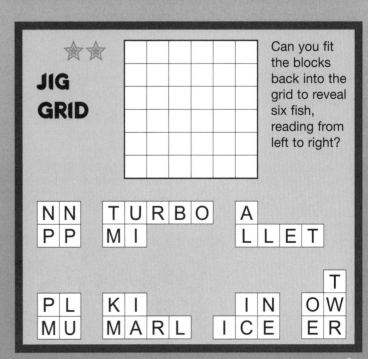

ON TARGET

Put the answers to the clues in the grid starting from the outside. Each answer has five letters and ends with the central letter R. When you've finished, the outer ring will reveal the name of a UK soccer team (7).

1 Heron for instance (5)
2 A snake (5)
3 Light beer (5)
4 Not as dangerous (5)
5 Change (5)
6 Subsequently (5)
7 Cruise ship (5)

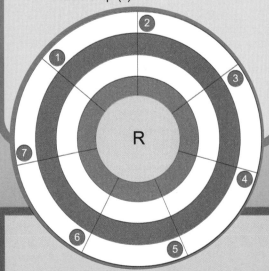

NINE NUMBERS

Try to fill in the missing numbers. Use the numbers 1 to 9 to complete the equations. Each number is only used once. Each row and column is an equation with the totals given below and to the right.

7	x		+	6	**13**
-		x		+	
	-		-	9	**-14**
-			/		-
	-		+		**3**

| **-1** | | **2** | | **13** | |

NOURISHING NINE

How many words of four letters or more can you track down in this game? At least one 'nourishing' word will contain all nine letters and all words must contain the central letter. Use each letter once only. No words with capital letters, foreign words, hyphens, or plurals and verb forms ending in -s are allowed.

UNDERDONE: 13 words, MEDIUM: 20 words, WELL DONE: 27 words

NATUREGRAMS

Solve each clue, then rearrange the five letters in every answer to form a set of three trees.

CLUES:
1 Sheets of glass
2 Of primary importance
3 Competed in a contest of speed

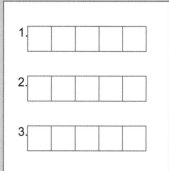

FLOWERY PHRASES

We have described a well known saying using flowery language. Can you uncover the more familiar form? For example, 'An eruption in the cook pot' would be 'A flash in the pan'.

The only entity in the universe that has the ability to accomplish intentions and fulfil desires is actual achievement and fruitful attainment of plans for prosperity.

ANAGRAM LADDERS

Solve the anagrams to reveal the names of seven British soccer teams. The shaded column in the middle will then reveal the name of another soccer team.

YCLED
HAMULF
ITCELC
NURYEBL
LLAWSLA
NOTVERE
LLOAA

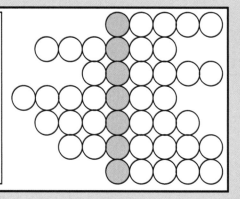

SUDOKU ★★★

To solve, fill in the grid so that every row, column and box contains the numbers 1 through 9.

4			7					
	7			2				6
	5				6	8		
		2	4		5			
5			8	2				7
	8			6				
						2	4	
		9			3			
			1				3	8

CODED CROSSWORD ★★★

Each number in the grid represents a different letter of the alphabet. Can you fill in the grid using the given letters to get you started?

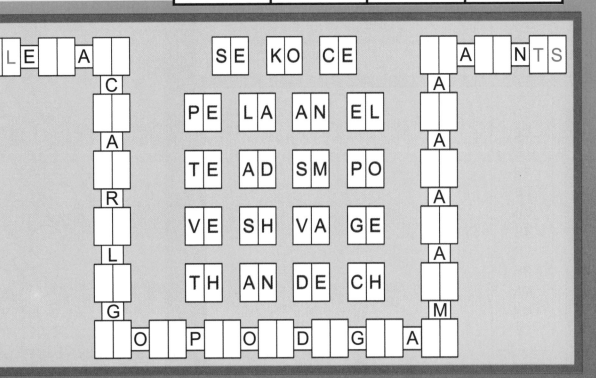

1	2	3	4 C	5	6	7	8	9	10	11	12	13
14	15 A	16	17	18	19	20	21	22 R	23	24	25	26

PYRAMID OF BRICKS ★

Fill in the bricks with numbers. Each brick must equal the sum of the two bricks directly below it.

96

48 | ☐

☐ | ☐ | 24

☐ | ☐ | 12 | ☐

☐ | 6 | ☐ | 6

☐ | ☐ | 3 | ☐ | ☐

THREE FOUR ALL ★★

The object is to find three four letter words using the letters given in each word without changing the order of the letters. For example, if the given word were PRICES, the first word might be PIES, the second might be RICE and the third would be ICES.

| INVERSION | _ _ _ _ | _ _ _ _ | _ _ _ _ |
| SQUANDER | _ _ _ _ | _ _ _ _ | _ _ _ _ |

CHAIN REACTION ★★★

Solve this puzzle by creating a 'chain reaction' of 20 five-letter words that run left to right, beginning in the upper-left hand corner, using the 19 two-letter tiles in the middle. A two-letter tile that ends one begins the next. Each tile will only be used once. The single letters already entered are the middle letters of the words you are to form. Start by finishing the word that begins PLE_ _.

Tiles: PLE E · A · SE · KO · CE · A · NTS · C · PE · LA · AN · EL · A · A · TE · AD · SM · PO · A · A · VE · SH · VA · GE · A · R · TH · AN · DE · CH · A · M · L · G · O · P · O · D · G · A

Middle letters column (left): C A A R L G

Right column middle letters: A A A A M

ZOO HUNT

An animal has escaped from the zoo and is hiding somewhere in the grid. If you cross out all the letters that appear more than twice, the remaining letters will spell out the missing creature.

THE MISSING CREATURE IS A

....

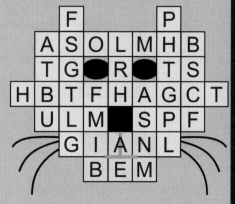

KAKURO

In Kakuro the numbers in the black squares refer to the SUMS of the digits 1-9 which you are to fill into the empty spaces. The number ABOVE the diagonal line refers to the empty spaces directly to the RIGHT of that number. A number BELOW the diagonal line refers to the empty spaces directly BELOW that number. No zeros are used here and a digit can only appear once in any particular digit combination.

HEN MAZE

Try and find your way from start to finish in the hen maze.

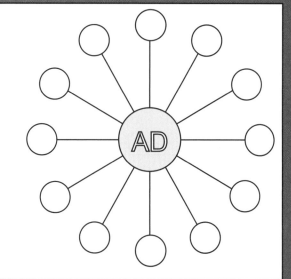

ARROWS

Put the following numbers in the arrows below:

1 1 2 2 3 3 3 4

Be careful though.
The numbers in the three arrows pointing at each other must add up to 10.

The numbers in the arrows which are back to back must add up to 5.

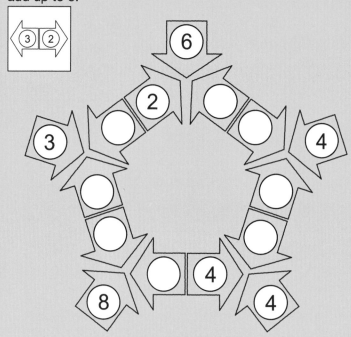

PAIR WHEELS

Place each of the 12 pairs of letters into one of the circles in the wheel, so that every line running through the central circle gives you a six-letter word with the middle letters AD.

ED
DE
LE
ER
LE
OW
TR
ER
SH
ME
CR
LY

WORD FIT

Can you fit all the writers into the grid below?

★★★

4 letter words
Hugo
Snow

5 letter words
Eliot
Joyce
Scott
Swift

Twain
Waugh

6 letter words
Austin
Conrad
Cronin
Graves
Greene

Orwell

7 letter words
Bennett
Kipling
Tolstoy

8 letter words
Christie
Fielding

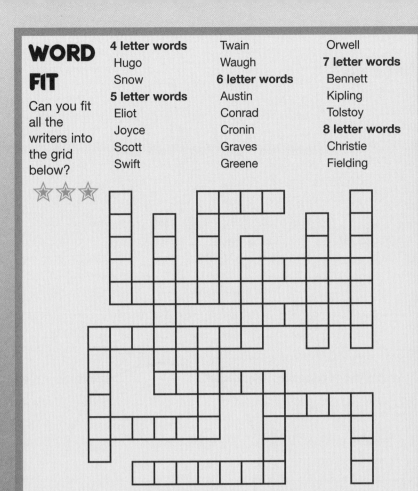

NINE NUMBERS

★★

Try to fill in the missing numbers.
Use the numbers 1 to 9 to complete the equations. Each number is only used once. Each row and column is an equation with the totals given below and to the right.

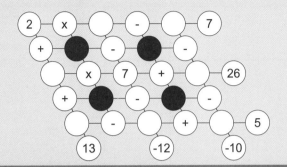

EURO TEASE

★

Can you work out the answer to this teaser?

After Ian found 2 Euros in the street, he then had three times as much as he would have had if he had lost 2 Euros. How much did he have before he found the 2 Euros?

STEP LADDER

★

Starting with the top word, change one letter at a time to make a new word at every step until you have reached the bottom word.

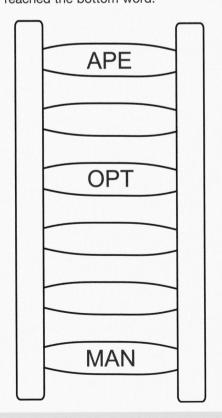

APE

OPT

MAN

BITS AND PIECES

The tiles in the top grid are all jumbled up. Can you rearrange them in the grid below using only one tile from each column to reveal four related words and their theme?

★★★

CO	R	EN	IC	S
F	HE	AS	E	E
C	ME	E	I	S
FR	EO	DI	D	S
TH	I	FF	R	ER

ALPHAFITS

★★

One of each of the 26 letters of the alphabet has been removed from the crossword grid below. Can you replace them all to fill the crossword with everyday words?

| A | B | C | D | E | F | G | H | I | J | K | L | M |
| N | O | P | Q | R | S | T | U | V | W | X | Y | Z |

SUDOKU ⭐⭐⭐

To solve, fill in the grid so that every row, column and box contains the numbers 1 through 9.

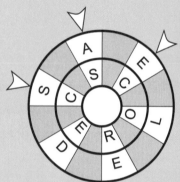

BLOCKBUSTERS ⭐⭐⭐

Complete the square by using each number and symbol provided in the top row ONCE only in every other row and column to equal the given answers. The first column and all the - signs have been put in to give you a start!

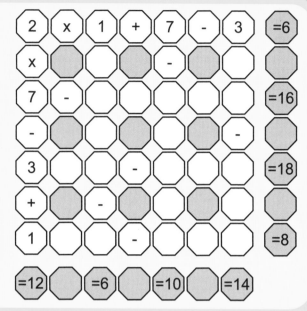

Top row: 2 × 1 + 7 - 3 =6

× − =16

7 − =18

Row answers: =6, =16, =18, =8
Column answers: =12, =6, =10, =14

First column: 2, x, 7, -, 3, +, 1

WORD WHEEL ⭐

For each of the circles, can you find two letters which, when placed in the middle, will form three six-letter words?

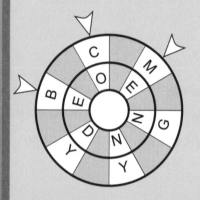

Circle 1 letters: C, M, O, E, N, Y, D, E, B
Circle 2 letters: A, E, L, O, R, E, D, C, S, S

COUNTING CRITTERS ⭐

Can you find the number that is represented by each animal face? You will find the total of the numbers below each column and to the right of each row.

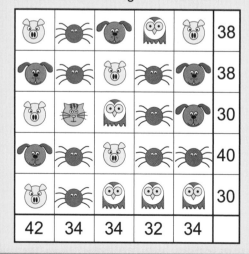

Row totals: 38, 38, 30, 40, 30
Column totals: 42, 34, 34, 32, 34

🐶 =
🐱 =
🦉 =
🕷 =
🐷 =

ODD ONE OUT

Can you spot the odd one out in this sequence of words?

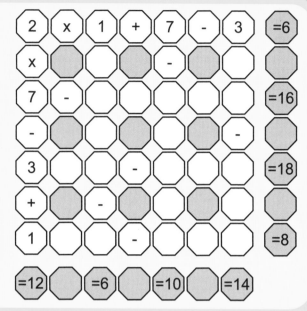

MONTH
Second
POUND
Week
MINUTE
YEAR

SPORTS QUIZ TENNIS ⭐⭐

What is the least number of points a player needs to have to win a singles game?

....

Who famously shouted at a Wimbledon umpire, 'you cannot be serious'?

....

Who was the last British female to win the French Open?

....

Which British singer and tennis fan entertained the crowd with a sing-along when rain stopped play at Wimbledon one year?

....

What nationality is tennis star Roger Federer?

....

OPPOSITES ATTRACT

Place each of the tiles in the boxes below to form two words with opposite meanings.

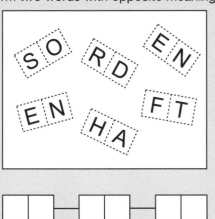

ADD THREE TO THREE

1. Do you **HATE** this small axe.

2. There'll be chuckles **LATER**

3. Difficulty encountered on the **PROM**.

Can you add three letters to the three words in red to make another word which solves the clue? For example, by adding three letters to the clue 'BAN this fruit', you can make the word BANANA.

LITTLE TOUGHIE

Across
4 A muffled groan from a goat (6)
5 Metal tester, for instance, one making a statement (7)
8 Frayed mat has to lead to chest condition (6)

Down
1 Farewell gratitude is repeated (2-2)
2 Publishing payment for top family (7)
3 Time to copy recording (4)
6 Kill left inside for instance (4)
7 Company traveler bringing in a harvest (4)

SKELETON CROSSWORD

Below is an incomplete quick crossword grid. Can you solve the puzzle by fitting the answers to the clues correctly into the grid, along with the remaining blocks and clue numbers? A few blocks have been shaded to give you a start. This puzzle has been rotated by 180 degrees.

Across
1 Unforeseen obstacles (5)
4 Breaks in two (5)
7 Atmosphere (3)
8 Consumed (3)
9 Light afternoon meal (3)
10 Shoe tie (4)
11 Tenth part (5)
14 Room in the roof (5)
16 Nobleman (4)
18 Girl's name (3)
20 Woman's name (3)
21 Beer (3)
22 Borders (5)
23 Member of boy's organization (5)

Down
1 Mammal with flippers (4)
2 Alongside each other (7)
3 Drudge (5)
4 Perspire (5)
5 Fitting (3)
6 Proclaims (6)
12 Violent tropical storm (7)
13 Procession (6)
15 Form in school (5)
16 Directs and guides (5)
17 Canvas shelter (4)
19 Continually grouse (3)

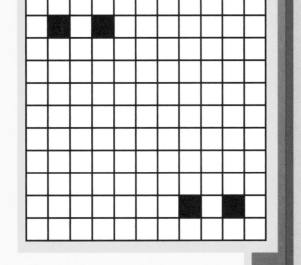

ON TARGET

Put the answers to the clues in the grid starting from the outside. Each answer has five letters and ends with the central letter A. When you've finished, the outer ring will reveal the name of a UK soccer team (7).

1 Plant life of an area (5)
2 First letter in Greek alphabet (5)
3 A stage of insect development (5)
4 Australian marsupial (5)
5 A republic in South Asia (5)
6 Ballroom dance (5)
7 Asian country (5)

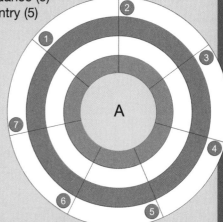

CODED CROSSWORD

Each number in the grid represents a different letter of the alphabet. Can you fill in the grid using the given letters to get you started?

17	10	19	25	8	14	12		12	16	7	11	8
7		25		20		16		20		2		25
20	21	8	20	24	10	5		7	2	21	8	20
22		14		2		10		15		8		12
20	26	16	24	21		20	11	20	2	7	20	12
				11		12				11		20
20	11	23	19	5	12		12	22	24	20	9	12
2		7				21		19				
20	11	8	21	8	20	18		10	19	1	16	5
24		12		5		4		19		21		19
8	24	21	12	17		20	3	25	21	10	10	5
20		9		12		24		24		12		19
18	25	12	16	5		13	21	12	6	20	16	12

1	2	3	4	5	6	7	8 G	9	10	11	12	13
14 H	15	16 T	17	18	19	20	21	22	23	24	25	26

GEMS WORDSEARCH

The grid contains 14 words connected with gems hidden vertically, horizontally or diagonally. Can you find them all?

AGATE
AMBER
BANGLE
BEAD
BROOCH
CAMEO
CORAL
CRYSTAL
DIAMOND
GARNET
JADE
LOCKET
RING
SIGNET

L	A	T	S	Y	R	C	D
C	H	Q	J	A	D	E	I
L	O	C	K	E	T	P	A
C	A	O	O	A	E	D	M
A	M	R	G	O	N	A	O
M	B	A	I	U	R	E	N
E	E	L	G	N	A	B	D
O	R	T	E	N	G	I	S

COMMON WORDS

Your task here is to determine the answers to each tricky definition below, as well as the word that is contained in all five of the answers. For example, if the five solutions were ERRAND, TERRIBLE, MERRY MEN, PREFERRED and PERRY, the word in the central circle would be ERR.
CLUES:
1 Portuguese navigator
2 007
3 Workplace for an actor
4 Scheme
5 Oz lion's lack

FIVE SNEAKY SNAKES

Can you add five letters to each of the words in capitals in the snakes below, to make another word which solves the clue? For example, by adding five letters to the clue 'A revolt can make you REEL', you can make the word REBELLION. Each of the answers shares a common theme.

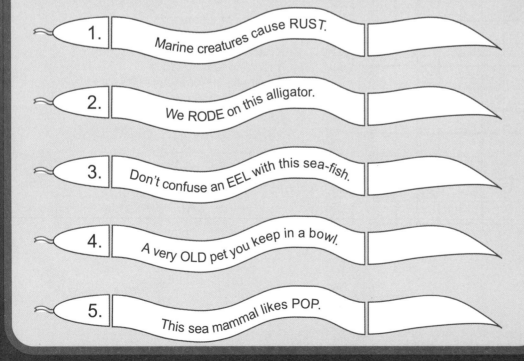

1. Marine creatures cause RUST.

2. We RODE on this alligator.

3. Don't confuse an EEL with this sea-fish.

4. A very OLD pet you keep in a bowl.

5. This sea mammal likes POP.

SUDOKU

To solve, fill in the grid so that every row, column and box contains the numbers 1 through 9.

	7				4	2		5
5		4		7		1		
		9				3	7	
		8						
			2		1		4	3
1		6				5		9
8			4		9		1	
9		7		3	6	4		2
	6				1	2		8

BITS AND PIECES

The tiles in the top grid are all jumbled up. Can you rearrange them in the grid below using only one tile from each column to reveal four related words and their theme?

GR	R	S	BO	Y
M	I	M	E	S
B	H	LL	A	O
W	AS	L	E	T
BA	A	E	E	T

(empty grid below)

ADD A LETTER

Add one letter to each word in capitals to create a new word that answers the clue. The order of the letters does not need to be changed.

For example – 'I BET it's more superior' would be BEST.

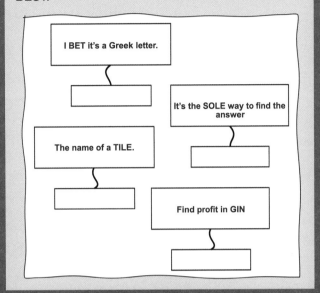

I BET it's a Greek letter.

It's the SOLE way to find the answer

The name of a TILE.

Find profit in GIN

AMPHIBIAN SQUIRCLE

Put vowels in the circles and consonants in the squares to make words in all the columns. Definitions of these words are given. When this has been done, the first and third rows will make the names of three amphibians.

DEFINITIONS
1 Lavish meal
2 To rest
3 Jewels
4 Contests for amusement
5 Express gratitude
6 Unit of weight
7 Kind of tree
8 Great fear
9 Increase suddenly

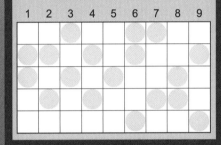

HOLLYWOOD ANAGRAMS ⭐⭐⭐

Below are four anagrams of films or film people. The number and length of words to find are shown in brackets. The four anagram solutions are all linked in some way – can you find the link?

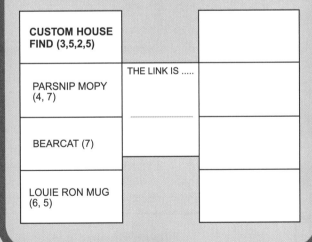

CUSTOM HOUSE FIND (3,5,2,5)	
PARSNIP MOPY (4, 7)	THE LINK IS .....
BEARCAT (7)	
LOUIE RON MUG (6, 5)	

ALPHAFITS ⭐⭐

One of each of the 26 letters of the alphabet has been removed from the crossword grid below. Can you replace them all to fill the crossword with everyday words?

(crossword grid)

A	B	C	D	E	F	G	H	I	J	K	L	M
N	O	P	Q	R	S	T	U	V	W	X	Y	Z

FLAG NUMBER PIC

Can you create a picture from the grid below?

Each number represents a group of shaded squares, so for example **3 2** means that on this row there is a group of 3 red squares to the left of a group of 2 green squares. The numbers are always in order, so **4 2** means a group of 4 red squares to the left of a group of 2 green squares in that row, and **5** means a block of 5 green squares **3** above a block of 3 red squares in that column.

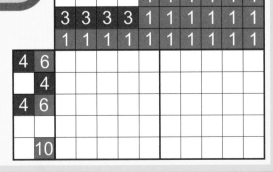

CHAIN REACTION

☆☆☆

Solve this puzzle by creating a 'chain reaction' of 20 five-letter words that run left to right, beginning in the upper left-hand corner, using the 19 two-letter tiles in the middle. A two-letter tile that ends one begins the next. Each tile will only be used once. The single letters already entered are the middle letters of the words you are to form. Start by finishing the word that begins BAN_ _.

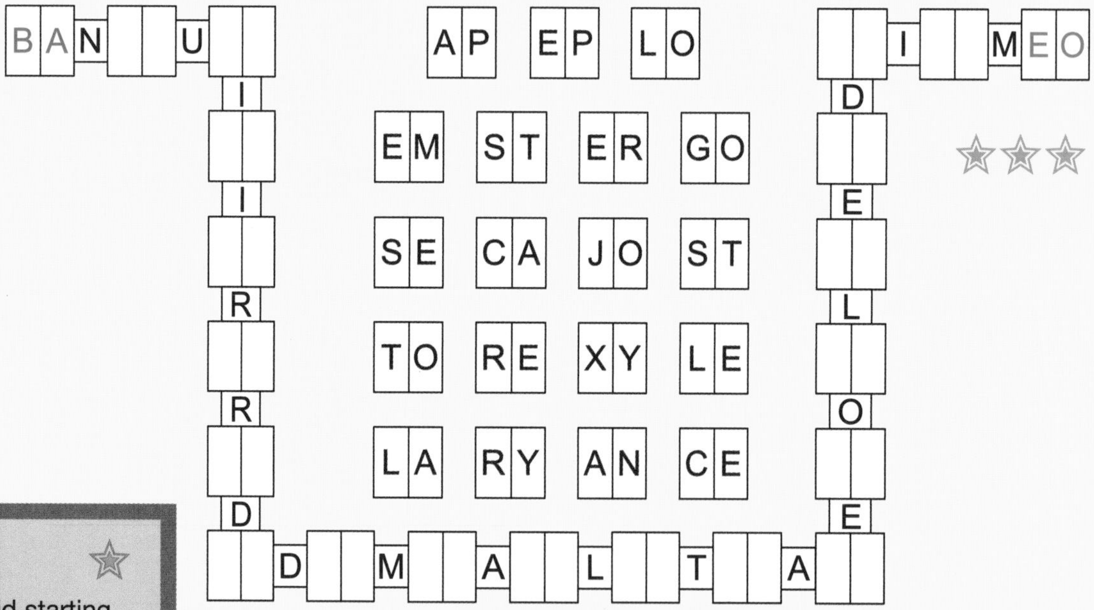

BAN
U
I
I
R
R
D
D
M
A
L
T
A
E
O
L
E
D
I
MEO
AP EP LO
EM ST ER GO
SE CA JO ST
TO RE XY LE
LA RY AN CE

ON TARGET

☆

Put the answers to the clues in the grid starting from the outside. Each answer has five letters and ends with the central letter R. When you've finished, the outer ring will reveal the name of a game (7).

1 Writing sheets (5)
2 Unpleasant smell (5)
3 More pleasant (5)
4 Asian wildcat (5)
5 Command (5)
6 Happen (5)
7 More modern (5)

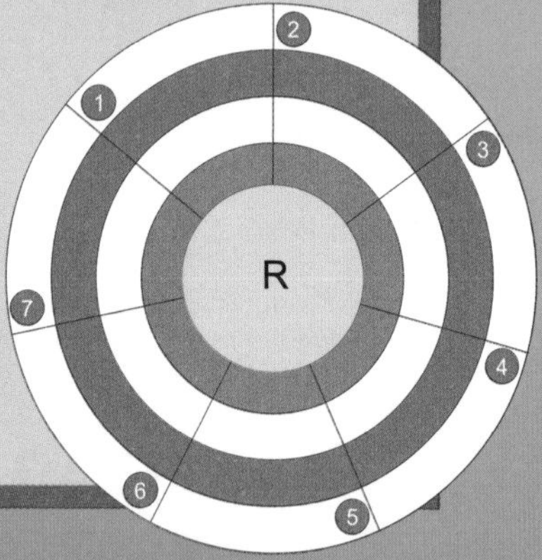

R
1
2
3
4
5
6
7

BIRD BOXES

☆

Shade in all the letters that appear in the word 'BIRDS' to reveal a hidden bird.

I	I	R	M	Q	E	C	L	D	P	B	H
B	T	S	E	G	H	K	G	B	E	D	C
S	D	B	Q	A	N	F	V	I	N	S	T
M	A	I	J	T	E	P	A	S	H	I	F
E	P	R	T	S	H	S	V	R	E	S	J
S	D	B	G	I	N	R	M	S	W	B	X
F	L	J	E	R	C	B	C	Q	J	G	C
H	C	G	K	D	I	R	K	F	A	Y	L

☆☆☆

MOVIE HOUSE

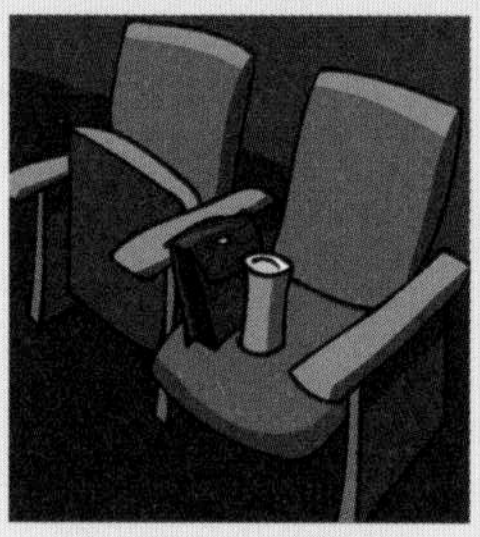

Hidden in the grid are six 80s sci-fi films. Can you find them all?

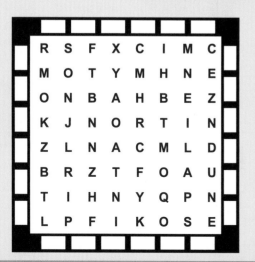

R	S	F	X	C	I	M	C
M	O	T	Y	M	H	N	E
O	N	B	A	H	B	E	Z
K	J	N	O	R	T	I	N
Z	L	N	A	C	M	L	D
B	R	Z	T	F	O	A	U
T	I	H	N	Y	Q	P	N
L	P	F	I	K	O	S	E

RIDDLE WORDS

☆

Can you answer these word riddles with dances?

Which dance can also be found on a fishing rod?

Which dance is also a strong throw?

Which dance can be served with tortilla chips?

Which dance is also an unsettled state?

ROTATION WORDS

Rotate each of the two sets of circles so that the letters reading across the top of the circles and the row across the bottom spell out everyday words. The circles don't have to rotate in the same direction and you will have to rotate some of the circles further than others in each puzzle.

1.

2.

1. (O P / C O) (P N / O V) (I N / S I) (T C / E E)

2. (D C / E O) (I L / V N) (G E / H N) (T I / F E) (T L / N U)

PLACE THE PLACES

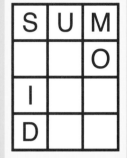

To solve the puzzle place the letters from the place in capitals into the empty spaces in the grid. Four everyday words should be formed reading across the grid and three everyday words reading down.

G A L L E Y

SKELETON CROSSWORD

Below is an incomplete quick crossword grid. Can you solve the puzzle by fitting the answers to the clues correctly into the grid, along with the remaining blocks and clue numbers? A few blocks have been shaded to give you a start. This puzzle has been rotated by 180 degrees.

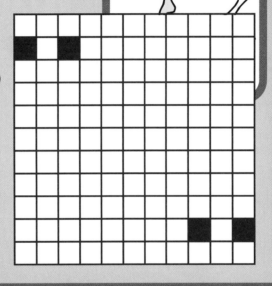

Across
1 Placed apart (8)
7 And so be it (4)
8 Large gun (6)
9 Welcomes (6)
13 That woman (3)
15 Espy (3)
16 Rodent (3)
18 Venomous snake (3)
20 Religious festival (6)
24 Tiles for the roof (6)
25 Charge for journey (4)
26 Threatening or ominous (8)

Down
2 Gaze fixedly (5)
3 Yearn (4)
4 Slight hint of colour (5)
5 To become old-fashioned (4)
6 Nuisance (4)
10 To hire (4)
11 Dame Everage (4)
12 Restrain (4)
13 Wish (4)
14 Gentle blows (4)
15 Painful (4)
17 Crime of fire raising (5)
19 Strainer (5)
21 Kind of horse (4)
22 Knots (4)
23 Bills in a restaurant (4)

ANAGRAM LADDERS

Solve the anagrams below to reveal the names of seven items of furniture. The shaded column in the middle will then reveal the name of another furniture item.

DIGEFR
NEORHT
FELSH
KEDS
FOSA
VENO
BIRC

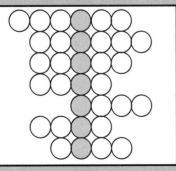

ALPHAFITS

One of each of the 26 letters of the alphabet has been removed from the crossword grid below. Can you replace them all to fill the crossword with everyday words?

U S T	S C	S
O	E
G L E	I N D I A
S A S	S D
A S	Y
H O U D C
L D I S
I K T E E
S L I G H S I E
N N L D
T O A V E T S

| A | B | C | D | E | F | G | H | I | J | K | L | M |
| N | O | P | Q | R | S | T | U | V | W | X | Y | Z |

SUDOKU

To solve, fill in the grid so that every row, column and box contains the numbers 1 through 9.

4		2		5		6		
	5		1		6	4		8
8	1	6	4	3	7		2	9
			8			7		6
9	8	7	6	1	4		5	
5	6		2		3		8	4
3	9		7			1	6	5
6	2		3	4		8	9	7
1	7	8			9			2

BITS AND PIECES ★★★

The tiles in the top grid are all jumbled up. Can you rearrange them in the grid below using only one tile from each column to reveal four related words and their theme?

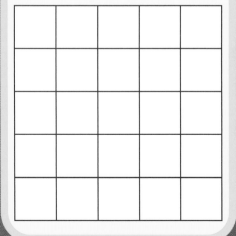

AR	AT	R	OC	S
PO	T	CK	S	K
T	L	I	N	EY
H	O	L	ST	E
M	U	IS	N	ER

PICTURE PHRASES

The images below represent three well-known phrases. Look carefully and see if you can work out what they are.

1. **HERRING**

2. **DEAL**

3. **ROADS**

OCCUPATIONS ★★★

How many words of four letters or more can you track down in this game? At least one will be a nine letter occupation and all contain the central letter. Use each letter once only. No words with capitals, foreign words, hyphens, or plurals and verb forms ending in -s are allowed.

GOOD: 12 words
VERY GOOD: 16 words
EXCELLENT: 21 words

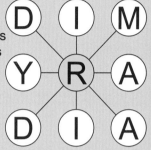

LETTER STEW ★

Use all the given letters in the stew to spell three words meaning hit.

DANCE WORDSEARCH ★★

The grid contains 14 dances hidden vertically, horizontally or diagonally. The unused letters spell out another connected dance.

BALLET
CLOG
CONGA
COUNTRY
CREEP
DISCO
FLING
FOLK
MAMBO
MORRIS
SHIMMY
SHUFFLE
SQUARE
TANGO

G	O	L	C	R	E	E	P
M	Y	B	A	L	L	E	T
O	M	F	M	F	R	K	T
R	M	A	F	A	L	A	A
R	I	U	U	O	M	G	N
I	H	Q	F	L	I	N	G
S	S	D	I	S	C	O	O
Y	R	T	N	U	O	C	N

NATURE TRAIL

Find the plant that is growing inside the tree by removing all the letters that appear more than twice.

THE HIDDEN PLANT IS A

....

```
        H I
    F G O P
  P N M R J A
M D I J F E R G
  J G A R I D
    Y P S U
      G C
      F J
      K D
      M L
      A E
```

PAIR WHEELS

Place each of the twelve pairs of letters into one of the circles in the wheel, so that every line running through the central circle gives you a six-letter word with the middle letters LA.

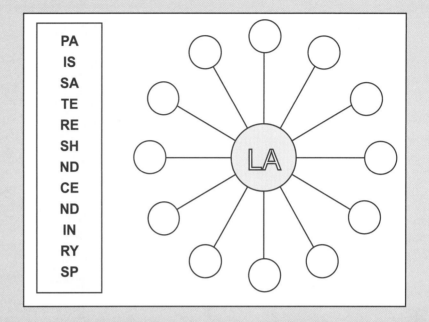

PA
IS
SA
TE
RE
SH
ND
CE
ND
IN
RY
SP

KAKURO

In Kakuro the numbers in the black squares refer to the SUMS of the digits 1-9 which you are to fill into the empty spaces. The number ABOVE the diagonal line refers to the empty spaces directly to the RIGHT of that number. A number BELOW the diagonal line refers to the empty spaces directly BELOW that number. No zeros are used here and a digit can only appear once in any particular digit combination.

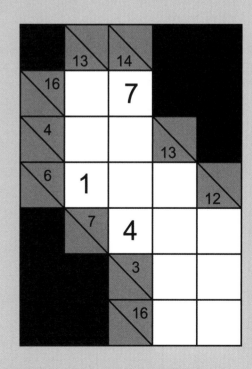

CROSSWORD

Across
2 Twilight (4)
4 Naked (4)
5 Close with a bang (4)
6 Fog (4)
7 Ridge of coral (4)
8 Trial (4)

Down
1 Armed conflict (7)
2 The sweet course (7)
3 Bladderwrack for instance (7)

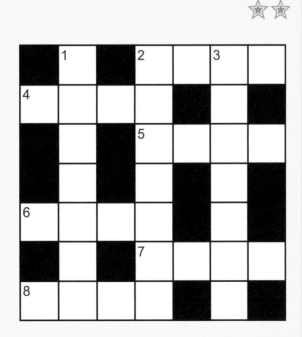

80s SPORTS QUIZ

Which UK soccer team did Gary Bailey keep goal for?

....

Who was Britain's first £2 million soccer player?

....

In which year was the first rugby world cup held?

....

Who beat Ivan Lendl to become the 1987 Wimbledon champion?

....

Which country came top of the medals table in the 1980 Olympics?

....

WORD SPLITZ

Each row of ten letters can be split into two five-letter British towns. These words read from left to right and are in order.

For example SMOKOSUENK can be split to reveal SKUNK and MOOSE.

① C D R E R E B W E Y

② D L U O T V O E R N

③ P R U O G O B Y L E

④ S T W I G O A K E N

ADDING GRIDS

Place any digits 0 to 9 into the empty circles. When complete each row should add up to the figures on the right and each column to the figures below. The shaded numbers are the total of the diagonal circles.

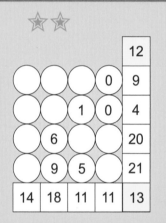

MEDIUM KAKURO

In Kakuro the numbers in the black squares refer to the SUMS of the digits 1-9 which you are to fill into the empty spaces. The number ABOVE the diagonal line refers to the empty spaces directly to the RIGHT of that number. The number BELOW the diagonal line refers to the empty spaces directly BELOW that number. No zeros are used here and a digit can only appear once in any particular digit combination.

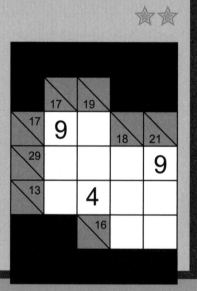

SUDOKU

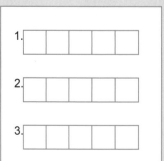

To solve, fill in the grid so that every row, column and box contains the numbers 1 through 9.

GEOGRAMS

Solve each clue, then rearrange the five letters in every answer to form three countries.

CLUES:
1 Cuban ballroom dance
2 Series of mountains
3 Flat sheet

1.
2.
3.

1.
2.
3.

CODED CROSSWORD ⭐⭐⭐

Each number in the grid represents a different letter of the alphabet. Can you fill in the grid using the given letters to get you started?

5	12	9	23	6	10	18	■	9	4	24	21	16
12	■	7	■	24	■	21	■	8	■	17	■	9
24	10	21	16	7	9	23	■	4	20	21	14	16
24	■	10	■	7	■	26	■	24	■	1	■	7
20	25	18	21	10	■	7	24	17	9	10	24	■
■	■	24	■	16	■	■	■	8	■	20	■	■
21	4	3	12	16	7	■	16	13	24	24	4	16
20	■	12	■	22	■	12	■	■	■	24	■	■
20	24	1	25	19	21	10	■	15	24	11	20	21
9	■	13	■	21	■	25	■	15	■	20	■	2
19	24	9	8	7	■	14	24	10	22	21	20	24
24	■	8	■	24	■	24	■	24	■	6	■	8
16	9	2	8	16	■	20	24	16	13	24	23	7

1	2	3	4	5	6	7 T	8	9	10 L	11	12	13
14	15	16	17	18 Y	19	20	21	22	23	24	25	26

ALPHAFITS ⭐⭐

One of each of the 26 letters of the alphabet has been removed from the crossword grid below. Can you replace them all to fill the crossword with everyday words?

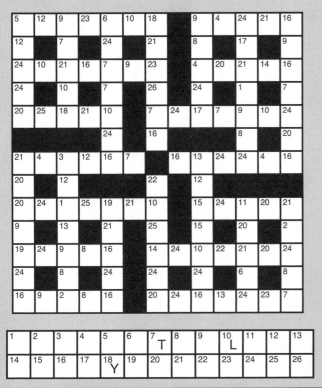

A	B	C	D	E	F	G	H	I	J	K	L	M
N	O	P	Q	R	S	T	U	V	W	X	Y	Z

ODD ONE OUT ⭐

Can you spot the odd one out in this set of numbers?

FALL WORDSEARCH ⭐

The grid contains 15 fall words hidden vertically, horizontally or diagonally. Can you find them all?

ACORN
APPLE
BERRY
BRAMBLE
CONKER
FIRE
HARVEST
LEAVES
MIST
OCTOBER
REAP
RUSSET
SEED
STORE
YELLOW

B	E	L	P	P	A	E	R
T	R	E	B	O	T	C	O
E	H	A	R	V	E	S	T
S	B	V	M	I	S	T	A
S	E	E	D	B	F	O	C
U	R	S	H	G	L	R	O
R	R	C	O	N	K	E	R
I	Y	E	L	L	O	W	N

JIG GRID ⭐⭐

Can you fit the blocks back into the grid to reveal five dances, reading from left to right?

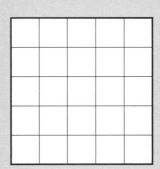

N	G
T	Z

U	M
A	M

B	A
	O

M	A
R	

M	R
	S
	T

	A
W	A	L

M	B	O
	B	A

BITS AND PIECES

The tiles in the top grid are all jumbled up. Can you rearrange them in the grid below using only one tile from each column to reveal four related words and their theme?

CH	IC	I	S	E
C	E	ME	TT	R
R	HE	D	LT	AN
PA	T	E	DA	A
S	R	O	S	ON

BIRTHDAY GIRL

Sue was 7 the day before yesterday. Next year she will be 10.

What is the date of Sue's birthday and on which date were the above statements made?

....

LETTER STEW

Use all the given letters in the stew to spell three words meaning fast.

CROSSWORD

Across
2 Glean information with electronic beam (4)
4 Cried (4)
5 Deferred (7)
6 People in general (4)
7 Marries (4)

Down
1 Protection from harm (7)
2 Sea channels (7)
3 Sticks to (7)

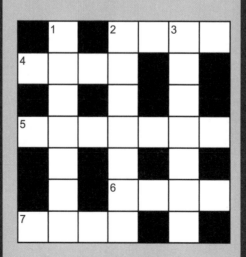

KAKURO

In Kakuro the numbers in the black squares refer to the SUMS of the digits 1-9 which you are to fill into the empty spaces. The number ABOVE the diagonal line refers to the empty spaces directly to the RIGHT of that number. The number BELOW the diagonal line refers to the empty spaces directly BELOW that number. No zeros are used here and a digit can only appear once in any particular digit combination.

SUDOKU

To solve, fill in the grid so that every row, column and box contains the numbers 1 through 9.

	2		4	9		8	5	1
5		6				9		7
	1				3			6
2	8	5	6				9	4
				2				5
4	7			8	5	6		
	3	4	9				5	7	8
8	9				7	4		
6	5		8	3		1	2	9

WHAT COMES FIRST?

⭐⭐

Can you work out which word commonly precedes the pairs of words below?

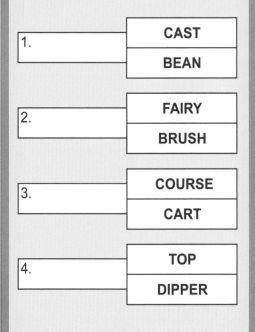

| 1. | CAST |
| | BEAN |

| 2. | FAIRY |
| | BRUSH |

| 3. | COURSE |
| | CART |

| 4. | TOP |
| | DIPPER |

CAGED ANIMALS

⭐

An animal has escaped from the zoo. To put him back in his cage answer the eight clues and put them in the grid starting from the outermost circle. When this is done the central circle, starting clockwise from number nine, will reveal the name of the animal who escaped.

1 Land measurement (4)
2 Computer information (4)
3 Scorch (4)
4 Pimple (4)
5 To grow weary (4)
6 It's rung at church (4)
7 Group of three (4)
8 Short shot in golf (4)

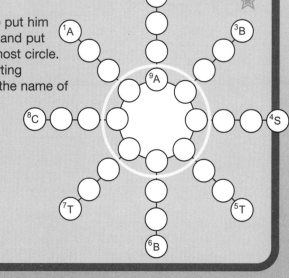

NINE NUMBERS

⭐⭐

Try to fill in the missing numbers. Use the numbers 1 to 9 to complete the equations. Each number is only used once. Each row and column is an equation with the totals given below and to the right.

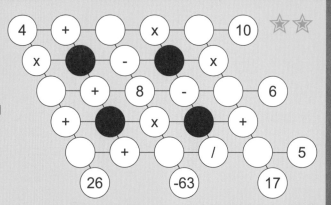

ALPHAFITS

⭐⭐

One of each of the 26 letters of the alphabet has been removed from the crossword grid below. Can you replace them all to fill the crossword with everyday words?

| A | B | C | D | E | F | G | H | I | J | K | L | M |
| N | O | P | Q | R | S | T | U | V | W | X | Y | Z |

STRING MAZE

⭐

Can you find your way through the maze of string?

START

FINISH

WORD FIT

Can you fit all the words linked with carpentry into the grid?

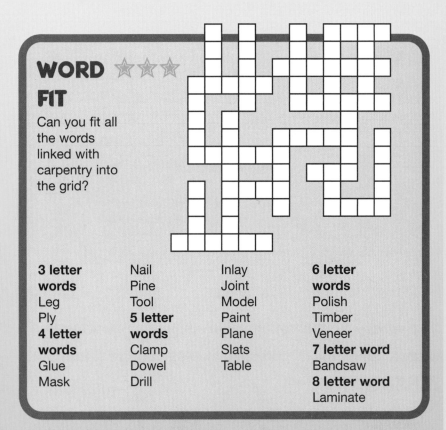

3 letter words
Leg
Ply

4 letter words
Glue
Mask

Nail
Pine
Tool

5 letter words
Clamp
Dowel
Drill

Inlay
Joint
Model
Paint
Plane
Slats
Table

6 letter words
Polish
Timber
Veneer

7 letter word
Bandsaw

8 letter word
Laminate

BATTLESHIPS

There are four ships hidden in the grid below. Look at the key to see which ships you have to find. The numbers on the grid tell you how many squares of each row or column part of a ship is found in. To get you started we've put a few parts of ships (in red) and a few squares with no ships (in black).

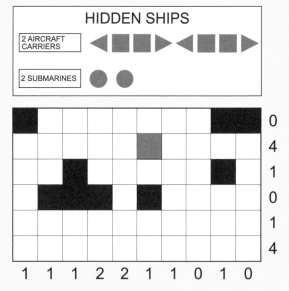

HINTS: Begin by shading in all the misses (all the columns which have a zero in them) as there are no ships here. When you have found a full ship you can shade all the blocks around that ship as misses because none of the ships are touching.

BLOCKBUSTERS

Complete the square by using each number and symbol provided in the top row ONCE only in every other row and column to equal the given answer. The first column and all the + signs have been put in to give you a start!

4	x	7	-	9	+	2	=21
+		+					
2					+		=15
x				+			
7					+		=29
-						+	
9			+				=31

=33   =56   =12   =6

WORD WHEEL

For each of the circles, can you find two letters which, when placed in the middle, will form three six-letter words?

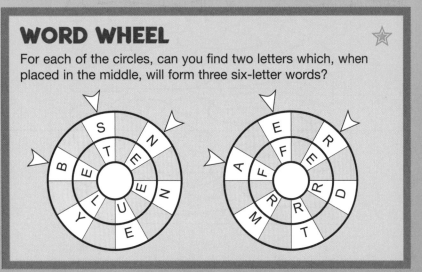

ARROWS

Put the following numbers in the arrows below:

1 1 3 3 3 4 5

Be careful though.
The total numbers in the three arrows pointing at each other must add up to 9:

The total numbers in the arrows which are back to back must add up to 6:

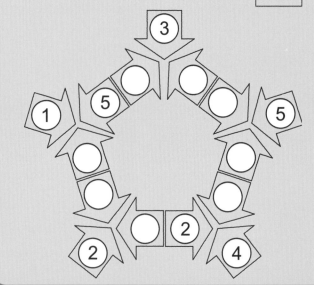

MINI MAZE ⭐⭐

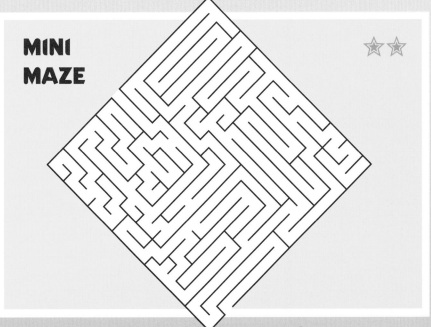

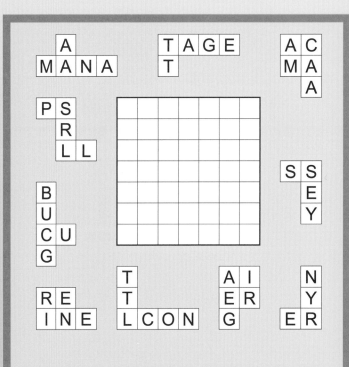

JIG GRID ⭐⭐⭐

Can you fit the blocks back into the grid to reveal, reading from left to right, seven theatrical terms?

MATCH STICKS ⭐⭐⭐

What is the fewest number of matches that need to be moved in order for the matchstick fish to swim in the opposite direction?

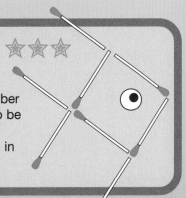

NATURE TRAIL ⭐

Find the plant that is growing inside the tree by removing all the letters that appear more than twice.

	X	C		
	S	A	G	B
B	T	N	U	H	P
M	L	G	M	B	I	N	S
P		F	X	T	X	L
	N	O	H	W
		B	S
		P	E
		P	G
		G	M
		N	T
		H	R

THE HIDDEN PLANT IS A

....

NATURAL NINE ⭐

Try and become king of the jungle in this natural puzzle.

How many words of four letters or more can you track down? At least one will use all nine letters and all contain the central letter U. Use each letter once only. No words with capitals, foreign words, hyphens, or plurals are allowed.

R Y
G R Y D
N U
H E

THE NINE LETTER WORD IS

....

PUSSYCAT STANDARD: 9 words
PANTHER STANDARD: 17 words
LION STANDARD: 24 words

HOLLYWOOD ANAGRAMS ⭐⭐⭐

Below are four anagrams of films or film people. The number and length of words to find is shown in brackets. The four solutions are all linked in some way – can you find the link?

BETTER HALF ASK CUB (3, 9, 4)	
SHELBY TOOTS (3, 4, 4)	THE LINK IS .....
KITTEN PIN PRY (6, 2, 4)	
GUN GUN SOY (5, 4)	

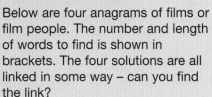

SKELETON CROSSWORD ⭐⭐⭐

Below is an incomplete quick crossword grid. Can you solve the puzzle by fitting the answers to the clues correctly into the grid, along with the remaining blocks and clue numbers? A few blocks have been shaded to give you a start. The grid has been rotated by 180 degrees.

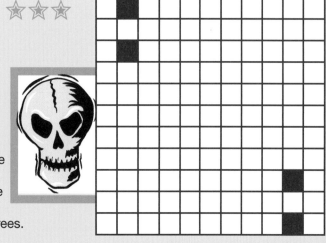

Across
6 In a foreign country (6)
7 Chum (4)
9 Old-fashioned girl's name (3)
10 Ardently serious (7)
11 Exchanges (5)
13 To playfully vex (5)
15 Holds back (7)
18 At the stern (3)
20 Hit with open hand (4)
21 Shooting star (6)

Down
1 To stun or stupefy (4)
2 A fleet of ships (6)
3 British system of withholding tax (4)
4 A counterfeit (4)
5 Soft, kind (6)
8 Unruly child (4)
11 Mental tension (6)
12 Brief satirical sketch (4)
14 Showy garden or house plant (6)
16 Hard wood (4)
17 To appear (4)
19 Period of school year (4)

HIDDEN COLORS ⭐

Shade in all the letters from the first half of the alphabet to reveal a hidden color.

Q	R	Y	I	Z	Q	T	Z	L	F	C	V
V	O	W	B	U	S	O	Y	A	R	T	O
E	S	Y	D	P	W	Q	S	E	G	K	S
C	U	P	F	T	Q	U	T	H	P	Q	U
F	T	X	R	I	Y	K	P	C	R	W	S
B	J	A	X	H	T	M	V	L	G	A	Y
I	R	J	V	B	E	H	R	Y	S	Z	P
D	G	D	P	T	X	Q	W	O	U	X	S

COUNTING CRITTERS ⭐⭐⭐

Can you find the number that is represented by each animal face? You will find the total of the numbers below each column and to the right of each row.

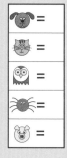

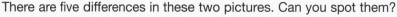

MOUNTAIN SQUIRCLE ⭐⭐

Put vowels in the circles and consonants in the squares to make words in all the vertical columns. Definitions of these words are given. When this has been done, the first and third horizontal lines will make the names of two mountains.

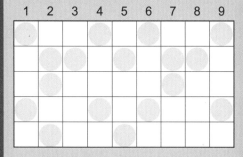

DEFINITIONS
1 Confess
2 Rope for hanging
3 Nursemaid
4 Caper
5 Spanish boy's name
6 Not illuminated
7 Kingdom
8 Widow of Mr Reagan
9 English racecourse

SPOT THE DIFFERENCE ⭐

There are five differences in these two pictures. Can you spot them?

GREEN WORDSEARCH

The grid contains 14 green things hidden vertically, horizontally or diagonally. The unused letters spell out another green item.

```
C P L S B S A E
U O E U S H P B
C E D A J A P U
U S R A R M L D
M G A R C R E G
B R O C C O L I
E T N I M C V E
R B E A N K F A
```

APPLE
AVOCADO
BEAN
BROCCOLI
BUDGIE

BUDS
CUCUMBER
GLASS
GRASS

JADE
MINT
PARROT
PEAR
SHAMROCK

ALPHAFITS

One of each of the 26 letters of the alphabet has been removed from the crossword grid. Can you replace them all to fill the crossword with everyday words?

```
A V E . L A S . E D
P . A . . . . I . A
L U . . . A M . E .
A . U . B . K . E S
S . E . . E S . . .
. M . C . . . . O . O
. . . . . W E . U .
B . S . M . D . F . D
E . O T . C . D I . E
E . F . N . . . C . S
S H . G . . . . E A T
```

```
A B C D E F G H I J K L M
N O P Q R S T U V W X Y Z
```

PYRAMID OF BRICKS

Fill in the bricks with numbers. They must equal the sum of the two bricks below.

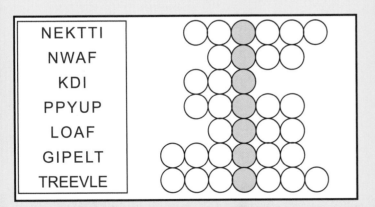

```
          415
       205    [ ]
    [ ]    [ ]   100
   [ ]  55   [ ]  [ ]
 [ ]  [ ]  [ ]  25
10  [ ]  20  [ ]  [ ]
```

QUICK QUIZ QUESTIONS

Can you get all of these quiz questions correct?

WHO IS THE LEAD SINGER OF.......	
1. REM ?	
2. U2 ?	
3. BLUR ?	
4. BON JOVI ?	
5. AEROSMITH ?	
6. THE DARKNESS ?	

ANAGRAM LADDERS

Solve the anagrams below to reveal the names of seven animal young. The shaded column in the middle will then reveal the name of another animal's young.

NEKTTI
NWAF
KDI
PPYUP
LOAF
GIPELT
TREEVLE

NATUREGRAMS

Solve each clue, then rearrange the five letters in every answer to form a set of three fruits.

CLUES:
1 Electronic beeper
2 Sweet gourd
3 In the middle of

1. [ ][ ][ ][ ][ ]   1. [ ][ ][ ][ ][ ]

2. [ ][ ][ ][ ][ ]   2. [ ][ ][ ][ ][ ]

3. [ ][ ][ ][ ][ ]   3. [ ][ ][ ][ ][ ]

OCCUPATIONS ⭐⭐⭐

How many words of four letters or more can you track down in this game? At least one will be a nine letter occupation and all contain the central letter. Use each letter once only. No words with capitals, foreign words, hyphens, or plurals and verb forms ending in -s are allowed.

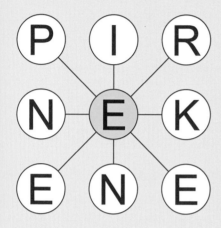

GOOD: 13 words
VERY GOOD: 18 words
EXCELLENT: 24 words

CROSSWORD ⭐

Across
1 High pitched laugh (6)
5 Eggs of a fish (3)
6 Atmosphere (3)
7 Fitting (3)
8 Low-lying flat land (3)
9 Concealed (3)
10 Academic award (6)

Down
1 Bottle for wine (6)
2 To remove dirt from (7)
3 Tanned hide (7)
4 Device to keep things cold (6)

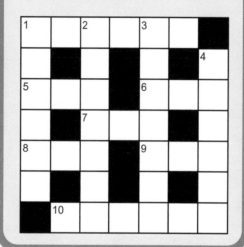

KAKURO ⭐⭐

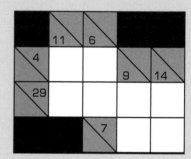

In Kakuro the numbers in the black squares refer to the SUMS of the digits 1-9 which you are to fill into the empty spaces. The number ABOVE the diagonal line refers to the empty spaces directly to the RIGHT of that number. The number BELOW the diagonal line refers to the empty spaces directly BELOW that number. No zeros are used here and a digit can only appear once in any particular digit combination.

COMMON WORDS ⭐⭐⭐

Your task here is to determine the answers to each set of tricky definitions below, as well as the word that is contained in all five of the set's answers. For example, if the five solutions were ERRAND, TERRIBLE, MERRY MEN, PREFERRED and PERRY, the word in the central circle would be ERR.

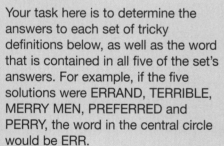

Clues:
1 Floorwear
2 Corolla leaves
3 Kin to clue number 2
4 Hook's foe
5 Rash

ALPHABET SUDOKU ⭐

To solve, fill in the grid so that every row, column and box contains the letters A through I.

G		C			B	F	E	A
I		F	C	A				B
			E	D		G		C
	H		B		I	A	C	D
	C	D	A				I	
A		I		E	C	H	G	F
	I		E				D	
D	G	A		B		C		
C		B	G	I	D	E	A	

ADD A LETTER ⭐

Add one letter to each word in capitals to create a new word that answers the clue. The orders of the letters do not need to be changed.

For example – 'I BET it's more superior' would be BEST.

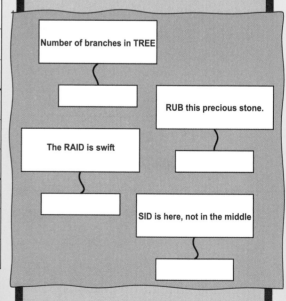

Number of branches in TREE

RUB this precious stone.

The RAID is swift

SID is here, not in the middle

NINE NUMBERS ★★

Try to fill in the missing numbers. Use the numbers 1 to 9 to complete the equations. Each number is only used once. Each row and column is an equation with the totals given below and to the right.

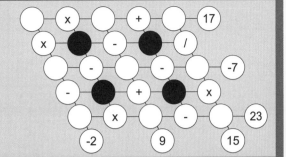

HOLLYWOOD ANAGRAMS ★★★

Below are four anagrams of films or film people. The number and length of words to find is shown in brackets. The four anagram solutions are all linked in some way – can you find the link?

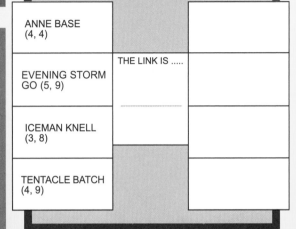

ANNE BASE
(4, 4)

EVENING STORM GO (5, 9)

ICEMAN KNELL
(3, 8)

TENTACLE BATCH
(4, 9)

THE LINK IS .....

CHAIN REACTION ★★★

Solve this puzzle by creating a 'chain reaction' of 20 five-letter words that run left to right, beginning in the upper-left hand corner, using the 19 two-letter tiles in the middle. A two-letter tile that ends one begins the next. Each tile will only be used once. The single letters already entered are the middle letters of the words you are to form. Start by finishing the word that begins BRI_ _.

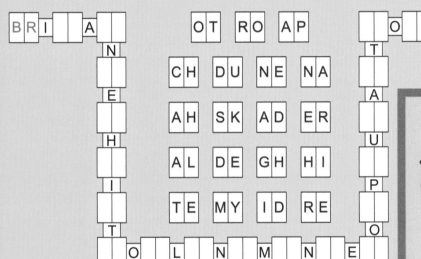

JIG GRID ★★

Can you fit the blocks back into the grid to reveal six computer terms, reading from left to right?

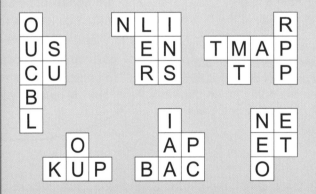

CAGED ANIMALS ☆

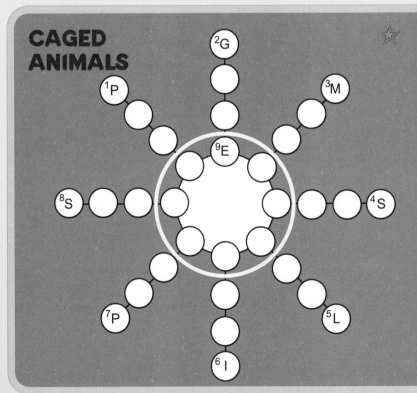

An animal has escaped from the zoo. To put him back in his cage, answer the eight clues and put them in the grid starting from the outermost circle. When this is done the central circle, starting clockwise from number nine, will reveal the name of the animal who escaped.

1 A portion (4)
2 Adhesive (4)
3 Post (4)
4 Ingredient of stuffing (4)

5 Jump (4)
6 Skin irritation (4)
7 Cougar (4)
8 Perceived (4)

NATURAL NINE

Try and become king of the jungle in this natural puzzle.

How many words of four letters or more can you track down? At least one will use all nine letters and all contain the central letter B. Use each letter once only. No words with capitals, foreign words, hyphens, or plurals are allowed.

THE NINE LETTER WORD IS

....

PUSSYCAT STANDARD: 9 words
PANTHER STANDARD: 17 words
LION STANDARD: 26 words

ZOO HUNT

An animal has escaped from the zoo and is hiding somewhere in the grid. If you cross out all the letters that appear more than twice, the remaining letters will spell out the missing creature.

THE MISSING CREATURE IS A

....

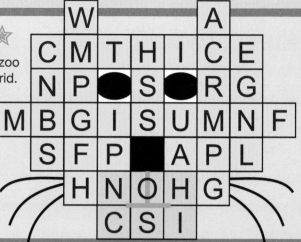

PAIR WHEELS

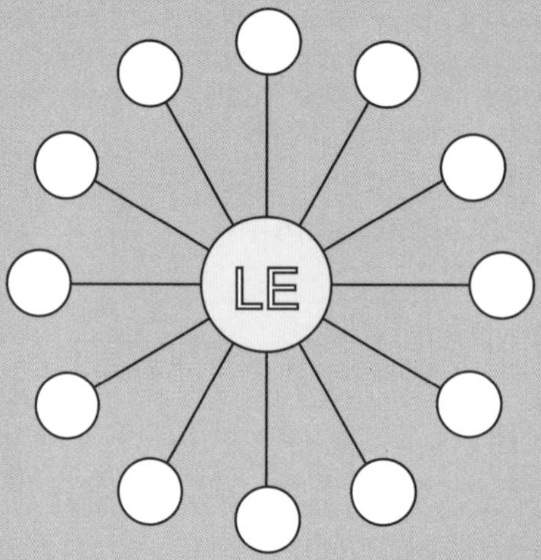

Place each of the twelve pairs of letters into one of the circles in the grid, so that every line running through the central circle gives you a six-letter word with the middle letters LE.

NT
NT
UN
SE
EP
CT
AS
SO
TA
SS
MN
SI

(central circle: LE)

FLOWERY PHRASES ☆☆☆

We have described a well-known saying using flowery language. Can you uncover the more familiar form? For example, 'An eruption in the cook pot' would be 'A flash in the pan'.

> Whatever constitutes tremendous power, force, or influence enjoys the privilege and protection of being correctly and properly deemed in control of either the truth or the situational parameters.

BITS AND PIECES ☆☆☆

The tiles in the top grid are all jumbled up. Can you rearrange them in the grid below using only one tile from each column to reveal four related words and their theme?

C	R	R	TT	E
F	AG	A	I	S
P	A	E	I	C
GA	H	L	NC	E
B	R	UE	ES	E

(empty answer grid below)

There are 15 sweets in a jar. If Steve eats twice as many as Nick, and Nick eats four times as many as Glenda, how many sweets are left for Mark?

SWEETIE TEASE ☆

Can you work out the answer to this teaser?

MARK HAS

_____ SWEETS

CROSSWORD

Across
2 Commits to memory (6)
5 Rescue (4)
6 Tree lined road (6)
7 Prepares a trap (4)
8 The Common Market (3)
11 Scented garden flower (4)
13 Spiritualist's meeting (6)
14 Scheme (4)
15 Gracefully slim (6)

Down
1 Cover in flagstones (4)
2 Tenant's contract (5)
3 Area of frozen ice (4)
4 Arm section of a garment (6)
7 The five faculties (6)
9 Crinkly fabric (5)
10 Strip the skin off (4)
12 Sharp protuberance (4)

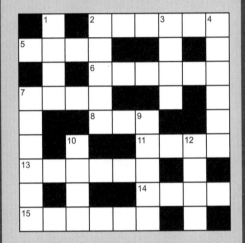

KAKURO

In Kakuro the numbers in the black squares refer to the SUMS of the digits 1-9 which you are to fill into the empty spaces. The number ABOVE the diagonal line refers to the empty spaces directly to the RIGHT of that number. The number BELOW the diagonal line refers to the empty spaces directly BELOW that number. No zeros are used here and a digit can only appear once in any particular digit combination.

THREE FOUR ALL

The object is to find three four-letter words using the letters given in each word without changing the order of the letters. For example, if the given word were PRICES, the first word might be PIES, the second might be RICE and the third would be ICES.

| CAUTIOUS | _ _ _ _ | _ _ _ _ | _ _ _ _ |
| MARBLE | _ _ _ _ | _ _ _ _ | _ _ _ _ |

ALPHAFITS

One of each of the 26 letters of the alphabet has been removed from the crossword grid below. Can you replace them all to fill the crossword with everyday words?

| A | B | C | D | E | F | G | H | I | J | K | L | M |
| N | O | P | Q | R | S | T | U | V | W | X | Y | Z |

LOLLIPOPS

By moving two of the lollipops below can you make seven squares?

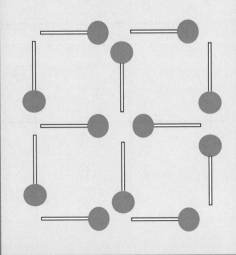

CHAIN REACTION

Solve this puzzle by creating a 'chain reaction' of 20 five-letter words that run left to right, beginning in the upper-left hand corner, using the 19 two-letter tiles in the middle. A two-letter tile that ends one begins the next. Each tile will only be used once. The single letters already entered are the middle letters of the words you are to form. Start by finishing the word that begins LAS_ _.

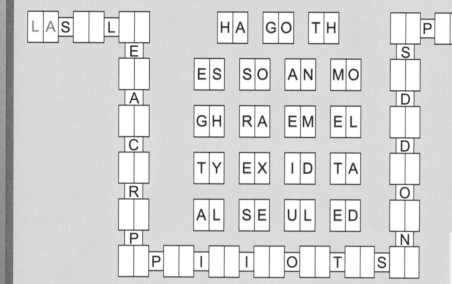

LAS | | L | | | HA | GO | TH | | | P | AND
E
ES | SO | AN | MO
A
GH | RA | EM | EL
C
TY | EX | ID | TA
R
AL | SE | UL | ED
P
P | I | I | O | T | S
S | D | D | O | N

WORD SPLITZ

Each row of ten letters can be split into two five-letter dog words. These words read from left to right and are in order.

For example

SMOKOSUENK

can be split to reveal SKUNK and MOOSE.

① BCAOIXRERN

② CDIONRGGIO

③ HPOOOUCNDH

④ HPUUSPKYPY

ODD ONE OUT

Can you spot the odd one out in this sequence of words?

Edam
Brie CHEDDAR
STILTON   CAMEMBERT
Ravioli

SUDOKU

To solve, fill in the grid so that every row, column and box contains the numbers 1 through 9.

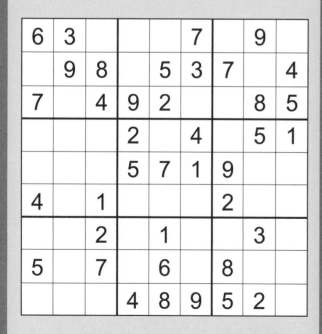

6	3				7		9	
	9	8		5	3	7		4
7		4	9	2			8	5
			2		4		5	1
			5	7	1	9		
4		1				2		
		2		1				3
5		7		6		8		
			4	8	9	5	2	

FRUIT SQURCLE

Put vowels in the circles and consonants in the squares to make words in all the columns. Definitions of these words are given. When this has been done, the first and third horizontal lines will make the names of four types of fruit.

DEFINITIONS
1 A wanderer
2 Hazards at sea
3 Siren, say
4 Political group
5 Rub out
6 Part of jacket
7 Drive on
8 A grinding tooth
9 Foe

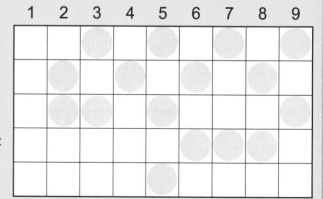

SOLUTIONS

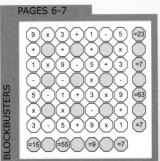

BLOCKBUSTERS

AWARDS WORDSEARCH

HOLLYWOOD ANAGRAMS

LINK: THEY ARE ALL
SUSAN SARANDON FILMS

ELIZABETHTOWN
STEPMOM
THE CLIENT
DEAD MAN WALKING

80s MOVIES QUIZ

1 KEVIN COSTNER
2 WISH YOU WERE HERE
3 TOP GUN
4 GORILLAS IN THE MIST
5 HELEN SLATER

WELL DONE:
27 WORDS

WORD SPLITZ

CLYDE, FORTH
LOIRE, SEINE
STOUR, RHINE
VOLGA, TRENT

NATURE TRAIL

THE HIDDEN PLANT IS
LEMON GRASS

STEP LADDER

BEAR
BEAT
BELT
BELL
BULL

ADD THREE TO THREE

1 WINDSOR
2 CARPET
3 SLEUTH

NOURISHING NINE

UNDERDONE: 13 WORDS

MEDIUM: 20 WORDS

CRACKLING

ARCING CACKLING CAIRN
CAKING CALK CALKING
CARING CIGAR CIRCA
CLACK CLACKING CLAN
CLANG CLANK CLICK
CLING CLINK
CRACK CRACKING
CRAG CRANK CRICK
GARLIC LACING LACK
LACKING LICK NICK
RACING RACK
RACKING RICK

BITS AND PIECES

C	LO	TH	IN	G
OV	ER	CO	A	T
T	UX	E	DO	
S	WE	A	T	ER
TR	O	U	SE	RS

LION
STANDARD:
24 WORDS

NATURAL NINE

PUSSYCAT STANDARD: 8 WORDS

arrow EARTHWORM harrow
marrow meow mower ower
rawer rower thaw thawer
threw throw thrower tower trow
ware warm warmer warmth
wart water wear wham what
wheat whet whoa whom wore
worm wormer worth wrath
wreath wrote

PANTHER STANDARD: 16 WORDS

ODD ONE OUT

CHINA, BECAUSE ALL THE
OTHERS ARE EUROPEAN
COUNTRIES

ARROWS

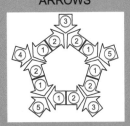

ADDING GRIDS

4	3	2	7	8	1	6	9	5
5	1	8	6	9	2	3	7	4
9	7	6	5	3	4	8	1	2
6	8	9	2	4	7	1	5	3
1	4	7	3	5	8	9	2	6
2	5	3	1	6	9	4	8	7
8	9	5	4	2	3	7	6	1
7	2	4	9	1	6	5	3	8
3	6	1	8	7	5	2	4	9

SHEEP WORDSEARCH

HIDDEN WORD: WOOL

NATUREGRAMS

1 EVICT	1 CIVET
2 DOING	2 DINGO
3 LADEN	3 ELAND

WORD WHEEL

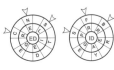

ON TARGET

1 SHOAL, 2 HOTEL,
3 OFFAL, 4 TRAIL,
5 PETAL, 6 UNTIL,
7 TROLL.

OUTER WORD:
SHOTPUT

BIRD BOXES

ANAGRAM LADDERS

TRADER
TUTOR
NURSE
AUTHOR
BARMAN
WHALER
MINER
CENTRAL WORD: DUSTMAN

PYRAMID OF APPLES

112
48 64
20 28 36
8 12 16 20
3 5 7 9 11
1 2 3 4 5 6

HALT WORDSEARCH

HIDDEN WORD: PAUSE

CHAIN REACTION

EAGLE LEAST, STAIN,
INANE, NEPAL, ALIAS,
ASSAM, AMUSE, SENNA,
NACHO, HOTEL, ELOPE,
PEACH, CHEAT, ATLAS,
ASHEN, ENROL, OLIVE,
VERGE, GENIE

OCCUPATIONS

EXCELLENT: 28 WORDS

aver averse avert ever harvest HARVESTER have haver heave rave raver revers revert save saver serve server sever shave shaver starve stave traverse vase vast veer verse vest

GOOD: 15 WORDS

LITTLE TOUGHIE

VERY GOOD: 20 WORDS

PLACE THE PLACES

C	A	B
O	R	E
D	I	N
E	A	T

D		A	S	S	U	R	E	S		B	
R		C		O		T		R		
A	G	U	E		S	T	R	A	T	A	
P			N	E	A	T		R		K	
E	L	S	E			C	E	N	T	R	E
		P		E	R	L				L	
S	E	R	E	N	E		B	E	S	S	
L		I		T	A	T	A				
O	U	T	F	I	T		S	O	Y	A	
O		E		R		I				L	
P			S	W	E	D	I	S	H		L

JIG GRID

A	U	T	H	O	R
B	A	R	M	A	N
C	L	E	R	I	C
D	O	C	K	E	R
F	A	R	M	E	R
J	O	I	N	E	R

FIVE SNEAKY SNAKES

ABERDEEN
NEWCASTLE
WAKEFIELD
ELDORADO
BRIGHTON

HOLLYWOOD ANAGRAMS

LINK: THEY ALL HAVE WON BEST ACTOR OSCARS
TOM HANKS
DENZEL WASHINGTON
MARLON BRANDO
DUSTIN HOFFMAN

ZOO HUNT

THE MISSING CREATURE
IS A ....

SNOW LEOPARD

CROSSWORD

ACROSS:
1 ADDING, 5 TOY, 6 PEA,
7 TOT, 8 SKI, 9 USE,
10 REMEDY

DOWN:
1 ARTIST, 2 DAYTIME,
3 NEPTUNE, 4 RARELY

CAGED ANIMALS

1 VEAL, 2 AIRS, 3 IRAQ,
4 MENU, 5 TAXI, 6 ROAR,
7 OVER, 8 BLUE.

CAGED ANIMAL:
SQUIRREL

NURSERY BLOCKS

ONE TWO BUCKLE
MY SHOE.

THREE FOUR
KNOCK AT THE DOOR.

COUNTING CRITTERS

 = 3

 = 5

= 1

 = 4

= 2

CULT TV SHOWS
SQUIRCLE

R	E	D	D	W	A	R	F	B
E	R	E	U	E	D	I	I	E
L	A	C	K	A	D	D	E	R
A	S	O	E	V	E	G	N	E
X	E	Y	S	E	R	E	D	T

NOURISHING NINE

WELL DONE: 18 WORDS

AGENT AGIN ANTIGEN
EATING FANG **FATTENING**
FEIGN GAIN GAIT GANNET
GATE GENT GENTIAN GIANT
GIFT GNAT NETTING TANG
TANGENT TING TINGE

UNDERDONE: 8 WORDS

MEDIUM: 13 WORDS

QUICK QUIZ QUESTIONS

1 BOB DYLAN
2 ELTON JOHN
3 BONO
4 STING
5 RINGO STARR
6 DAVID BOWIE

GEOGRAMS

¹SERIAL	¹ISRAEL
²BRAISE	²SERBIA
³ASPIRE	³PERSIA

NATURE TRAIL

THE HIDDEN PLANT IS A
WATER LILY

COOKIE WORDSEARCH

BATTLESHIPS

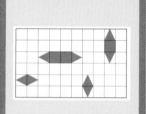

NINE NUMBERS

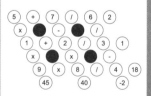

OCCUPATIONS

EXCELLENT: 31 WORDS

CONSCRIPT
corps cost crisp piston posit
post prison rosin scion scorn
script snip snort snot sonic
sort spin spit sport spot sprint
sprit stir stoic stop strip strop

GOOD: 15 WORDS

VERY GOOD: 22 WORDS

80s TV QUIZ

BRIDESHEAD REVISITED
PETER BOWLES
GORDON KAYE
JAZZ
KENNY EVERETT

LITTLE TOUGHIE

	¹R		G		³R	
⁴D	E	B	A	T	E	
	P		B		G	
⁵O	A	F		⁶T	A	N
	I		⁷P		L	
⁸R	O	O	K	I	E	
	S		D		A	

KAKURO

	4	9		
	3	1		
	5	3	1	2
8	5	7	9	
		9	7	
		2	1	

3	2	4	9	5	1	8	7	6
8	9	1	6	2	7	4	3	5
5	7	6	8	4	3	9	2	1
4	6	7	1	8	2	5	3	9
1	5	8	3	9	4	2	6	7
2	3	9	7	6	5	1	8	4
9	4	5	2	7	6	3	1	8
7	1	2	4	3	9	6	5	8
6	8	3	5	1	9	7	4	2

BITS AND PIECES

ST	AR	TR	E	K
S	P	O	C	K
EN	TE	RP	RI	SE
KL	IN	G	O	N
P	HA	S	E	R

TREE NUMBER PIC

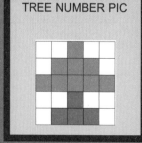

ON TARGET

1 RANCH
2 EARTH
3 ALLAH
4 DEATH
5 IRISH
6 NEIGH
7 GRAPH

OUTER WORD: READING

BIRD BOXES

1	27	15	7	11	3	19	33	17	9
23	36	2	31	16	8	22	7	3	25
19	20	5	3	28	21	29	12	23	9
27	6	24	39	34	2	4	7	17	11
15	14	17	12	2	19	33	1	13	29
1	25	37	8	19	21	3	34	21	22
33	20	30	7	5	7	19	3	4	18
17	3	7	23	17	15	29	21	14	26

PAGES 16-17

QUICK MOVIE QUIZ

1 JIM CARREY
2 TOBEY MAGUIRE
3 HOGWARTS
4 WARDROBE
5 DINOSAURS

PAGES 16-17

RIDDLE WORDS

STORM
HAIL
BRIGHT
LIGHTNING

PAGES 16-17

ADD THREE TO THREE

1 BOUNTY
2 SHAMROCK
3 PALETTE

PAGES 16-17 SUDOKU

3	7	9	1	4	8	5	6	2
6	2	1	3	5	7	8	9	4
4	5	8	2	9	6	1	3	7
1	6	3	9	7	2	4	5	8
8	9	2	4	1	5	6	7	3
5	4	7	6	8	3	2	1	9
7	1	5	8	2	9	3	4	6
2	3	4	7	6	1	9	8	5
9	8	6	5	3	4	7	2	1

PAGES 16-17

REBUS TOWER

EGGS ON TOAST

FRIENDS, ROMANS AND COUNTRYMEN

MOTHER IN LAW

PAGES 16-17

COMMON WORDS

ACORN, CORNET, SCORNED, CAPRICORN, UNICORN — CORN

PAGES 16-17

PLACE THE PLACES

ARC
CAR
ICE
DEW

PAGES 16-17 CROSSWORD

B	A	L	E		S	C	O	U	T
D		C		Y		H		U	
O	N	T	H	E	B	O	T	T	L	E
M			L		O		C		M
E	S	T	E	E	M		N	O	S	E
	O			T		T		M	
B	Y	R	E		L	A	Y	E	R	S
R		P		S		P			A
O	V	E	R	T	H	E	H	I	L	L
K		D		Y		R		B		T
E	R	O	D	E		S	E	A	M

PAGES 16-17

LETTER STEW

TINY
MINUTE
LITTLE

PAGES 18-19

SWEETIE TEASE

DAY 1 = 4
DAY 2 = 7
DAY 3 = 10
DAY 4 = 13
DAY 5 = 16

PAGES 18-19

ZOO HUNT

GRIZZLY BEAR

PAGES 18-19 BLOCKBUSTERS

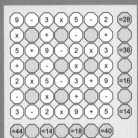

9	-	3	x	5	-	2	=28
x		+		x		+	
5	+	9	x	2	x	3	=36
+		+		+		x	
2	x	9	+	9	+	9	=16
-		-		+		-	
3	+	9	x	9	+	7	=14
=44		=14		=18		=40	

PAGES 18-19

WORD SPLITZ

WALTZ, TANGO
SAMBA, POLKA
FLING, LIMBO
CONGA, RUMBA

PAGES 18-19

PICTURE PHRASES

JACK IN A BOX
TOO FUNNY FOR WORDS
A CUT ABOVE THE REST

PAGES 18-19

NOURISHING NINE

COURGETTE
CERE CERT CORE COTTER
COURT CURE CURETTE
CURT CUTER ECRU EGRET
ERGO ERGOT ERUCT EURO
GOER GORE GREET GROUT
OTTER OUTER RECTO RETE
ROGUE ROUGE ROUT ROUTE
TORE TORT TORTE TOUR
TREE TROT TROUT TRUCE
TRUE TUTOR URGE UTTER

PAGES 18-19

SPORTS EQUIPMENT WORDSEARCH

Hidden word: Bait

PAGES 18-19

CROSSWORD

ACROSS:
2 FISH, 4 TALL, 5 LIBRARY,
6 SKIN, 7 NEXT

DOWN:
1 RADIATE, 2 FLORIST,
3 SCORPIO

PAGES 18-19

THREE FOUR ALL

OINTMENT
OMEN, TENT

DEBONAIR
DEAR, BOAR

SUGARED
SURE, SUED

PAGES 18-19

BITS AND PIECES

SC	O	T	LA	ND
T	AR	T	A	N
G	L	AS	GO	W
C	A	ST	L	E
HA	G	G	I	S

PAGES 18-19

HOLLYWOOD ANAGRAMS

LINK: THEY ARE ALL MOVIES THAT STEVEN SPIELBERG HAS DIRECTED OR PRODUCED
SAVING PRIVATE RYAN
THE TERMINAL
WAR OF THE WORLDS
MEMOIRS OF A GEISHA

PAGES 20-21

NATURAL NINE

cell cent cite client
CLIENTELE elect
entice inlet lent lentil lice
line lintel nice niece
tell tile tine

PAGES 20-21

ARROWS

PAGES 20-21 SUDOKU

h	g	a	b	f	d	e	c	i
c	i	d	g	e	a	b	h	f
f	b	e	c	h	i	d	a	g
e	h	i	f	d	c	a	g	b
g	a	f	i	b	e	h	d	c
d	c	b	h	a	g	f	i	e
b	d	g	e	c	h	i	f	a
a	f	c	d	i	b	g	e	h
i	e	h	a	g	f	c	b	d

PAGES 20-21

NINE NUMBERS

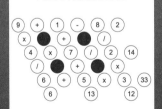

PAGES 20-21 CROSSWORD

PAGES 20-21

NATUREGRAMS

1 AMBER 1 BREAM
2 HARKS 2 SHARK
3 KEATS 3 SKATE

PAGES 20-21 CLUB HOUSE

CLUB HOUSE

Alonso, Button, Heidfeld, Rosberg, Trulli, Webber

H	W	K	G	S	R	X	A
R	E	X	A	J	S	L	A
M	B	I	P	Y	O	W	S
O	B	E	D	N	A	R	K
T	E	C	S	F	Y	Q	M
R	R	O	S	B	E	R	G
V	I	T	R	U	L	L	I
B	U	T	T	O	N	Y	D

PAGES 20-21

PLACE THE PLACES

BAG
AGE
GUN
SEE

PAGES 20-21 KAKURO

(Kakuro grid with solution)

PAGES 20-21

FLOWERY PHRASES

THE PROOF OF THE PUDDING IS IN THE EATING

191

PAGES 20-21
ODD ONE OUT

T, BECAUSE THE REST ARE VOWELS

PAGES 22-23
HIDDEN COLORS

36	50	10	16	21	54	37	24	32	14	18	46
48	6	13	44	33	24	16	5	20	10	30	38
16	2	35	4	9	27	45	12	38	36	14
30	52	23	14	22	6	30	26	28	20	20
2	19	39	26	46	32	50	47	31	7	40	38
6	3	2	12	40	6	10	41	16	34
11	25	43	12	48	20	50	20	19	22	42
24	4	44	2	26	8	42	18	24	48	8

PAGES 22-23
PETS WORDSEARCH

PAGES 22-23
ADD A LETTER

LIME, FAWN,
TRUCK, BEAST

PAGES 22-23
CHAIN REACTION

DRAMA, MACRO, ROUTE,
TEETH, THEME, METAL,
ALLAH, AHEAD, ADORE,
RECAP, APPLE, LEACH,
CHAFE, FEAST, STATE,
TELEX, EXTRA, RAISE,
SEIZE, ZESTY

PAGES 22-23
SODUKU

4	1	6	9	2	7	3	8	5
3	7	2	5	8	1	6	4	9
8	9	5	6	4	3	2	1	7
1	8	4	7	3	6	9	5	2
9	2	7	4	5	8	1	3	6
6	5	3	1	9	2	8	7	4
5	6	8	2	1	4	7	9	3
2	3	9	8	7	5	4	6	1
7	4	1	3	6	9	5	2	8

PAGES 22-23
WORD FIT

SALMON, TUNA, CHAD, HADDOCK, FLOUNDER, BASS, COLEY, TURBOT, SHAD, SKATE, BLENNY

PAGES 22-23
PLACE THE PLACES

T	W	O
H	O	P
A	R	E
T	E	N

PAGES 22-23 WORD WHEEL

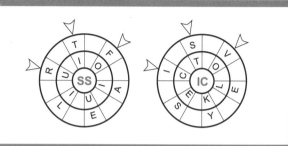

PAGES 22-23
NUMBER HEX

PAGES 22-23
ON TARGET

1 RAPID, 2 ACHED,
3 NAKED, 4 GLUED,
5 EASED, 6 RATED,
7 SALAD.

OUTER WORD:
RANGERS

PAGES 22-23
KITCHEN SQUIRCLE

F	R	I	D	G	E	C	O	O
L	I	N	R	O	X	A	F	B
O	D	F	I	O	A	D	F	E
C	G	E	N	S	C	E	A	S
K	E	R	K	E	T	T	L	E

PAGES 24-25
SODUKU

2	5	3	4	8	1	7	9	6
6	9	8	5	7	3	1	4	2
7	4	1	9	2	6	8	3	5
1	8	6	3	4	7	9	5	2
4	6	7	3	1	9	2	5	8
3	8	9	2	5	7	6	1	4
5	3	2	7	4	8	9	6	1
8	7	1	6	9	5	4	2	3
9	4	6	1	3	2	5	8	7

PAGES 24-25
BIRD BOXES

A	B	O	E	A	E	U	K	A	E	P	I
E	U	A	U	I	O	I	L	I	O	C	O
I	X	O	L	R	D	E	C	V	T	H	U
O	F	E	Y	E	F	A	U	I	E	W	E
M	S	I	B	A	P	U	E	A	O	M	A
U	A	O	C	K	J	O	I	J	X	N	E
I	E	U	Q	O	G	I	U	A	E	I	U
U	O	I	E	U	E	A	E	O	U	A	O

WELL DONE: 26 WORDS

PAGES 24-25
ANAGRAM LADDERS

MOTOR, TRAM
CAR, TRUCK
CART, MOPED
LORRY

CENTRAL WORD:
TRACTOR

PAGES 24-25
OPPOSITES ATTRACT

PUSH AND PULL

PASS AND FAIL

PAGES 24-25
NINE NUMBERS

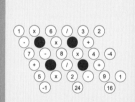

PAGES 24-25
NOURISHING NINE

UNDERDONE: 14 WORDS

MEDIUM: 20 WORDS

CIST CITRUS CRIT
CRUD CRUST CURD
CURST CURT CUTIS
DICTUM DISC DRUMSTICK
DUCK DUCT ICTUS
MICK MUCID MUCK
MUSCID MUSIC RICK
RICTUS RUCK RUSTIC
SCRIM SCRUM SCUD
SCUM SCUT SICK
STICK STRUCK STUCK
SUCK TICK TRICK
TRUCK TUCK URIC

PUSSYCAT STANDARD: 7 WORDS

PAGES 24-25 MOVIE HOUSE

COZY, CRAMP, RUG, POT, MAGS, VAT, MIRTH, FEE, XEN, CUP, KEY, COMB, BY, ARB, EQFAA, WDLCVN, LEGEND

PAGES 24-25
CODED CROSSWORD

WIZARD, UNEVEN, WEAR, IMPROVED, SPECIES, METER, WOVEN, REQUEST, EGYPTIAN, KISS, DEGREE, TUNING

PAGES 24-25
HOLLYWOOD ANAGRAMS

LINK: THEY ALL WON
OSCARS IN 2006
GEORGE CLOONEY
RACHEL WEISZ
REECE WITHERSPOON
ANG LEE

PAGES 24-25
LETTER SWAP

IT NEVER RAINS BUT IT
POURS.

LION STANDARD: 16 WORDS

PAGES 24-25
ODD ONE OUT

ANKLE, ALL THE REST
ARE ON THE HEAD

PAGES 26-27
NATURAL NINE

cent cite iciest incite insect
inset insist nest nett nicest
scent SCIENTIST sect sent
sett site stet stint tent test
tine tiniest tint

PANTHER STANDARD: 11 WORDS

PAGES 26-27
CAGED ANIMALS

1 CLOG, 2 BUSH, 3 CONE,
4 RIND, 5 SLUG, 6 ROPE,
7 RICH, 8 YOYO

CAGED ANIMAL:
HEDGEHOG

192

PAGES 26-27

ARROWS

PAGES 26-27

PYRAMID OF EGGS

108

62 46

34 28 18

16 18 10 8

6 10 8 2 6

3 3 7 1 1 5

PAGES 26-27 SUDOKU

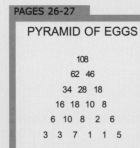

PAGES 26-27

CROSSWORD

Across: 2 Masses, 5 Tape,
6 Eclair, 7 Seat, 8 SAS,
11 Pose, 13 Sparse, 14 Char,
15 Sweats

Down: 1 Sate, 2 Meets,
3 Seam, 4 Scribe, 7 Spasms,
9 Specs, 10 Dare, 12 Stag

PAGES 26-27

FIVE SNEAKY SNAKES

SCULPTOR
PUBLICAN
OPTICIAN
CRAFTSMAN
MERCHANT

PAGES 26-27

COMMON WORDS

PAGES 26-27

SWEET NUMBER PIC

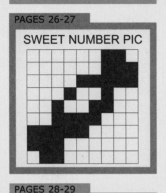

PAGES 26-27

GEOGRAMS

PAGES 26-27 KAKURO

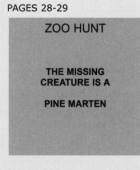

PAGES 28-29

ZOO HUNT

THE MISSING
CREATURE IS A

PINE MARTEN

PAGES 28-29 CROSSWORD

PAGES 28-29

ODD ONE OUT

CUBE, THE OTHERS
ARE ALL SHAPES

PAGES 28-29

ADD A LETTER

PALACE, FORT,
RINSE, TRAY

PAGES 28-29

ADD THREE TO THREE

1. ARMADA
2. PIGLET
3. DESERT

PAGES 28-29

LOLLIPOPS

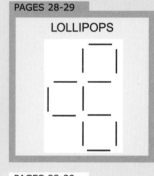

PAGES 28-29

MALE ACTORS WORDSEARCH

HIDDEN WORD: NEWMAN

PAGES 28-29

BLOCKBUSTERS

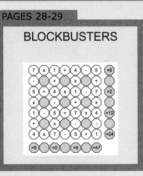

PAGES 28-29

REBUS TOWER

PUBLIC RIGHT OF WAY
SPLIT SECOND TIMING
RETURN TICKET

PAGES 28-29

LITTLE TOUGHIE

Across: 4 Behave, 5 Cob,
6 Ram, 8 Stages.

Down: 1 Remorse, 2 Tag,
3 Belated, 7 Gas.

PAGES 28-29

LETTER STEW

POOR, WICKED, EVIL

PAGES 30-31

BITS AND PIECES

F	LO	W	E	RS
T	U	L	I	P
DA	F	FO	DI	LL
B	L	UE	BE	L
CO	W	S	L	IP

PAGES 30-31

MATCHING PAIR

2 AND 5

PAGES 30-31

HIDDEN COLORS

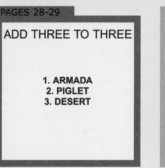

PAGES 30-31

CROSSWORD

ACROSS: 1 SUSPECTED,
6 ARABS, 7 ANT, 8 SACK,
10 PENS, 13 TOE, 14 ONION,
16 PARALLELS
DOWN: 1 SEALS, 2 SEA,
3 EASE, 4 TRACE, 5 DOT,
9 CHEER, 11 SONGS,
12 GOAL, 13 TOP, 15 ICE

PAGES 30-31 ADDING GRIDS

PAGES 30-31

NOURISHING NINE

CEIL CELL CELLULE
CELLULITE CILL CLUE
CULL CULLET CULT ELECT
ELUTE LEET LICE LIEU LILT
LUCE LUETIC LULL LUTE
TELIC TELL TILE TILL TULLE
UTILE

PAGES 30-31 SUDOKU

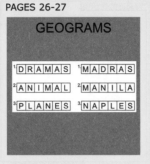

PAGES 30-31

DIZZY DICTATION

1. Have you seen their son's
new wild hairstyle.
2. Cheap shoes might cause
sore feet.
3. Weather forecasters
guessed their would be rain
hail and snow.

PAGES 30-31

GEOGRAMS

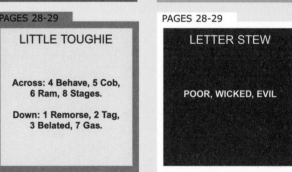

PAGES 30-31

A'MAZE'ING NUMBERS

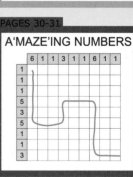

193

DANCE NUMBER PIC

NINE NUMBERS

ADD A LETTER

THREE, RUBY, RAPID, SIDE

PAIR WHEELS

AGREED, CEREAL, PARENT, CAREER, THREAD, SCREAM

CHAIN REACTION

BALSA, SABRE, REPRO, ROUTE, TENTH, THEME, METAL, ALPHA, HARSH, SHOVE, VETCH, CHOKE, KENYA, YAHOO, OOMPH, PHOTO, TOKYO, YODEL, ELUDE, DEALT

CODED CROSSWORD

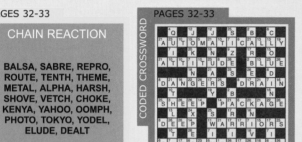

KAKURO

OCCUPATIONS

ASPIC CASH CHAIN
CHAP CHIN CHINA
CHIP INCH PANIC
PHYSICIAN PICA
PINCH PSYCH
SCAN SPICY
SPINACH SYNC SYNCH

COUNTING CRITTERS

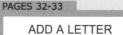=5

=15

=25

=20

=10

JIG GRID

S	P	A	N	N	E	R
H	A	C	K	S	A	W
C	L	E	A	V	E	R
P	I	C	K	A	X	E
C	R	O	W	B	A	R
H	A	T	C	H	E	T
S	C	A	L	P	E	L

WORD SPLITZ

DINAR, FRANC
KOPEK, KRONA
POUND, RUPEE
PENNY, CENTS

BIRD BOXES

ARROWS

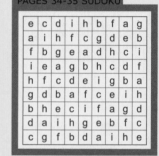

WORD WALL

AIRY
AIRS
FIRS
FURS
BURS
BURN
TURN

NINE NUMBERS

MATCH STICKS

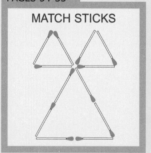

PLACE THE PLACES

B	I	B
R	O	E
A	T	E
T	A	N

NUMBER HEX

CODED CROSSWORD

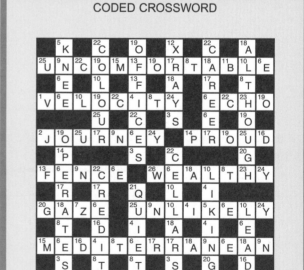

ZOO HUNT

THE MISSING CREATURE IS AN ELEPHANT

SOUNDS WORDSEARCH

NURSERY BLOCKS

JACK SPRAT COULD
EAT NO FAT.
HIS WIFE COULD EAT NO
LEAN.

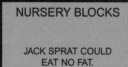

NINE NUMBERS

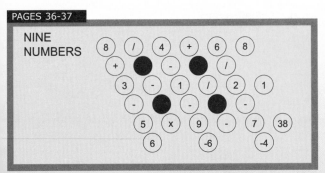

NOURISHING NINE

APHIS ASPIC ATOP CHAP
CHIP CHOP HASP OPTIC
PACT PAST PATCH PATH
PATHOS PATIO PATOIS PICA
PICOT **PISTACHIO** PITCH
PITH POACH POSH POSIT
POST POTASH SHIP SHOP
SOAP SPAR SPIT SPOT
STOP TOPI TOPIC

WORD WHEEL

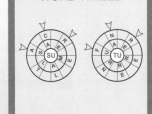

HOLLYWOOD ANAGRAMS

**LINK: THEY ARE ALL
BRITISH FILMS**
LOVE ACTUALLY
SHAUN OF THE DEAD
THE FULL MONTY
SHALLOW GRAVE

QUICK QUIZ QUESTIONS

1 INSANITY
2 HEIGHTS
3 SMALL SPACES
4 TIME
5 SPIDERS
6 GOD

COUNTING CRITTERS

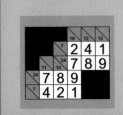 = 2

= 4

= 5

= 1

= 3

WORD SPLITZ

1 ITALY, INDIA
2 JAPAN, BURMA
3 GHANA, LIBYA
4 MALTA, YEMEN

NINE NUMBERS

2	-	4	-	8	-10
+		+		-	
1	+	7	+	6	14
+		-		x	
5	-	3	x	9	18
8		8		18	

CROSSWORD

ACROSS:
1 COCKLE, 5 AGE, 6 TOR,
7 ACT, 8 EON, 9 LAD,
10 DEGREE

DOWN:
1 CHAPEL, 2 CLEANSE,
3 LITTLER, 4 TRUDGE

STEP LADDER

**HAND
BAND
BOND
FOND
FONT
FOOT**

PAIR WHEELS

**BELONG, COLONY,
COLONS, MELODY,
PILOTS, UNLOAD.**

CHAIN REACTION

RUCHE, HENCE, CELLO,
LOYAL, ALIAS, ASIDE,
DENSE, SEIZE, ZEBRA,
RADAR, AROMA, MACAW,
AWASH, SHAPE, PERTH,
THEME, METAL, ALIEN,
ENROL, OLDIE

COMMON WORDS

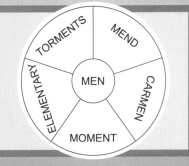

TORMENTS, MEND, CARMEN, MOMENT, ELEMENTARY / MEN

OCCUPATIONS

hurt reuse ruse rush rust
shut shutter strut suet sure
thrust thus true truest trust
trustee truth user usher
USHERETTE utter

KAKURO

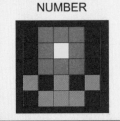

BITS AND PIECES

GE	M	ST	ON	ES
S	A	PP	HI	RE
T	O	P	A	Z
EM	ER	A	L	D
DI	A	M	O	ND

LITTLE FLOWER NUMBER

NATURAL NINE

SOME POSSIBLE WORDS:
brute burp butt butter
BUTTERCUP cruet cube
curb cure curt cute cuter
cutter erupt puce pure putt
putter rebut truce true tube
tuber tutu utter

TRUE OR FALSE WORDSEARCH

THE HIDDEN WORD IS **ACT**

NATURE TRAIL

THE HIDDEN PLANT IS A
EUCALYPTUS

ANAGRAM LADDERS

BRAKE
WHEEL
TANK
HORN
CLUTCH
TYRE
FILTER

CENTRAL WORD: BATTERY

PYRAMID OF BRICKS

66
35 31
18 17 14
9 9 8 6
5 4 5 3 3
4 1 3 2 1 2

ADD THREE TO THREE

1 BRIDGE
2 GAZELLE
3 METEOR

A'MAZE'ING NUMBERS

FIVE SNEAKY SNAKES

1 BADMINTON
2 SURFBOARD
3 GOALPOSTS
4 GRIDIRON
5 HANDICAP

PAGES 40-41

REBUS TOWER

COAST TO COAST

THE FOLLOWING DAY

HOME IS WHERE
THE HEART IS

PAGES 40-41

LITTLE TOUGHIE

PAGES 40-41 CROSSWORD

P	E	R	S	E	C	U	T	E
T	X		T	A		E		D
A	B	A	T	E		S	T	A	G	E

(crossword grid)

PAGES 42-43 SUDOKU

E	B	G	D	I	C	A	H	F
D	A	C	G	H	F	I	E	B
I	F	H	A	B	E	G	D	C
H	E	I	F	G	D	B	C	A
G	C	B	H	E	A	F	I	D
F	D	A	I	C	B	H	G	E
A	G	F	E	D	I	C	B	H
C	I	D	B	F	H	E	A	G
B	H	E	C	A	G	D	F	I

PAGES 42-43

ODD ONE OUT

REAL MADRID,
ALL THE REST ARE
ENGLISH TEAMS

PAGES 42-43

ARROWS

PAGES 42-43

RIDDLE WORDS

GRUB, BUG,
FLY, TICK

PAGES 42-43

PICTURE PHRASES

SOLUTION:

CRYING SHAME
ICE CUBE
TOO BIG TO IGNORE
FOREIGN LANGUAGE

PAGES 42-43

CODED CROSSWORD

PAGES 42-43

NATUREGRAMS

¹VERDI ¹DIVER

²GREET ²EGRET

³SPINE ³SNIPE

PAGES 42-43

EDIBLE EIGHT

AVER DERV DOVE
DROVE FLAVOR
FLAVORED
FOVEA FOVEAL LAVE LAVED
LAVER LEVA LOVE
LOVED LOVER OVAL
OVER RAVE RAVED
RAVEL ROVE ROVED
VALE VEAL VELA
VELAR VELD VELOUR
VOLE VOLED

PAGES 42-43

BLOCKBUSTERS

(number puzzle grid)
=11, =15, =17, =40
=19, =16, =6, =16

PAGES 42-43

JIG GRID

M	A	R	A	C	A	S
P	A	N	P	I	P	E
B	A	G	P	I	P	E
C	O	W	B	E	L	L
W	H	I	S	T	L	E
U	K	U	L	E	L	E
P	I	C	C	O	L	O

PAGES 42-43

EURO TEASE

8, 4, 6, 2

PAGES 44-45

ON TARGET

1 COAST, 2 HEART,
3 EGRET, 4 LEAST,
5 SHIFT, 6 ERUPT,
7 ABOUT

OUTER WORD: CHELSEA

PAGES 44-45

CAGED ANIMALS

1 BEAR, 2 ANNA,
3 AMEN, 4 AUNT,
5 ABLE, 6 AREA,
7 WEST, 8 SORE.

CAGED ANIMAL: ANTEATER

PAGES 44-45

ADD A LETTER

FLEET, WARD,
BLIND, PASTRY

PAGES 44-45

LOLLIPOPS

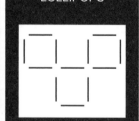

PAGES 44-45

FAMOUS BATTLES
SQUIRCLE

G	A	L	L	I	P	O	L	I
R	L	E	I	R	U	C	A	N
E	L	A	L	A	M	E	I	N
E	O	V	T	T	P	A	R	E
D	W	E	S	E	S	N	D	R

PAGES 44-45

CROSSWORD

Across: 1 Surprise, 6 NCO,
7 Patio, 9 Seen, 11 Ta-ta,
12 Nine, 14 Swan, 16 Rupee,
18 Ape, 19 Repented.

Down: 1 Sanitary, 2 Roost,
3 Rope, 4 Sat, 5 Forehead,
8 Anna, 10 Ease, 13 Inapt,
15 Were, 17 Pie.

PAGES 44-45

BLOCKBUSTERS

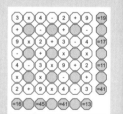

=19, =17, =11, =41
=16, =45, =41, =13

LION
STANDARD:
20 words

PAGES 44-45

FLOWERY PHRASES

TIME AND TIDE
WAIT FOR NO MAN.

PAGES 44-45

BITS AND PIECES

OL	Y	M	PI	CS
CE	RE	MO	N	Y
M	E	DA	L	S
S	I	L	VE	R
A	TH	LE	T	E

PAGES 44-45

LETTER SWAP

TWO WRONGS
DO NOT MAKE
A RIGHT.

PAGES 44-45

BOOT NUMBER

PAGES 46-47

PUSSYCAT STANDARD: 8 WORDS

NATURAL NINE

boring born brig bring brink
brisk broking giro grin grip
groin iron poring pork porn
prig prison probing prong
ring rink risk robin robing
roping signor sprig spring
SPRINGBOK

PANTHER STANDARD: 13 WORDS

196

PAGES 46-47
NINE NUMBERS

2	x	1	-	8	-6
x		-		-	
6	-	4	x	5	10
/		x		x	
3	+	7	+	9	19

4	-21	27

PAGES 46-47
QUICK TV QUIZ

1 CENTRAL PERK
2 THE QUEEN VICTORIA
3 EDDIE
4 JOEY

PAGES 46-47 SUDOKU

PAGES 46-47
PAIR WHEELS

BATTLE, BOTTOM,
KITTEN, SETTEE,
LATTER, BUTTON.

PAGES 46-47
CHAIN REACTION

PAGAN, ANGST, STASH,
SHADE, DELTA, TAIGA,
GAUGE, GEESE, SEINE,
NEPAL, ALPHA, HASTE,
TEACH, CHEAP, APACE,
CELLO, LOTTO, TORSO,
SOGGY, GYPSY.

AGES 46-47 KAKURO

PAGES 46-47 WORD FIT

PAGES 46-47
MOVIE HOUSE
**Das Boot, Mash, Patton,
Platoon, Red Dawn, Zulu**

PAGES 46-47
PLACE THE PLACES

PAGES 46-47
NUMBER HEX

PAGES 48-49
WORD SPLITZ

1 CARVE, DRAIN
2 GRILL, POACH
3 ROAST, STEAM
4 BASTE, GLAZE

PAGES 48-49
NATURE TRAIL

RUBBER PLANT

PAGES 48-49
DEER WORDSEARCH

PAGES 48-49
ADDING GRIDS
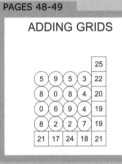

PAGES 48-49
NOURISHING NINE

AIRY AMIR ARIA ARID
ARMY DAIRY **DAIRYMAID** DARI
DIARY DRAM DRAMA DRAY
DRYAD MARIA MIRY MYRIAD
RADII RAID
RAMI RIMY YARD

PAGES 48-49 SUDOKU
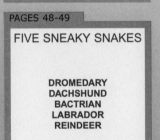

PAGES 48-49
FIVE SNEAKY SNAKES

DROMEDARY
DACHSHUND
BACTRIAN
LABRADOR
REINDEER

PAGES 48-49
REBUS TOWER

LIFT OUT OF ORDER
LOOK ON THE BRIGHT SIDE
THE MIDDLE OF NOWHERE

PAGES 48-49
LITTLE TOUGHIE

Across: 4 Vacate, 5 Was,
6 Sag, 8 Closet.

Down: 1 Valance, 2 Tax,
3 Delayed, 7 Toy.

PAGES 48-49 CROSSWORD

PAGES 48-49
COUNTING CRITTERS

=100
=6
=10
=1
=2

PAGES 50-51
ON TARGET

1 SCORE, 2 NUDGE,
3 OUNCE, 4 OLIVE,
5 KNIFE, 6 ELOPE,
7 RIDGE.

OUTER WORD: SNOOKER

PAGES 50-51
NINE NUMBERS

7	-	2	+	9	14
x		-		/	
8	/	4	-	3	-1
+		-		-	
5	-	6	+	1	0

61	-8	2

PAGES 50-51
ADD A LETTER

DUET, LAMB,
PLANE, COST

PAGES 50-51
BATTLESHIPS
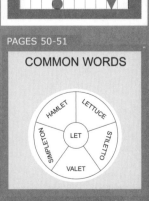

PAGES 50-51
PAIR WHEELS

EDITOR, GUITAR,
SWITCH, UNITED,
WAITER, WRITES

PAGES 50-51
EGYPT WORDSEARCH
Hidden word: Sun

PAGES 50-51
OCCUPATIONS

atom farm firm foam form
format from inform
INFORMANT main manor mart
martin matron mina minor
mint moan moat morn motif
norm omit roam roman
tram trim

PAGES 50-51
COMMON WORDS
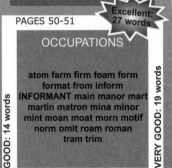

KAKURO

```
M   S L   H F
JACK ADORES
L Y   S   L
STREET   TATE
P U   H   W V
ASSUMEDNAME
D T   T   R N
EAST   ASSESS
X U   B A L
PETROL   SHAH
S N   E   H
```

NAME THE DATE

55BC

1777

1994

```
3 2 7 6 5 4 1 8 9
8 6 4 1 7 9 2 5 3
5 9 1 8 3 2 4 7 6
6 7 2 3 4 8 9 1 5
1 5 3 9 6 7 8 4 2
9 4 8 2 1 5 3 6 7
2 1 6 5 8 3 7 9 4
7 3 5 4 9 1 6 2 8
4 8 9 7 2 6 5 3 1
```

CAGED ANIMALS

1 MORE, 2 MINT,
3 SILO, 4 POOR,
5 NEXT, 6 ZERO,
7 YETI, 8 OILS

CAGED ANIMAL: TORTOISE

CROSSWORD

ACROSS:
2 DISC, 4 BALE,
5 STAY, 6 LIAR,
7 TIER, 8 AGES

DOWN:
1 LASTING,
2 DESERTS,
3 SLACKEN

NURSERY BLOCKS

SEE-SAW MARJORY
DAW. JACKY SHALL
HAVE A NEW MASTER.

ADD THREE TO THREE

1 COSMETIC
2 FINISH
3 CURATE

NINE NUMBERS

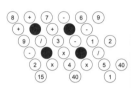

FIVE SNEAKY SNAKES

SATELLITE
ASTRONOMER
ASTEROID
FIRMAMENT
SPACEMAN

HOLLYWOOD ANAGRAMS

SOLUTION:
LINK: THEY ARE ALL JACK
NICHOLSON FILMS
AS GOOD AS IT GETS
CHINA TOWN
EASY RIDER
THE SHINING

JIG GRID

```
A N K A R A
A T H E N S
B E R L I N
P E K I N G
L I S B O N
L O N D O N
```

LETTER STEW

PREVENT,
END,
IMPEDE

Lion standard: 24 words

NATURAL NINE

Pussycat standard: 8 words

adorn angry argon darn drag
dragon DRAGONFLY dray
flora foray ford fray frog
frond glory gory gran grand
grandly groan gyro lard lord
oral organ radon rand rang
rangy rayon road roan royal
yard yarn

Panther standard: 15 words

ON TARGET

1 NASTY, 2 ENEMY,
3 TABBY, 4 BULLY,
5 ANNOY, 6 LOLLY,
7 LORRY

OUTER WORD: NETBALL

ANAGRAM LADDERS

SHAWL
DRESS
TUTU
MASK
BUSBY
TUNIC
TIE

CENTRAL WORD: WETSUIT

```
d c h e i a b g f
i a f b c g d h e
e g b f h d a c i
g i e a f b h d c
b d c i g h e f a
f h a c d e i b g
c b g h e i f a d
h e d g a f c i b
a f i d b c g e h
```

CARTOON CHARACTERS SQUIRCLE

```
S C I A G K S F A
T I N T I N T O M
A G A L A E U R E
B A N A N A M A N
S R E S T D P Y D
```

NINE NUMBERS

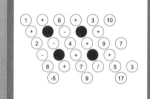

```
U M   S   B
ENCYCLOPAEDIA
I   S   I A   F K
ATTENDED   OXEN
L   I   E R
SURFING   BEGIN
N   G L   S
FINDS   DAISIES
I   Q   T
JEWS   UNIFORMS
R   M   E   R
ESTABLISHMENT
T   Y   T   S E
```

MATCH STICKS

MOVIE HOUSE

Berry, Kidman, Lange,
Paltrow, Roberts, Sarandon

```
L A N G E S A S
T Y Q Z N T A X
G P A L T R O W
U P X X A E W P
R K U N Q B C H
T S D Y I O C B
Y O W Y R R E B
N A M D I K Y N
```

JIG GRID

```
B A R N O W L
B U Z Z A R D
V U L T U R E
S E A G U L L
K E S T R E L
J A C K D A W
S P A R R O W
```

WORD WHEEL

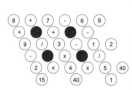

ZOO HUNT

THE MISSING
CREATURE IS A
CHIMPANZEE

NINE NUMBERS

```
2 + 1 - 3     0
x       +   +
4 + 9   - 8   5
-   +   +
5 - 7 x 6   -12
3     17   5
```

ARROWS

PYRAMID OF EGGS

311

158153

82 76 77

45 37 39 38

27 18 19 20 18

16 11 7 12 8 10

MILITARY PEOPLE WORDSEARCH

HIDDEN WORD: HUSSAR

```
R L B A T M A N
E T E D A C D I
C G U N N E R A
I U H U O S A T
F A S A R L G P
R O J A M O A
O D N A M M O C
A D J U T A N T
```

WELL DONE 18 words

PAGES 56-57
NOURISHING NINE

CIRQUE CLIQUE CLUE
COIL COIR CORE CRUEL
CURE CURIE CURIO
CURL ECRU ICIER LICE
LIQUORICE LOCI LUCRE
RECOIL RELIC RICE ULCER

UNDERDONE 9 words

PAGES 56-57 KAKURO

MEDIUM 13 words

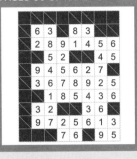

PAGES 56-57 WORD FIT

PAGES 56-57
NATUREGRAMS

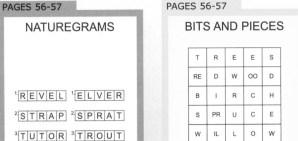

¹ REVEL ¹ ELVER
² STRAP ² SPRAT
³ TUTOR ³ TROUT

PAGES 56-57
BITS AND PIECES

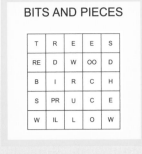

PAGES 56-57
SUN NUMBER PIC

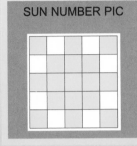

PAGES 58-59 SUDOKU

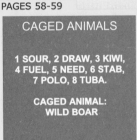

PAGES 58-59
CAGED ANIMALS

1 SOUR, 2 DRAW, 3 KIWI,
4 FUEL, 5 NEED, 6 STAB,
7 POLO, 8 TUBA.

CAGED ANIMAL:
WILD BOAR

PAGES 58-59
PANTOMIME WORDSEARCH

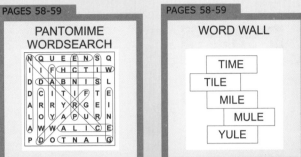

PAGES 58-59
WORD WALL

TIME
TILE
MILE
MULE
YULE

PAGES 58-59
CROSSWORD

Across: 1 Test tube, 6 Sea,
7 Padre, 9 Tier, 11 Cleo,
12 Urge, 14 Tame, 16 Satan,
18 Ace, 19 Defected.

Down: 1 Test case, 2 State,
3 Type, 4 Bad, 5 Reverend,
8 Arum, 10 Iota, 13 React,
15 Ante, 17 Tee.

PAGES 58-59
CHAIN REACTION

WIDTH, THEME, MECCA,
CACTI, TIARA, RADAR,
AROSE, SEDGE, GEODE,
DELLA, LABEL, ELITE, TELEX,
EXTOL, OLIVE, VENOM,
OMAHA, HARSH, SHOAL,
ALARM

PAGES 58-59
BLOCKBUSTERS

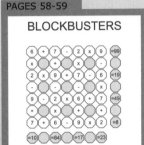

PAGES 58-59
WHAT COMES FIRST?

LEMON
CHURCH
ROBIN
BEEF

PAGES 58-59 ALPHAFITS

PAGES 58-59
PLACE THE PLACES

A R T
L A Y
A R K
S E E

PAGES 58-59
NUMBER HEX

PAGES 60-61
HOLLYWOOD ANAGRAMS

LINK: THEY ARE ALL FILM
STUDIOS
PARAMOUNT
METRO GOLDWYN MAYER
DREAMWORKS
BUENA VISTA

PAGES 60-61
NATURAL NINE

Pussycat standard: 8 words

chin cling coding coin ding
dingo doing doling dong
finch find flinch fling flong
folding fond **GOLDFINCH**
hind holding holing icon
inch info infold ling lingo
lino lion loin long nigh

Panther standard: 14 words

LION STANDARD: 21 WORDS

PAGES 60-61
BIRD BOXES

PAGES 60-61
ADD A LETTER

HERD, BARN,
PASTE, CLUE

PAGES 60-61 SUDOKU

PAGES 60-61
NINE NUMBERS

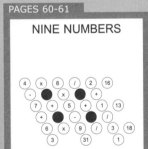

PAGES 60-61
TRUE OR FALSE WORDSEARCH

HIDDEN WORD: ACT

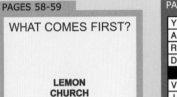

PAGES 60-61
QUICK QUIZ QUESTIONS

PABLO PICASSO
LEONARDO DA VINCI
JOHN CONSTABLE
EDVARD MUNCH
VINCENT VAN GOGH
EDWIN LANDSEER

PAGES 60-61
COUNTING CRITTERS

= 5
= 3
= 1
= 2
= 4

PAGES 60-61
WORD WHEEL

PAGES 60-61 CROSSWORD

PAGES 62-63
ZOO HUNT

THE MISSING CREATURE
IS A
FIELD MOUSE

199

NINE NUMBERS

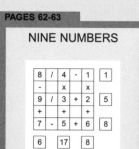

ACROSS: 1 DIAGNOSIS, 6 SPADE, 7 APT, 8 OUST, 10 REST, 13 AWE, 14 AGATE, 16 THREE FEET.

DOWN: 1 DISCO, 2 AVA, 3 NEED, 4 SHAKE, 5 SAT, 9 STEER, 11 TRENT, 12 PALE, 13 AFT, 15 APE.

STEP LADDER

KISS
MISS
MOSS
LOSS
LOSE
LOVE

ADD THREE TO THREE

1. SALARY
2. DANGER
3. NEPHEW

NOURISHING NINE

AFAR AFRO AORTA AROMA ARROW FARM FARO FARROW FORA FORM FORMAT FORT FROM MARROW **MARROWFAT** MART MORA MORRA MORTAR RAFT RATA ROAM ROAR ROMA ROTA TARO TORR TRAM TROW WARM WART WORM WORT

UNDERDONE: 10 words
MEDIUM: 19 words

WELL DONE: 26 words

REBUS TOWER

SCRAMBLED EGGS
A PLAY ON WORDS
NO TURNING BACK

PLACE THE PLACES

BITS AND PIECES

CAGED ANIMALS

1 OPEN, 2 BENT, 3 LURE, 4 MOOR, 5 HOUR, 6 SAGA, 7 LAMP, 8 ANTI.

CAGED ANIMAL:
TERRAPIN

WORD SPLITZ

1 EAGLE, CRANE
2 FINCH, GOOSE
3 QUAIL, ROBIN
4 SWIFT, STORK

HIDDEN COLORS

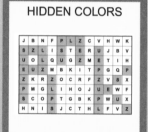

ARROWS

SWIMMING TRAINING

16 LENGTHS

PAIR WHEELS

CASTLE, LISTEN, PASTRY, PISTOL, SYSTEM, SISTER

BLOCKBUSTERS

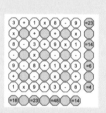

LITTLE TOUGHIE

Across:
4 Beware, 5 Bee, 6 Ham, 8 Scared.

Down:
1 Reverse, 2 Fad, 3 Related, 7 Cap.

MOVIE HOUSE

Aladdin, Bambi, Dumbo, Fantasia, Mulan, Peter Pan

CHAIN REACTION

PADRE, REPLY, LYMPH, PHOTO, TORTE, TETRA, RASTA, TANYA, YAHOO, OOZED, EDGAR, AROMA, MACAW, AWAIT, ITCHY, HYENA, NAOMI, MINIM, IMAGE, GENUS

LETTER STEW

LARGE, HUGE, IMMENSE

WELL DONE: 18 WORDS

ZOO HUNT

THE MISSING CREATURE IS A **SPRINGBOK**

ROWING WORDSEARCH

ADDING GRIDS

NOURISHING NINE

CALF CALICO **CALORIFIC** CAROL COAL COIL COLIC CORAL FAIL FLAIR FLORA FOAL FOCAL FOIL FRAIL FROLIC ILIAC LAIR LIAR LOAF ORAL RAIL

UNDERDONE: 9 WORDS
MEDIUM: 13 WORDS

A'MAZE'ING NUMBERS

COMMON WORDS

RECORD, CORDIAL, CONCORD, CORD, ACCORDION, CORDUROYS

NATUREGRAMS

[1] DREAD [1] ADDER
[2] SNEAK [2] SNAKE
[3] CAROB [3] COBRA

JIG GRID

M	O	H	A	I	R
M	U	S	L	I	N
V	E	L	V	E	T
C	A	L	I	C	O
T	A	R	T	A	N
C	A	N	V	A	S

HELLO NUMBER PIC

ON TARGET

1 WAGES, 2 ABYSS,
3 TACKS, 4 FACES,
5 OASIS, 6 RACES,
7 DARTS.

OUTER WORD: WATFORD

NINE NUMBERS

3	x	2	+	5		11
x		-		-		
4	+	9	+	6		19
+		x		+		
1	-	7	+	8		2

| 13 | -49 | 7 |

CROSSWORD

ACROSS:
2 BUSY, 4 FADE,
5 BIZARRE, 6 SEAT,
7 CAFE.

DOWN: 1 VANILLA,
2 BECAUSE, 3 SPORRAN.

a	h	i	d	b	f	g	c	e
g	d	e	c	i	a	b	h	f
c	b	f	h	e	g	d	a	i
h	c	b	i	d	e	a	f	g
d	i	a	g	f	h	c	e	b
f	e	g	b	a	c	i	d	h
e	a	c	f	g	b	h	i	d
i	g	h	e	c	d	f	b	a
b	f	d	a	h	i	e	g	c

UK TV SLEUTHS SQUIRCLE

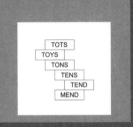

M	A	R	P	L	E	T	A	G
A	H	O	A	L	L	H	B	R
N	E	A	R	A	B	O	U	E
G	A	R	T	M	O	R	S	E
O	D	S	Y	A	W	N	E	D

CHAIN REACTION

CRUST, STOOP, OPIUM,
UMBER, ERWIN, INFRA,
RAZOR, ORATE, TEETH,
THEME, METRO, ROWAN,
ANGLO, LOYAL, ALAMO,
MOTTO, TONGA, GAUDY,
DYLAN, ANTIC

OCCUPATIONS

 EXCELLENT 29 WORDS

apron harp harpoon
HARPOONER heap hope
hoper nape neap open opera
orphan pane pare parer pear
phone pooh poor poorer pore
porn porno prone rape raper
reap rope roper

GOOD 15 WORDS — VERY GOOD 22 WORDS

FIVE SNEAKY SNAKES

RECTANGLE
PENTAGON
GEOMETRY
TRIANGLE
DIAMETER

FLOWERY PHRASES

IF THE SHOE
FITS, WEAR IT

QUESTION NUMBER PIC

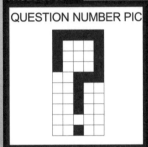

NAME THE DATE

1939
1066
1896

NAME THE DATE

1. 1876
2. 1944
3. 1923

NATURAL NINE

PUSSYCAT STANDARD: 8 WORDS

acorn action anoint anon anti
cairn cannot canon cant canton
CARNATION carton citron coin
contain contra corn icon into iron
nation ocarina rain raincoat rant
ration roan tarn tonic torn train

LION STANDARD: 20 WORDS — PANTHER STANDARD: 13 WORDS

ODD ONE OUT

GLASGOW, BECAUSE
IT IS NOT IN ENGLAND

ANAGRAM LADDERS

SPROUT
POTATO
CARROT
RADISH
SPINACH
ONION
PEPPER

CENTRAL WORD: PARSNIP

WORD WALL

TOTS
TOYS
TONS
TENS
TEND
MEND

NINE NUMBERS

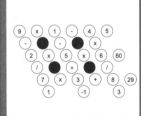

PAIR WHEELS

ABROAD, EUROPE,
STRONG, THROAT,
HEROIC, ACROSS

3	5	9	8	7	6	1	2	4
8	1	7	5	4	2	3	9	6
2	4	6	3	9	1	8	5	7
5	9	4	2	3	8	7	6	1
6	8	2	7	1	9	4	3	5
7	3	1	4	6	5	9	8	2
1	2	3	9	5	4	6	7	8
4	7	8	6	2	3	5	1	9
9	6	5	1	8	7	2	4	3

[1] T	O	N	G	A				[2] D		
			R		[3] L	E	S	O	T	H	O
[4] B	R	U	N	E	I		[5] F	M			
				N				I		[6] U	
[7] S	W	A	Z	I	L	A	N	D		S	
I				D		J				T	
[8] T	A	N	Z	A	N	I	A			R	
C						C				A	
A				[9] I	G	T			[10] H	L	
I				N		E			I	I	
R				D		I			[11] U	G	A	N	D	A
N				I							
			[12] C	A	N	A	D	A			

KAKURO

		1	2	
	9	7		
	8	1		
		8	9	
		9	7	

NUMBER HEX

(Hexagon with outer labels A, B, C, D, E, F and inner values: 2, 3, 5, 7, 8, 9)

CLOWN WORDSEARCH

Y	M	Y	C	L	A	P	Q
N	T	E	Y	O	J	N	E
N	H	E	S	U	M	A	T
U	Y	Y	G	K	S	D	I	K
F	P	S	U	C	R	I	C
A	P	P	L	A	U	D	I
W	A	T	E	R	L	B	R
V	H	R	E	K	O	J	T

ADD A LETTER

BROOK, CELLO,
SUNK, CAMEL

BATTLESHIPS

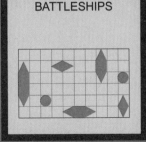

WORD SPLITZ

1. NANCY, MEGAN
2. ALICE, WENDY
3. TANYA, SUSAN
4. POLLY, PEGGY

NINE NUMBERS

(Number puzzle with circles)

2	4	7	6	1	9	5	3	8
9	1	8	5	3	4	7	6	2
5	3	6	2	8	7	4	1	9
1	7	5	9	2	3	6	8	4
4	8	9	1	7	6	3	2	5
3	6	2	4	5	8	1	9	7
7	2	4	8	6	1	9	5	3
6	5	3	7	9	2	8	4	1
8	9	1	3	4	5	2	7	6

PAGES 72-73

OCCUPATIONS

GOOD: 18 WORDS

ameer emmer hammer hare harem hark harm hear here herm hero hoar HOMEMAKER horme maker mare mark marm mere merome mora more okra rake rakee ream reek remake rhea roam

EXCELLENT: 30 WORDS

LION STANDARD: 16 WORDS

VERY GOOD: 22 WORDS

CODED CROSSWORD

PAGES 72-73

PAGES 72-73

HOLLYWOOD ANAGRAMS

LINK: THEY WERE ALL MARRIED TO ELIZABETH TAYLOR

LARRY FORTENSKY
EDDIE FISHER
RICHARD BURTON
MICHAEL WILDING

PAGES 72-73

WORD WHEEL

PAGES 72-73

COUNTING CRITTERS

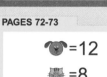 =12

 =8

 =2

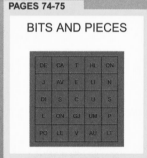 =4

 =16

PAGES 74-75

NATURAL NINE

PUSSYCAT STANDARD: 7 WORDS

bigot BIOLOGIST blot boil bolt boost boot glob igloo logo loot lost silo slob slog slot soil solo soot stool toil tool

PANTHER STANDARD: 11 WORDS

PAGES 74-75

ZOO HUNT

THE MISSING CREATURE IS A **GUINEA PIG**

PAGES 74-75

ARROWS

PAGES 74-75

ADDING GRIDS

				9
4	9	8	0	21
7	3	2	5	17
8	1	5	2	16
6	6	3	1	16
25	19	18	8	13

PAGES 74-75

ADD THREE TO THREE

1. PARCEL
2. CATTLE
3. BUNKER

PAGES 74-75

PAIR WHEELS

CHEESE, GREEDY,
SLEEPY, SNEEZE,
SPEECH, QUEENS

PAGES 74-75

ANTIQUES WORDSEARCH

Hidden word: Art

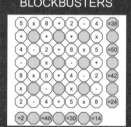

G	N	I	Y	U	B	N	A
A	H	P	R	R	O	P	R
M	S	R	E	I	E	E	T
E	U	C	I	T	W	P	L
U	C	C	T	P	E	B	A
L	U	E	O	T	T	A	P
A	R	C	P	L	A	T	E
V	T	C	E	J	B	O	T

PAGES 74-75

REBUS TOWER

QUITE RIGHT
ONWARD CHRISTIAN SOLDIERS
MAN IN THE MOON

PAGES 74-75

LITTLE TOUGHIE

Across: 1 Suburb, **5** Run, **6** Pie, **7** Awl, **8** Win, **9** Eye, **10** Latest

Down: 1 Strewn, **2** Bonanza, **3** Replete, **4** Repent

PAGES 74-75

BITS AND PIECES

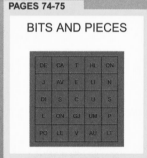

DE	CA	T	HL	ON
J	A	VE	LI	N
DI	S	C	U	S
L	ON	GJ	UM	P
PO	LE	V	AU	LT

PAGES 74-75 CROSSWORD

T	R	A	N	S	F	E	R	R	E	D
U		G		I		N		A		R
S	T	A	R	T		T	R	I	P	E
K		I		E	Y	E		D		G
S	A	N	D	S		R	O	S	E	S
		T		O		W		A		
P	E	A	C	E		S	N	O	R	T
O		L		A	G	O		V		O
S	P	E	N	T		B	R	A	I	N
S		R		E		E		L		G
E	N	T	E	R	P	R	I	S	E	S

PAGES 76-77

BIRD BOXES

70	15	350	60	170	45	140	110	175	155	120	175
225	175	140	125	150	210	100	285	65	20	160	
185	115	30	160	205	205	155	100	10	235	130	
25	250	40	115	165	15	180	120	325	375	440	
65	300	5	70	155	50	300	175	85	275	230	75
25	100	100	25	100	60	190	145	140	200	220	125
110	45	135	60	70	100	215	175	180	45	170	115
10	160	30	185	100	155	215	175	160	5	145	70

PAGES 76-77

ADD A LETTER

EVEN, IRISH,
HEDGE, BITE

PAGES 76-77

NURSERY BLOCKS

SIMPLE SIMON MET
A PIEMAN GOING
TO THE FAIR

PAGES 76-77

ON TARGET

1 AGILE, 2 NOBLE,
3 GEESE, 4 LEAVE,
5 IMAGE, 6 NOISE,
7 GLIDE.

OUTER WORD: ANGLING

PAGES 76-77

NOURISHING NINE

UNDERDONE: 13 WORDS

ABAFT ABASE ABATE ABET
ABREAST BAKE BAKER BARE
BAREST BARK BASE BASER
BASK BASKET BAST BASTE
BATS BEAK BEAR BEAST
BEAT BERK BEST BETA BRAE
BRAKE BRAT BREAK
BREAKFAST BREAST KERB
SABRE STAB

MEDIUM: 20 WORDS

WELL DONE: 27 WORDS

PAGES 76-77

CROSSWORD

Across: 2 Twists, **5** Hare,
6 Square, **7** Sect, **8** Yes, **11**
Lose, **13** Rabble, **14** Peak,
15 Extort.

Down: 1 Bake, **2** Testy, **3** Scar,
4 Sneeze, **7** Source, **9** Slept,
10 Abet, **12** Sham.

AGES 76-77

BLOCKBUSTERS

5	x	8	+	2	-	4	=38
+		+		+		+	
4		3		6		5	=50
+		+		+		+	
8		9		4		5	=42
+		+		+		+	
2		5		9		1	=24
=2		=46		=30		=14	

PAGES 76-77

COMMON WORDS

SKINNY, BILLY-JEAN KING, MACAULAY CULKIN, JOKING, KINDERGARTEN — KIN

PAGES 76-77

PLACE THE PLACES

S	P	A
L	A	G
A	R	E
B	A	D

PAGES 76-77

HOLLYWOOD ANAGRAMS

LINK: THEY ARE SIBLING PAIRS

WARREN BEATTY
SHIRLEY MACLAINE

CHARLIE SHEEN
EMILIO ESTEVEZ

PAGES 76-77

LETTER STEW

BURLY, MUSCULAR, STOUT

PAGES 78-79

CONNECT THE DOTS

ODD ONE OUT

14, BECAUSE IT CANNOT BE DIVIDED BY SIX

MONOPOLY WORDSEARCH

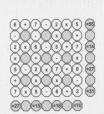

9	3	4	6	8	7	1	5	2
1	8	2	9	5	4	7	6	3
5	7	6	2	3	1	8	4	9
3	6	5	1	2	8	9	7	4
4	1	7	3	9	5	2	8	6
2	9	8	4	7	6	3	1	5
6	4	3	7	1	9	5	2	8
8	2	1	5	6	3	4	9	7
7	5	9	8	6	2	4	3	1

CHAIN REACTION

GYPSY, SYNCH, CHINO, NOMAD, ADDED, EDITH, THROW, OWNER, ERROR, ORGAN, ANODE, DEGAS, ASSAM, AMUSE, SERVO, VOILA, LASSO, SONAR, ARUBA, BASIN

NINE NUMBERS

OCCUPATIONS

GOOD: 11 WORDS

acne arcane arena cane canvas canvass CANVASSER cavern crane craven earn nacre nave near ness raven sane scan snare vane

EXCELLENT: 20 WORDS

CODED CROSSWORD

VERY GOOD: 14 WORDS

DIZZY DICTATION

1. I must check eight ceilings for leaks
2. We've grown roses, tulips and daisies.
3. I suppose I'd like a nice steak, well-done, and some salad.

NATUREGRAMS

1 HOLST, SLOTH
2 TOAST, STOAT
3 WHEAL, WHALE

FORK AND KNIFE NUMBER PIC

NATURAL NINE

PUSSYCAT STANDARD: 8 WORDS

abate abet able abler albeit arable bacteria BACTERIAL bail bailer bait baiter bale baler bare bear beat belt beta bile bite biter blare bleat brace bract brae brat cabaret caber cable CALIBRATE calibre crab crib table tribal tribe

LION STANDARD: 23 WORDS

PANTHER STANDARD: 15 WORDS

CAGED ANIMALS

1 BELT, 2 BEEF,
3 YEAR, 4 PERU,
5 MINI, 6 GOAT,
7 LIMB, 8 SOFA.

CAGED ANIMAL: FRUITBAT

QUICK SPORTS QUIZ

1 BOBBY CHARLTON
2 GRASS
3 PHIL 'THE POWER' TAYLOR
4 DIAMONDBACKS
5 TEN

PICTURE PHRASES

ROBIN HOOD
FOR ONCE IN MY LIFE
SKATE ON THIN ICE

PAIR WHEELS

AMOUNT, AROUND, ENOUGH, GROUND, HOULD, THOUGH

TRANSPORT SQUIRCLE

S	B	W	M	S	O	S	T	S
T	R	A	I	N	S	C	O	O
O	A	G	R	A	A	O	I	L
U	K	E	T	R	K	U	L	V
T	E	R	H	E	A	R	S	E

BLOCKBUSTERS

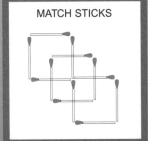

MATCH STICKS

LITTLE TOUGHIE

KAKURO

NINE NUMBERS

4	-	6	x	8	-16
/		-		+	
2	+	5	-	1	6
+		x		/	
7	-	9	/	3	4
9		-36		3	

8	6	9	2	7	4	3	5	1
3	5	7	1	6	8	9	2	4
4	1	2	3	9	5	7	8	6
9	3	1	6	4	2	8	7	5
2	4	5	8	3	7	6	1	9
6	7	8	9	5	1	2	4	3
7	8	3	5	1	6	4	9	2
5	9	4	7	2	3	1	6	8
1	2	6	4	8	9	5	3	7

WELL DONE: 27 WORDS

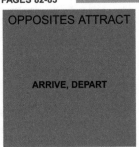

OPPOSITES ATTRACT

ARRIVE, DEPART

PYRAMID OF APPLES

206
110 96
57 53 43
28 29 24 19
13 15 14 10 9
6 7 8 6 4 5

NOURISHING NINE

UNDERDONE: 13 WORDS

ACHE CACHE CHAIN CHALICE CHANCE CHANCEL CHIC CHICANE CHICLE CHIN CHINA CHINE CHOICE CINCH CLENCH CLINCH CLOCHE COACH **COCHINEAL** COCHLEA CONCH EACH ECHO HAIL HALE HALO HEAL HOLE HONE INCH INHALE LEACH LICHEN LOACH LOCH NICHE

MEDIUM: 20 WORDS

FIVE SNEAKY SNAKES

BAGPIPES
BALMORAL
HEBRIDEAN
CLAYMORE
SCOTSMAN

PAGES 82-83 WORD FIT

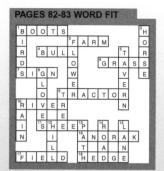

PAGES 82-83 CLUB HOUSE

Clarke, Garcia, Goosen, Langer, Singh, Woods

PAGES 82-83 JIG GRID

A	B	I	G	A	I	L
S	A	B	R	I	N	A
V	A	L	E	R	I	E
S	I	O	B	H	A	N
P	A	U	L	I	N	E
R	A	C	H	A	E	L
N	I	C	H	O	L	A

PAGES 82-83 NUMBER HEX

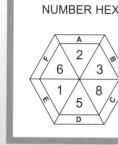

PAGES 84-85 ODD ONE OUT

FROG, THE OTHERS ARE REPTILES

PAGES 84-85 CROSSWORD

ACROSS: 2 DASH, 4 LAME, 5 PLAN, 6 SALE, 7 SOAP, 8 MEWS.

DOWN: 1 CABBAGE, 2 DEPRESS, 3 SPARTAN.

PAGES 84-85 WORD WALL

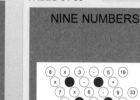

BACK
RACK
RANK
RANT
RENT
REST

PAGES 84-85 NINE NUMBERS

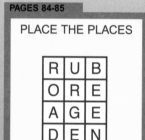

PAGES 84-85 BOOT MAZE

PAGES 84-85 SEA WORDS WORDSEARCH

Hidden word: Shore

PAGES 84-85 OCCUPATIONS

EXCELLENT: 47 WORDS

agent angst ante east eaten ensate gannet gate genet gennet gent geta gnat neat neaten negate nest newest NEWSAGENT newt sate sateen seat senate sent seta setae stag stage stang sten stew swat sweat sweet tang tawse tease teen tense twang twas twee want waste went west

GOOD: 29 WORDS

VERY GOOD: 34 WORDS

PAGES 84-85 QUICK QUIZ QUESTIONS

1 THE BRAIN
2 THE THROAT
3 THE WRIST
4 THE EYE
5 THE KNEE
6 THE FEET

PAGES 84-85 PLACE THE PLACES

R	U	B
O	R	E
A	G	E
D	E	N

PAGES 84-85 GEOGRAMS

1. STONED — 1. OSTEND
2. ANTHER — 2. TEHRAN
3. LOOTED — 3. TOLEDO

PAGES 86-87 NAME THE DATE

1783
1848
1972

PAGES 86-87 NATURAL NINE

PUSSYCAT STANDARD: 7 WORDS

LION STANDARD: 17 WORDS

deli dell dill dimple elide idle impel impelled implied lied lime limed limp limped mild mile mill MILLIPEDE peel pile piled pill plied

PANTHER STANDARD: 11 WORDS

PAGES 86-87 ADD A LETTER

CARP, GOING, KEEN, SAME

PAGES 86-87 SUDOKU

8	6	9	4	2	5	1	3	7
5	4	7	6	1	3	8	9	2
3	2	1	7	9	8	5	4	6
4	7	6	8	3	1	9	2	5
9	3	5	2	7	4	6	8	1
1	8	2	5	6	9	4	7	3
6	5	8	3	4	7	2	1	9
7	9	4	1	5	2	3	6	8
2	1	3	9	8	6	7	5	4

PAGES 86-87 ADD THREE TO THREE

1. CACTUS
2. SINGLE
3. BILLION

PAGES 86-87 CHAIN REACTION

PRIMA, MACRO, ROAST, STYLE, LEAVE, VERSE, SENNA, NANNY, NYMPH, PHOTO, TORCH, CHASM, SMASH, SHAME, METRO, ROUTE, TENTH, THROW, OWLET, ETHIC

PAGES 86-87 KAKURO

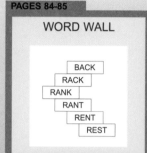

PAGES 86-87 REBUS TOWER

A LITTLE LIGHT RELIEF
ONE MISTAKE ON TOP OF ANOTHER
ONE FINE DAY

PAGES 86-87 LITTLE TOUGHIE

Across: 2 Rock, 4 Tame, 5 Smug, 6 Dawn, 7 Ties, 8 Jets.

Down: 1 Baggage, 2 Resents, 3 Couplet.

PAGES 86-87 BITS AND PIECES

P	A	S	T	A
R	A	V	I	O	LI
LA	S	A	G	N	E
N	O	O	D	L	E
MA	C	AR	O	NI

PAGES 86-87 CROSSWORD

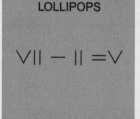

PAGES 88-89 LOLLIPOPS

VII − II = V

PAGES 88-89 SUDOKU

H	E	A	F	G	C	I	D	B
F	D	I	A	E	B	C	H	G
C	B	G	I	H	D	E	F	A
E	F	D	B	C	I	G	A	H
B	A	C	G	D	H	F	I	E
I	G	H	E	A	F	B	C	D
D	H	B	C	I	G	A	E	F
G	C	E	H	F	A	D	B	I
A	I	F	D	B	E	H	G	C

PAGES 88-89 CAGED ANIMALS

1 NEWS, 2 CROP, 3 NOEL, 4 ASIA, 5 MEET, 6 PLAY, 7 SHIP, 8 TUTU.

CAGED ANIMAL

204

PAGES 88-89

ANAGRAM LADDERS

DIPPER
GREBE
EAGLE
EIDER
FINCH
CANARY
CONDOR

CENTRAL WORD: PELICAN

PAGES 88-89

SPORTS QUIZ
RUGBY

WALES
THE SHARKS
TWICKENHAM
IRELAND
ITALY

PAGES 88-89

WELL DONE: 27 WORDS

NOURISHING NINE

AVENGE AVENGER AVER
ENGRAVE EVEN EVER GAVE
GIVE GIVEN GIVER
GRAPEVINE GRAVE GRAVEN
GREAVE GRIEVE NAEVI NAVE
NERVE NEVER PAVE PAVING
RAVEN RAVINE RAVING
RIVEN VAIN VAINER VANE
VEER VEGAN VEIN VERGE
VINE VINEGAR VIPER

UNDERDONE: 13 WORDS MEDIUM: 20 WORDS

PAGES 88-89

BLOCKBUSTERS

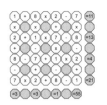

PAGES 88-89

LITTLE TOUGHIE

PAGES 88-89

MOVIE HOUSE

Big, Castaway, Dragnet, Splash, The Burbs, Toy Story.

PAGES 88-89

KAKURO

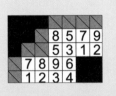

PAGES 88-89

LETTER STEW

LIKE, RELISH, APPRECIATE

PAGES 90-91

ON TARGET

1 ANVIL, 2 REGAL,
3 SKULL, 4 EXPEL,
5 NASAL, 6 ANGEL,
7 LABEL.

OUTER WORD: ARSENAL

PAGES 90-91

NATURE TRAIL

THE HIDDEN PLANT IS A
VENUS FLYTRAP

PAGES 90-91

OPPOSITES ATTRACT

CHAOS, ORDER

PAGES 90-91

RIDDLE WORDS

COMIC, PAGE,
PUPIL, HEAD

PAGES 90-91

PICTURE PHRASES

REPEAT AFTER ME
ONCE UPON A TIME
SAFETY IN NUMBERS
A SQUARE MEAL

PAGES 90-91

CROSSWORD

Across: 2 Berths, 5 Bade,
6 Averse, 7 Seat, 8 Sit,
11 Rise, 13 Rookie,
14 Swan, 15 Shears
Down: 1 Rake, 2 Beats,
3 Torn, 4 Swerve, 7 Stares,
9 Tress, 10 Mope, 12 Soap

PAGES 90-91

EXCELLENT: 35 WORDS

OCCUPATIONS

ALAR ALIBI ANAL ANIL ARIA
ARIL BAIL BAIRN BANAL
BANIA BARN BLAIN BRAIL
BRAIN BRAN BRIAR ILIA
LABIA LABRA LAIN LAIR LARN
LIANA LIAR LIBRA **LIBRARIAN**
LIRA NAIL NAIRA NARIAL RABI
RAIL RAIN RANI RIAL

GOOD: 21 WORDS VERY GOOD: 25 WORDS

PAGES 90-91

FLOWERY PHRASES

KNOW WHICH SIDE YOUR
BREAD IS BUTTERED.

PAGES 90-91

GEOGRAMS

PAGES 90-91

WORD WHEEL

PAGES 90-91

SHOP TEASE

THE PRICE MUST
BE PUT UP BY 33.33%
TO GET TO ITS
ORIGINAL PRICE.

PAGES 92-93

LION STANDARD: 28 WORDS

NATURAL NINE

feign finger fling flog
FLOWERING flowing foreign
forge fowling fringe frog girl
giro glen glow glower goer golf
golfer gone gore gown grew
grief grin groin grow growl
grown ignore legion ling linger
lingo long lowering lowing ogle
ogler ogre owing region reign
ring rowing wigeon wing
winger wolfing wring wrong

PUSSYCAT STANDARD: 12 WORDS PANTHER STANDARD: 20 WORDS

PAGES 92-93

NINE NUMBERS

1	+	8	−	6	3
−		+		+	
4	+	9	+	5	18
×		+		−	
3	−	7	−	2	−6
−9		24		9	

PAGES 92-93

ADD A LETTER

COAST, HALT,
COPY, MOTOR

PAGES 92-93 SUDOKU

a	c	i	f	b	g	h	d	e
g	d	h	i	e	c	b	a	f
e	f	b	d	h	a	g	c	i
c	a	d	b	f	h	e	i	g
b	e	f	g	d	i	a	h	c
h	i	g	c	a	e	f	b	d
i	b	e	h	g	d	c	f	a
f	g	c	a	i	b	d	e	h
d	h	a	e	c	f	i	g	b

PAGES 92-93

TV COMEDY SQUIRCLE

A	S	D	B	G	O	S	F	E
C	H	E	E	R	S	T	A	X
R	A	M	A	E	C	I	I	C
I	R	O	S	E	A	N	N	E
D	K	N	T	D	R	K	T	L

PAGES 92-93

PAIR WHEELS

BREATH, GREASY,
STEADY, CREATE,
TREATY, PLEASE.

PAGES 92-93

CODED CROSSWORD

PAGES 92-93

FIVE SNEAKY SNAKES

JAPANESE
CANADIAN
HAWAIIAN
MUSCOVITE
AMERICAN

PAGES 92-93

COMMON WORDS

REBELLED BELLOWS
BELLY BELL BELLES
BARBELLS

PAGES 92-93

HOLLYWOOD ANAGRAMS

LINK: THEY ARE ALL BOOKS
MADE INTO FILMS
THE DA VINCI CODE
JURASSIC PARK
LORD OF THE RINGS
THE GRAPES OF WRATH

SMILIE NUMBER PIC

PICTURE TILES

CAGED ANIMALS

1 HAIR, 2 SOAR, 3 KNEE, 4 SARI, 5 KEEN, 6 WEED, 7 NOSE, 8 OBOE. CAGED ANIMAL: REINDEER

FAIRYTALE WORDSEARCH

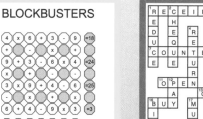

PYRAMID OF EGGS

```
        224
      96  128
    40  56  72
  16  24  32  40
 6  10  14  18  22
2  4  6  8  10  12
```

WELL DONE: 33 WORDS

NOURISHING NINE

BONCE BONE BONY BOOH BOOM BOON COHO COHOE COMB COMBO COME CONE CONEY CONY COOEY COOMB COON EBON EBONY ECHO ECONOMY HOBO HOME HOMEY HOMO HOMY HONE HONEY **HONEYCOMB** HOOEY MONEY MONO MONY MOOCH MOON MOONY OBEY OBOE OCHONE OHONE OMEN ONCE

UNDERDONE: 13 WORDS

```
7 1 2 5 9 4 3 8 6
8 3 9 6 1 7 2 4 5
6 4 5 2 8 3 1 7 9
1 6 4 7 3 5 8 9 2
5 7 8 1 2 9 6 3 4
2 9 3 8 4 6 7 5 1
3 5 7 9 6 2 4 1 8
9 2 1 4 7 8 5 6 3
4 8 6 3 5 1 9 2 7
```

MEDIUM: 22 WORDS

BLOCKBUSTERS

(crossword grid with words: RECEIPT, COUNT, COUNTER, SHOP, STILL, OPEN, GOODS, BUY, STORE, LABEL, etc.)

KAKURO

```
29
12
8796
3896
48
13
```

JIG GRID

```
A N E M O N E
B E G O N I A
C A M P I O N
L O B E L I A
P E T U N I A
P R I M U L A
C O W S L I P
```

NUMBER HEX

```
    A
  7
F     B
 8   5
 1   9
E     C
  6
    D
```

```
5 3 9 1 8 4 7 6 2
6 1 2 5 3 7 4 8 9
8 4 7 2 9 6 3 5 1
7 6 4 9 1 3 2 8 5
2 5 8 7 6 1 9 4 3
3 9 1 6 4 5 8 2 7
9 8 5 3 7 2 1 4 6
1 7 3 4 5 2 6 9 8
4 2 6 8 5 9 5 1 3
```

NINE NUMBERS

```
6  x  5  +  8    38
-     x     /
7  x  3  +  4    25
x     +     +
2  x  1  -  9    -7
-2    16    11
```

CROSSWORD

ACROSS: 1 RECOGNIZE, 6 LABEL, 7 NET, 8 YELL, 10 TRIM, 13 PEA, 14 CLEAR, 16 BUTTERFLY.

DOWN: 1 RELAY, 2 CUB, 3 GOLD, 4 INNER, 5 EAT, 9 LEAST, 11 MARRY, 12 ACRE, 13 PUB, 15 ELF.

EXCELLENT: 47 WORDS

STEP LADDER

SHIP
SLIP
SLAP
SOAP
SOAK
SOCK
DOCK

PAIR WHEELS

FINISH, GENIUS, JUNIOR, TUNING, PONIES, DENIED.

EATING OUT WORDSEARCH

HIDDEN WORD: Hot

(wordsearch grid ending with SERVICE E)

OCCUPATIONS

amend ardent armed dame damn dare darn dart date dean dear dent dram drama dream dreamt made mandate mansard mated mead mend named rand ranted rased rated read remand rend sand sated sedan send smarted snared stand stared stead strand tamed tandem tend trade TRADESMAN tread trend

GOOD: 22 WORDS

VERY GOOD: 33 WORDS

WHAT COMES FIRST?

GOLDEN
STAGE
BUTTER
RAG

HOLLYWOOD ANAGRAMS

LINK: THEY ARE ALL BRAD PITT FILMS
THELMA AND LOUISE
FIGHT CLUB
TWELVE MONKEYS
OCEANS ELEVEN

LETTER SWAP

DO AS YOU WOULD BE DONE BY.

COUNTING CRITTERS

🐶 =8
🐱 =5
🦉 =7
🕷 =6
🐭 =9

HEART NUMBER PIC

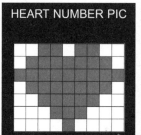

BITS AND PIECES

```
C  LO  TH  IN  G
OV  ER  CO  A  T
T  U  X  E  DO
S  WE  A  T  ER
TR  O  U  SE  RS
```

WELL DONE: 26 WORDS

LITTLE TOUGHIE

Across: 1 Simmer, 5 Ann, 6 Spa, 7 Sin, 8 Pit, 9 And, 10 Grieve.

Down: 1 Scampi, 2 Monster, 3 Ensnare, 4 Waddle.

REBUS TOWER

READING BETWEEN THE LINES

THE JOKES ON YOU

BAGS UNDER THE EYES

BLOCKBUSTERS

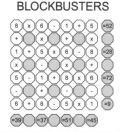

NOURISHING NINE

CEIL CELERY CERE CERGE CERING CIRL CLEG CLERGY CLINE CLING CLINGY CREEL CRENEL CRINGE CRINGLE CRYING GENERIC GENIC GLYCERIN **GLYCERINE** GLYCIN GLYCINE ICER LICE LYRIC NICE NICELY NICER NIECE RECLINE REGENCY RELIC RICE RICEY RICY

UNDERDONE: 14 WORDS

MEDIUM: 20 WORDS

SKELETON CROSSWORD

PUSSYCAT STANDARD: 7 WORDS

PANTHER STANDARD: 11 WORDS

MATCH STICKS

VERY GOOD: 28 WORDS

GOOD: 20 WORDS

PAGES 98-99

AND THREE TO THREE

1 PENSION
2 CHUTNEY
3 PASTURE

PAGES 98-99

ADD A LETTER

EARL, SLOW,
RIND, TUBA

PAGES 98-99 SUDOKU

PAGES 98-99

BIRD BOXES

PAGES 98-99

ON TARGET

1 MAIZE, 2 ADORE,
3 RANGE, 4 BADGE,
5 LADLE, 6 EVADE,
7 SAUCE

OUTER WORD: MARBLES

PAGES 100-101

PAGES 100-101 SUDOKU

6	8	1	4	2	3	9	7	5
5	2	4	7	1	9	8	3	6
3	9	7	5	8	6	4	2	1
7	6	5	8	3	1	2	4	9
1	4	2	9	6	7	5	8	3
8	3	9	2	4	5	6	1	7
4	7	6	3	5	8	1	9	2
9	5	8	1	7	2	3	6	4
2	1	3	6	9	4	7	5	8

PAGES 100-101 KAKURO

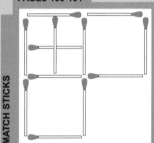

PAGES 100-101

ANAGRAM LADDERS

DEE
MERSEY
LOIRE
WEAR
TRENT
DANUBE
TYNE

CENTRAL WORD: DERWENT

PAGES 100-101

ADDING GRIDS

			23
9	1	9	28
5	5	5	21
3	4	2	1
5	1	2	8
22	11	18	16

LION STANDARD: 15 WORDS

PAGES 100-101

NATURE TRAIL

THE HIDDEN PLANT IS A
DOUGLAS FIR

PAGES 100-101

NATURAL NINE

admiral alarm amid amoral
ARMADILLO aroma diorama
dram drama llama loam maid
mail mall mallard mild mill
molar moll moral roam

PAGES 100-101

PAIR WHEELS

ACTION, DATING,
ARTIST, NOTICE,
UNTIDY, ENTIRE

PAGES 100-101

PAGES 100-101

HOLLYWOOD ANAGRAMS

LINK: THEY HAVE ALL WON BEST ACTRESS OSCARS.

KATHERINE HEPBURN
SALLY FIELD
JODIE FOSTER
GLENDA JACKSON

PAGES 100-101

PLACE THE PLACES

S	A	P
A	R	E
S	E	A
H	A	T

PAGES 102-103

JIG GRID

N	E	W	Y	O	R	K
V	E	R	M	O	N	T
W	Y	O	M	I	N	G
M	O	N	T	A	N	A
F	L	O	R	I	D	A
A	R	I	Z	O	N	A
A	L	A	B	A	M	A

PAGES 102-103

NATUREGRAMS

¹ SHORE ¹ HORSE
² TORTE ² OTTER
³ BALES ³ SABLE

PAGES 102-103

CROSSWORD

ACROSS:
2 POSE, 4 SAGE, 5 ROAR,
6 CAGE, 7 CREW, 8 FEET.

DOWN:
1 PACKAGE, 2 PERFECT,
3 SLAPPED.

PAGES 102-103

WORD SPLITZ

BARON, CHIEF
JUDGE, MAYOR
NOBLE, QUEEN
RABBI, VICAR

PAGES 102-103

NINE NUMBERS

4	x	7	+	5	33
x		+		-	
6	+	9	/	3	5
-		+		-	
2	+	8	/	1	10
22		24		1	

PAGES 102-103

NAME THE DATE

1 1953
2 1901
3 1981

PAGES 102-103

NURSERY BLOCKS

HUMPTY DUMPTY SAT
ON A WALL. HUMPTY
DUMPTY HAD A
GREAT FALL

PAGES 102-103

SPORTS QUIZ

1 SAND WEDGE
2 SCOTLAND
3 THE USA & EUROPE
4 ERNIE ELS
5 TWO

PAGES 102-103

CHAIN REACTION

FUNGI, GIZMO, MOCHA,
HAITI, TIARA, RAZOR,
ORATE, TENCH, CHIDE,
DEATH, THOSE, SEOUL,
ULTRA, RABBI, BINGO,
GOUDA, DAISY, SYNOD,
ODOUR, URGED

EXCELLENT: 39 WORDS

PAGES 102-103

OCCUPATIONS

acme acne acre agency cage
cagey calm calmer came
camel cane care clam clan
clang clanger clay clean clear
clergy CLERGYMAN crag
cram crane cream creamy
glance grace lace lacy lance
lancer larceny legacy mace
mercy nacre race racy

PAGES 102-103

COMMON WORDS

HEARTTHROB
ROBIN
AEROBICS
ROB
COROBORATE
ROBERT E

PAGES 104-105 KAKURO

PAGES 104-105

GEOGRAMS

¹ HERMAN ¹ ARNHEM
² HASTEN ² ATHENS
³ TOBAGO ³ BOGOTA

PAGES 104-105 CROSSWORD

207

SHIP NUMBER PIC

BIRD BOXES

LOLLIPOPS

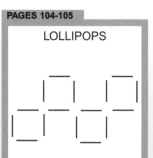

TV PROGRAM TYPES SQUIRCLE

ARROWS

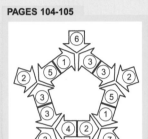

FIVE SNEAKY SNAKES

CARDIGAN
FURNITURE
CUPBOARD
TROUSERS
MOTHBALL

MOVIE HOUSE

Capote, Crash, Junebug,
King Kong, Munich, Syriana

ODD ONE OUT

13 BECAUSE IT IS NOT A
SQUARE NUMBER

WORD FIT

LION STANDARD: 24 WORDS

PANTHER STANDRAD: 14 WORDS

NATURAL NINE

apse bare barer base bear
berry brae byre easy espy
pare parer parse payer pear
perry prayer prey pryer
pyre rare rarer rase
RASPBERRY rasper reap
rear repay respray sabre
sayer sear spare sparer
spear sprayer spryer year

PUSSYCAT STANDARD: 8 WORDS

ALIENS WORDSEARCH

PYRAMID OF BRICKS

92

44 48

21 23 25

10 11 12 13

5 5 6 6 7

2 3 2 4 2 5

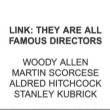

BLOCKBUSTERS

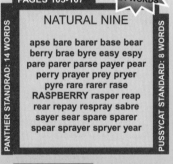

PLACE THE PLACES

B R A
R O B
A L E
Y E T

WORD WHEEL

NUMBER HEX

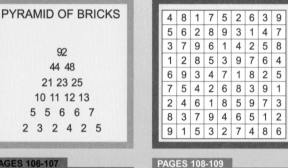

HOLLYWOOD ANAGRAMS

LINK: THEY ARE ALL
FAMOUS DIRECTORS

WOODY ALLEN
MARTIN SCORCESE
ALDRED HITCHCOCK
STANLEY KUBRICK

OPPOSITES ATTRACT

FORMER, LATTER

CODED CROSSWORD

LION STANDARD: 16 WORDS

PANTHER STANDARD: 11 WORDS

NATURAL NINE

albino anabolic bacon
bail bait banal baton
blain bloat bloc blot
boat boil bolt botanic
BOTANICAL cabal
cabin cobalt obtain

PUSSYCAT STANDARD: 7 WORDS

NINE NUMBERS

BATTLESHIPS

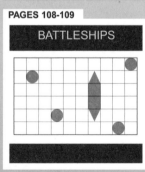

PAIR WHEELS

CARTON, DARTED,
PARTLY, TURTLE,
WORTHY, EARTHS

PEACE WORDSEARCH

SKELETON CROSSWORD

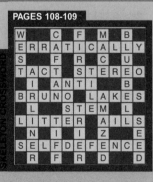

LITTLE TOUGHIE

Across: 2 Duck,
4 Gape, 5 Stag,
6 Cake, 7 Reef, 8 Heat.

Down: 1 Rat race,
2 Dessert,
3 Clamber.

COUNTING CRITTERS

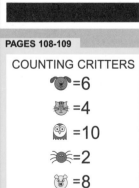

=6

=4

=10

=2

=8

PAGES 110-111

PAGES 110-111 — ADD THREE TO THREE

1 CASINO
2 COURAGE
3 CAMELOT

PAGES 110-111 KAKURO

LION STANDARD 23 WORDS

PAGES 110-111 — WORD SPLITZ

BARGE, CANOE
FERRY, KAYAK
LINER, CRAFT
YACHT, SCULL

PAGES 110-111 — HIDDEN COLORS

26	10	32	34	38	17	25	5	6	37	23	28
1	16	11	40	28	1	19	24	4	8	17	
41	15	2	1	15	5	18	5	20	11	20	
16	9	13	22	1	37	6	29	6	21	36	30
23	30	14	15	19	7	27	12	27	24	14	3
12	27	4	3	9	2	32	29	22	18	15	5
10	38	15	3	18	10	24	33	35	2		
34	14	5	21	19	31	5	3	15	21		

PAGES 110-111 SUDOKU

1	7	5	8	2	9	4	6	3
8	2	3	6	7	4	5	9	1
9	6	4	3	1	5	2	8	7
4	8	2	7	9	6	3	1	5
3	5	9	1	4	8	7	2	6
7	1	6	2	5	3	9	4	8
2	4	1	5	6	7	8	3	9
6	3	7	9	8	2	1	5	4
5	9	8	4	3	1	6	7	2

PAGES 110-111 — NATURAL NINE

PANTHER STANDRAD: 9 WORDS

aged dirge drag gait gaited gaiter gape gaped gaper garter gate gear girder grade grader grape grate grated grater great grid grip gripe griped griper grit page paged pager PARTRIDGE rage raged rager regard ridge tiger

PUSSYCAT STANDARD: 9 WORDS

PAGES 110-111 — BLOCKBUSTERS

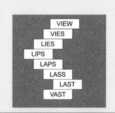

PAGES 110-111 — LITTLE TOUGHIE

PAGES 110-111 — REBUS TOWER

BACK DOOR
HIGH EXPLOSIVE
A TOUCHING MOMENT

PAGES 110-111 — ADD A LETTER

DESK, HALF, MEAN, NEWT

PAGES 112-113 SUDOKU

6	7	8	3	2	1	5	4	9
1	4	3	9	8	5	6	7	2
2	9	5	4	6	7	8	1	3
7	3	6	8	9	2	1	5	4
4	2	1	5	7	6	3	9	8
5	8	9	1	4	3	2	6	7
8	1	7	2	5	9	4	3	6
9	5	4	6	3	8	7	2	1
3	6	2	7	1	4	9	8	5

PAGES 112-113 — LETTER STEW

NICE, LOVELY, PLEASANT

PAGES 112-113 SUDOKU — WORD WALL

VIEW, VIES, LIES, LIPS, LAPS, LASS, LAST, VAST

PAGES 112-113 — NOURISHING NINE

WELL DONE 22 WORDS

ALARM ALARMED ARMADA ARMED DAME DRAM DRAMA DREAM LAMA LAME LAMED LAMER MADAM MADE MALE MAMA MARE MARL **MARMALADE** MEAD MEAL MEDAL MEDLAR RAMMED REALM REAM

UNDERDONE: 10 WORDS — MEDIUM: 16 WORDS

PAGES 112-113 — CROSSWORD

ACROSS: 2 TEST, 4 MATE, 5 FEATHER, 6 TREE, 7 HARE

DOWN: 1 MAGENTA, 2 TESTATE, 3 SCHEMER

PAGES 112-113 — NINE NUMBERS

6	-	9	-	4	-7
/		/		x	
2	-	3	+	5	4
+		+		+	
8	-	1	x	7	49
11		4		27	

PAGES 112-113 — CHAIN REACTION

HOUSE, SEDAN, ANGLE, LEASH, SHAKE, KETCH, CHAFE, FEMME, MECCA, CACHE, HEATH, THERE, RECAP, APPAL, ALIBI, BIMBO, BOAST, STATE, TEXAS, ASCOT

PAGES 112-113 — A'MAZE'ING NUMBERS

PAGES 112-113 — COMMON WORDS

REWIND, SWINDLE, WINDOW, DWINDLING, THE WINDY CITY, WIND

PAGES 112-113 — PLACE THE PLACES

ALL
SEA
INN
ADD

PAGES 112-113 — COUNTING CRITTERS

 =8, =10, =6, =4, =2

PAGES 114-115 — NATUREGRAMS

¹OATHS, ¹HOSTA, ²LOUTS, ²LOTUS, ³NASTY, ³TANSY

PAGES 114-115 — ON TARGET

1 CATER, 2 AFTER, 3 NEVER, 4 ACTOR, 5 SAFER, 6 TUTOR, 7 AMBER.

OUTER WORD: CANASTA

PAGES 114-115 — BIRD BOXES

1	13	6	10	24	7	8	16	6	24	11	3
14	5	20	21	6	15	3	5	11	2	21	14
3	17	14	4	12	9	25	8	14	10	16	25
24	2	26	3	1	16	6	19	1	15	5	19
9	17	20	8	18	11	22	18	23	23	18	8
12	4	21	20	3	22	7	4	26	3	11	5
13	19	21	11	23	5	12	1	10	8	1	16
18	6	1	17	8	20	9	2	15	14	6	23

PAGES 114-115 — ARROWS

PAGES 114-115 — BRICK TEASE

4 MINUTES

PAGES 114-115 — IN A... WORDSEARCH

HIDDEN WORD: **MUDDLE**

PAGES 114-115 — NINE NUMBERS

PAGES 114-115 — CROSSWORD

Across: 1 Case-load, 6 Eta, 7 Lynch, 9 Blue, 11 So-so, 12 Tome, 14 Spin, 16 Agree, 18 Set, 19 Ben Elton.
Down: 1 Chessman, 2 Stabs, 3 Lulu, 4 Ann, 5 Threaten, 8 Yeti, 10 Lose, 13 Onset, 15 Peke, 17 Roe.

209

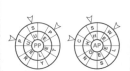

PAGES 114-115

OCCUPATIONS

VERY GOOD: 33 WORDS

enter erne nest peer pert pest pester preen present **PRESENTER** rent renter repent repenter **REPRESENT** resent resenter rest rester seen seep seer sent serene serpent sneer sneerer spent spree steep steepen steeper steer steerer step stern sterner tense tenser tepee tern terse terser tree

GOOD: 22 WORDS

PAGES 114-115

DIZZY DICTATION

1. Their neighbor's Great Dane howls all night.
2. We try to pay our rent on time but on occasion it's late.
3. He'd peddle his wares by the mall on Sundays.

PAGES 114-115

JIG GRID

C	H	E	M	I	S	E
C	U	L	O	T	T	E
G	A	R	M	E	N	T
C	A	S	S	O	C	K
O	V	E	R	A	L	L
P	Y	J	A	M	A	S
S	W	E	A	T	E	R

PAGES 116-117

FLOWERY PHRASES

LAST BUT NOT LEAST

PAGES 116-117

NATURAL NINE

PUSSYCAT STANDARD: 7 WORDS

beer bore borer breve brier brio ever heir herb **HERBIVORE** here hero hire hirer hover over rieve riever rive river robe rove rover veer verb

PAGES 116-117

CAGED ANIMALS

1 TANK, 2 DISC, 3 PATH, 4 SEMI, 5 PULP, 6 ROOM, 7 ZULU, 8 RUIN

CAGED ANIMAL: CHIPMUNK

PAGES 116-117

QUICK NATURAL WORLD QUIZ

1 FOAL
2 PYRENEES
3 SWITZERLAND
4 EUCALYPTUS
5 BAMBOO SHOOTS

PAGES 116-117

STEP LADDER

HEAD
HEAL
TEAL
TELL
TALL
TAIL

PAGES 116-117

EYE SQUIRCLE

A	M	T	G	T	V	C	M	I
C	O	R	N	E	A	R	O	D
R	U	A	A	M	L	Y	V	Y
I	R	I	S	P	U	P	I	L
D	N	T	H	O	E	T	E	L

PAGES 116-117 SUDOKU

8	4	1	7	9	5	3	6	2
5	7	3	2	8	6	1	9	4
9	6	2	1	4	3	8	5	7
6	3	5	4	1	9	7	2	8
2	1	9	6	7	8	4	3	5
7	8	4	3	5	2	9	1	6
3	9	6	8	2	4	5	7	1
1	5	8	9	6	7	2	4	3
4	2	7	5	3	1	6	8	9

CODED CROSSWORD

PAGES 116-117

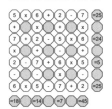

PAGES 116-117

FIVE SNEAKY SNAKES

DOUGHNUT
MOUSSAKA
COLESLAW
DUMPLING
TAKEAWAY

PAGES 116-117

LETTER SWAP

JACK OF ALL
TRADES MASTER
OF NONE

PAGES 116-117

FISHY NUMBER PIC

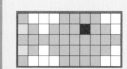

PAGES 118-119 SUDOKU

G	I	E	A	B	H	C	D	F
F	B	H	G	D	C	E	A	I
C	D	A	F	E	I	G	H	B
D	E	F	I	A	B	H	G	C
H	A	G	D	C	F	I	B	E
B	C	I	H	G	E	A	F	D
E	H	D	C	F	A	B	I	G
A	G	B	E	I	D	F	C	H
I	F	C	B	H	G	D	E	A

PAGES 118-119

NATURE TRAIL

THE HIDDEN PLANT
IS A
CHRYSANTHEMUM

PAGES 118-119 CROSSWORD

ACROSS:
1 SPLASH OUT, 6 ORATE, 7 ALE, 8 SO-SO, 10 NAPE, 13 ACE, 14 SNARE, 16 ARTHRITIS.

DOWN:
1 SLOWS, 2 LEA, 3 SLED, 4 OMAHA, 5 TOE, 9 SLEPT, 11 EVENS, 12 USER, 13 ADA, 15 ACT.

PAGES 118-119

PYRAMID OF EGGS

594
267327
197 170157
108 89 81 76
55 53 36 45 31
21 34 19 17 28 3

PAGES 118-119

NOURISHING NINE

UNDERDONE: 17 WORDS

ACME ACMITE AMEN AMENE AMENT AMICE AMINE CAME CEMENT CENTIME CINEMA EMETIC EMIT EMMET ENEMA ICEMAN ICEMEN IMAM INMATE ITEM MACE MAIM MAIN MANE MANIC MANTIC MATE MATIN MATINEE MEAN MEANIE MEANT MEANTIME MEAT MEET MENACE METE MICA MICE MIEN MIME MINA MINCE **MINCEMEAT** MINE MINT MITE MNEME MNEMIC NAME TAME TEAM TEEM TIME

PAGES 118-119

CHAIN REACTION

LYMPH, PHONE, NEGRO, ROACH, CHAFE, FEAST, STARE, RECAP, APACE, CELLO, LOBBY, BYLAW, AWASH, SHAPE, PECAN, ANITA, TAMPA, PABLO, LOOFA, FACIA

PAGES 118-119

BLOCKBUSTERS

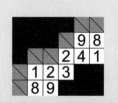

PAGES 118-119

WHAT COMES FIRST?

DOG
GREASED
LAUGHING
SOAP

PAGES 118-119

KAKURO

		9	8
	2	4	1
1	2	3	
8	9		

PAGES 118-119

WORD WHEEL

PAGES 118-119

NUMBER HEX

PAGES 120-121

WORD SPLITZ

PERCH, SHARK
SKATE, TENCH
TROUT, ANGEL
BREAM, PRAWN

PAGES 120-121

NINE NUMBERS

7	+	5	x	2	24
x		-		+	
1	-	8	+	6	-1
+		+		+	
3	-	4	+	9	8
10		1		17	

PAGES 120-121

WEATHER

S	L	U	S	H	T	O	M
L	D	L	O	C	B	J	R
E	Z	E	E	R	F	C	O
E	C	H	I	L	L	F	T
T	T	G	P	O	O	W	S
B	H	M	U	G	O	A	U
T	A	D	G	V	D	R	G
D	W	Y	T	S	I	M	U

PAGES 120-121 SUDOKU

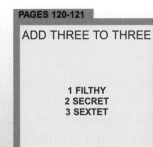

9	5	1	7	2	8	6	3	4
6	7	2	4	5	3	9	8	1
4	8	3	6	9	1	2	5	7
5	3	9	1	4	7	2	6	
7	1	8	2	6	5	3	4	9
2	4	6	9	3	7	8	1	5
1	6	7	3	4	2	5	9	8
8	2	4	5	7	9	1	6	3
3	9	5	8	6	4	7	2	

PAGES 120-121
ADD THREE TO THREE

1 FILTHY
2 SECRET
3 SEXTET

PAGES 120-121
FIVE SNEAKY SNAKES

ASBESTOS
NITROGEN
MERCURY
PLATINUM
FLUORIDE

PAGES 120-121
80S MUSIC QUIZ

1 PHIL COLLINS
2 SPANDAU BALLET
3 ELTON JOHN
4 NOWHERE
5 1985

PAGES 120-121
LITTLE TOUGHIE

Across: 4 Albino,
5 Strides, 8 Eureka.

Down: 1 Sags, 2 Riviera,
3 Hole, 6 Tree, 7 Sway.

PAGES 120-121
BITS AND PIECES

MO	TO	R	IN	G
GA	R	A	GE
EN	G	I	N	E
WH	EE	L	S
S	TE	ER	IN	G

PAGES 120-121
SKELETON CROSSWORD

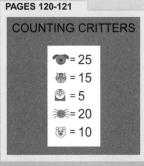

PAGES 120-121
COUNTING CRITTERS

🐶 = 25
🐱 = 15
👾 = 5
🕷 = 20
🐯 = 10

PAGES 122-123 ALPHAFITS

PAGES 122-123
SOCCER RIDDLES

KEANE

PAGES 122-123
ON TARGET

1 ELATE, 2 VAGUE,
3 ELITE, 4 RAISE,
5 TABLE, 6 OBESE,
7 NIECE.

OUTER WORD: EVERTON

PAGES 122-123
GEOGRAMS

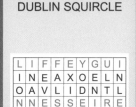

1 VENDER   1 DENVER
2 DENUDE   2 DUNDEE
3 AVENGE   3 GENEVA

PAGES 122-123
DUBLIN SQUIRCLE

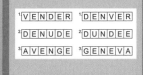

L I F F E Y G U I
I N E A X O E L N
O A V L I D N T L
N N E S S E I R E
S E R E T L E A T

PAGES 122-123
WORD WALL

FUND
FIND
WIND
WILD
WILT
GILT
GIFT

PAGES 122-123
HIDDEN COLORS

PAGES 122-123
MOVIE HOUSE

PAGES 122-123
WORD FIT

PAGES 122-123
BLOCKBUSTERS

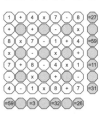

PAGES 122-123 SUDOKU

3	4	6	7	1	2	5	9	8
2	1	8	4	5	9	7	6	3
7	9	5	3	6	8	4	2	1
5	8	2	9	3	6	1	7	4
1	7	4	2	8	5	3	1	9
6	3	9	1	7	4	8	5	2
9	5	3	8	4	7	2	1	6
8	2	7	6	9	1	3	4	5
4	6	1	5	2	3	9	8	7

PAGES 124-125 SUDOKU

7	1	9	4	5	6	8	3	2
3	6	4	1	2	8	5	7	9
5	8	2	9	7	3	6	1	4
2	7	6	8	3	5	4	9	1
4	5	3	6	9	1	7	2	8
1	9	8	7	4	2	3	5	6
8	2	1	5	6	7	9	4	5
9	3	5	2	8	4	1	6	7
6	4	7	5	1	9	2	8	3

PAGES 124-125
NINE NUMBERS

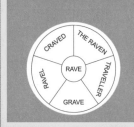

5	x	3	-	4	11
+		+		x	
9	+	2	-	6	5
-		-		-	
7	x	8	-	1	55
7		-3		23	

PAGES 124-125
SPORTS QUIZ – SNOOKER

JIMMY WHITE
147
THE CRUCIBLE THEATRE,
SHEFFIELD
SIX
FIFTEEN

PAGES 124-125
NOURISHING NINE

WELL DONE: 24 WORDS

MEDIUM: 17 WORDS

BEER BIER BORE BORER
BREVE BRIER BRIO EVER
HEIR HERB **HERBIVORE**
HERE HERO HIRE HIRER
HOVER OVER REBORE
REIVE REIVER RIEVE
RIEVER RIVE RIVER ROBE
ROVE ROVER VEER
VERB VERIER

UNDERDONE: 10 WORDS

PAGES 124-125
CHAIN REACTION

WHEEL, ELOPE, PEACH,
CHAFE, FEAST, STRAP,
APPLE, LEASE, SELMA,
MARGO, GOUDA, DAIRY,
RYDER, ERODE, DEPTH,
THROB, OBOES, ESTER,
ERROL, OLDIE

PAGES 124-125 KAKURO

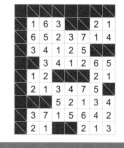

PAGES 134-135
CROSSWORD

ACROSS: 1 STAYED, 5 ERR,
6 SEE, 7 ANT, 8 EON, 9 ERA,
10 NEEDLE

DOWN: 1 STEWED,
2 ARRANGE, 3 EAST END,
4 SENATE

PAGES 124-125
COMMON WORDS

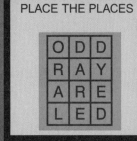

THE RAVEN
CRAVED
RAVEL
RAVE
TRAVELLER
GRAVE

PAGES 124-125
PLACE THE PLACES

O D D
R A Y
A R E
L E D

PAGES 124-125
JIG GRID

B R A Z I L
L A T V I A
K U W A I T
C A N A D A
G R E E C E
M O N A C O

PAGES 124-125
PLUG NUMBER PIC

PAGES 126-127
NATURAL NINE

apace aped apse aspen cape
clap clasp clasped
LANDSCAPE lapse lapsed leap
nape pace paced palace pale
paled panda pane panel pascal
peal pecan pedal penal place
placed plan plane planed plea
plead scalp scalped sepal slap
snap space spaced spade span
spec sped spend

PAGES 126-127
NINE NUMBERS

2	-	7	-	3		-8
x		+		-		
6	+	8	x	9		126
+		-		x		
4	x	1	+	5		9
16		14		-30		

PAGES 126-127
ANAGRAM LADDERS

CHISEL
SPADE
PLANE
TONGS
WRENCH
MALLET
FORK

CENTRAL WORD: SPANNER

PAGES 126-127 SUDOKU

3	6	8	5	7	2	1	4	9
2	1	7	4	3	9	5	6	8
5	4	9	6	1	8	7	3	2
4	9	2	7	6	1	3	8	5
6	3	1	8	9	5	4	2	7
7	8	5	2	4	3	9	1	6
8	2	3	1	5	7	6	9	4
1	7	6	9	2	4	8	5	3
9	5	4	3	8	6	2	7	1

PAGES 126-127
CEREMONY WORDSEARCH
HIDDEN WORD: QUEEN

PAGES 126-127
CODED CROSSWORD

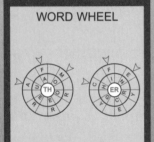

PAGES 126-127
REBUS TOWER

RIGHT BETWEEN THE EYES
FAIR AND SQUARE
A BIT OF THIS AND THAT

PAGES 126-127
KAKURO

PAGES 126-127
HOLLYWOOD ANAGRAMS

LINK: THEY ARE ALL
FAMOUS MOVIE THEME
COMPOSERS

JOHN WILLIAMS
VANGELIS
ELTON JOHN
ENNIO MORRICONE

PAGES 126-127
NAME THE DATE

1 1954
2 1988
3 1936

PAGES 126-127
WORD WHEEL

PAGES 128-129
ODD ONE OUT

6/12

ALL THE REST ARE THE
SAME NUMBER

PAGES 128-129
ARROWS

PAGES 128-129
ADDING GRIDS

				19
0	0	3	5	8
7	2	7	1	23
0	6	4	3	13
1	0	7	8	16
8	8	21	23	14

PAGES 128-129
NOURISHING NINE

ABATE ABET ABLE BALE
BALLET BEAT BELL BELT
BETA BLEAT LABEL LAPEL
LATE LEAP LEAPT PAELLA
PALATABLE PALATE PALE
PALLET PATE PATELLA PEAL
PEAT PELT PETAL PLATE
PLEA PLEAT TABLE TALE
TAPE TEAL TELL

PAGES 128-129 SUDOKU

6	1	7	3	2	4	8	9	5
5	4	8	9	1	6	7	3	2
9	2	3	8	7	5	6	4	1
7	5	6	1	4	9	3	2	8
1	9	2	6	8	3	5	7	4
3	8	4	2	5	7	1	6	9
2	6	5	4	3	1	9	8	7
4	7	9	5	6	8	2	1	3
8	3	1	7	9	2	4	5	6

PAGES 128-129
BLOCKBUSTERS

9	-	1	x	4	+	7	=39
x		x		x		x	
4	+	7	+	1	x	9	=90
-		+		+		-	
5	+	2	-	8	+	3	=12
x		-		x		x	
7	-	4	x	9	+	1	=28
=30		=68		=30		=60	

PAGES 128-129 ALPHAFITS

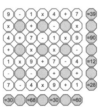

	C	A	M	P	A	I	G	N
X		R		E		L	R	N
Y	O	U	L	L		S	K	A	T	E
L		D		T	O	Z		W
O	B	E	Y	E	D		J	E	T	S
P			D	Q				P
H	E	L	P		R	U	S	S	I	A
O		A		F		I		P
N	E	R	V	E		L	E	D	G	E
E		G		L		T		E		R
	D	E	N	T	I	S	T	S		

PAGES 128-129
LITTLE TOUGHIE

Across:
4 Aspire, 5 Straits, 8 Cornea

Down:
1 Eats, 2 Bizarre, 3 Deft,
6 Taco, 7 Scab

PAGES 128-129
GEOGRAMS

1 PAINS 1 SPAIN
2 TANGO 2 TONGA
3 ENEMY 3 YEMEN

PAGES 128-129

	F	A	L	S	E	A	L	A	R	M
S		M		L		I		L		I
A	R	O	M	A		S	H	O	P	S
F		U		Y		L		F		E
E	I	R	E		P	E	S	T	E	R
		V		A				O		
S	E	L	E	C	T		S	A	Y	S
I			L		G		W		W	
G	L	A	Z	E		O	M	A	H	A
H		M		A		R				G
S	T	A	R	R	Y	E	Y	E	D	

PAGES 128-129
ON TARGET

1 CANDY, 2 RALLY,
3 IMPLY, 4 CRAZY,
5 KIDDY, 6 EARLY, 7 TATTY

OUTER WORD: CRICKET

PAGES 130-131
HIDDEN COLORS

7	11	19	9	7	3	17	6	11	9	3	7
9	6	4	8	20	12	5	8	2	9	11	14
3	17	8	6	5	19	10	7	4	6	2	10
16	7	10	20	2	13	4	20	8	19	5	6
2	10	19	9	16	9	11	15	4	7	4	20
12	15	16	7	3	7	3	18	2	12	20	13
5	9	19	12	15	14	6	5	10	9	2	8
4	5	17	9	6	16	7	19	3	12	3	14	6

PAGES 130-131
OPPOSITES ATTRACT

TEACH, LEARN

PAGES 130-131
LOLLIPOPS

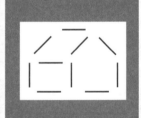

PAGES 130-131
NINE NUMBERS

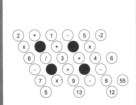

PAGES 130-131
CHAIN REACTION

FIRST, STOLE, LEACH, CHINA,
NACHO, HORDE, DELHI,
HIPPO, POLKA, KARMA,
MAMBO, BOMBE, BEIGE,
GENRE, RECCE, CEDAR,
AROSE, SERVO, VOCAL,
ALBUM

PAGES 130-131
ANAGRAM RIDDLE

1 IMPASSABLE
2 ANNIVERSARY
3 COMMERCIALLY
4 SPECIFICATION

PAGES 130-131
PLACE THE PLACES

O	W	E
B	I	N
E	N	D
Y	E	S

PAGES 130-131
WORD SPLITZ

BUGGY, COACH
CYCLE, LORRY
MOPED, WAGON
SEDAN, TRAIN

PLANE NUMBER PIC

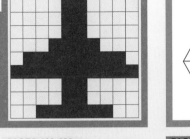

NUMBER HEX

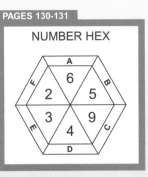

ON TARGET

1 KNEEL, 2 APRIL, 3 ROYAL,
4 TOTAL, 5 IDEAL, 6 NOVEL,
7 GROWL

OUTER WORD: KARTING

LION STANDARD: 24 WORDS

PUSSYCAT STANDARD: 17 WORDS

NATURAL NINE

arch batch bract
BUSHCRAFT butch cart
cash cast char chart
chat chub crab craft
crash crush crust curb
curt fact scab scar
scarf scat scrub scuba
starch such

PANTHER STANDARD: 14 WORDS

PULLING WORDSEARCH

QUICK SPORTS QUIZ

1 LEEDS UNITED
2 ENGLAND
3 ATHENS, GREECE
4 TWO
5 LANCE ARMSTRONG

ADD THREE TO THREE

1 BASOON
2 HEADGEAR
3 RATION

PAIR WHEELS

BARREL, BORROW,
CARROT, HORROR,
NARROW, BARREN.

BLOCKBUSTERS

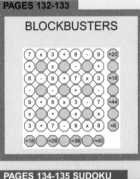

LITTLE TOUGHIE

Across: 2 Loch,
4 Gone, 5 Tray,
6 Hope, 7 Reel, 8 News

Down: 1 Pothole,
2 Letters, 3 Charted

KAKURO

COUNTING CRITTERS

=40
=20
=50
=10
=30

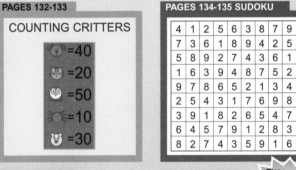

ZOO HUNT

THE MISSING CREATURE
IS A
RHINOCEROS

CROSSWORD

ACROSS: 2 STAY, 4 PELT, 5
ATHLETE, 6 SLOT, 7 JEST.

DOWN: 1 LETTUCE, 2
STYLIST, 3 AUCTION.

RIDDLE WORDS

BAT, BOWL, DUCK, OVER

GREEK GODS SQUIRCLE

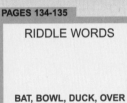

EXCELLENT 23 WORDS

OCCUPATIONS

GOOD: 12 WORDS

VERY GOOD: 18 WORDS

biscuit blip built clip
cubist cubit ibis licit lisp
list pistil pubic pubis
public **PUBLICIST** silt slip
slit spilt spit split suit tulip

MOVIE HOUSE

BITS AND PIECES

WORD WHEEL

TELEPHONE NUMBER PIC

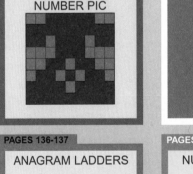

FIVE SNEAKY SNAKES

TOMORROW
NOWADAYS
CALENDAR
SATURDAY
TIMEPIECE

ADD A LETTER

LONG
LOST
DAWN
HARD

ON TARGET

1 ALERT, 2 REACT,
3 CARAT, 4 HABIT,
5 EXIST, 6 ROAST, 7 YEAST.

OUTER WORD: ARCHERY

NINE NUMBERS

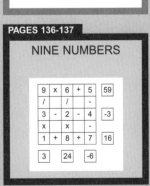

ANAGRAM LADDERS

INPUT, CURSOR
MODEM, LOGIN
SCROLL, ESCAPE
FORMAT

CENTRAL WORD: PROGRAM

NURSERY BLOCKS

RING-A-RING O'ROSES A
POCKET FULL OF POSIES

WELL DONE! 29 WORDS

NOURISHING NINE

UNDERDONE: 12 WORDS

ACHE CACHE CACHET CATCH
CHALET CHAT CHEAT
CHOCOLATE CLEAT CLOCHE
CLOT CLOTH CLOTHE COACH
COAL COAT COCA COCHLEA
COCO COCOA COLA COLT
COOL COOT COTE EACH
ECHO ETCH LACE LATCH
LEACH LOACH LOCATE LOCH
LOCO
OCELOT TALC TEACH

MEDIUM: 20 WORDS

CROSSWORD

Across: 2 Arable, 5 Laps,
6 Tyrant, 7 Peke, 8 Rat,
11 Hose, 13 Cradle,
14 Roam, 15 Sledge.

Down: 1 Sane, 2 Aster,
3 Boat, 4 Entire, 7 Pisces,
9 There, 10 Sage, 12 Slam.

COMMON WORDS

PLACE THE PLACES

G	A	S
A	R	E
S	I	N
P	A	T

LETTER SWAP

ONE SWALLOW DOES
NOT MAKE A SUMMER

LETTER STEW

BRIGHT, SMART,
INTELLIGENT

ZOO HUNT

THE MISSING ANIMAL IS A
VAMPIRE BAT

CAGED ANIMALS

1 PAGE, 2 SLIM, 3 ALSO,
4 TOWN, 5 TWIG, 6 HERO,
7 OSLO, 8 MISS.

CAGED ANIMAL:
MONGOOSE

ARROWS

PICTURE PHRASES

ADD INSULT TO INJURY
HITTING BELOW THE BELT
GET UP AND GO

SHELLED CREATURES WORDSEARCH

HIDDEN WORD: WHELK

5	1	2	8	4	7	9	3	6
4	6	9	2	1	3	8	7	5
8	3	7	5	6	9	2	1	4
7	2	4	3	8	5	1	6	9
1	8	3	6	9	4	5	2	7
6	9	5	7	2	1	4	8	3
2	7	6	4	5	8	3	9	1
9	4	8	1	3	6	7	5	2
3	5	1	9	7	2	6	4	8

EXCELLENT: 22 WORDS

OCCUPATIONS

VERY GOOD: 15 WORDS

arch ARCHIVIST astir
cart chair char chart
crash hair hart iris racist
rash ravish rich scar shirt
star starch stir trash vicar

GOOD: 10 WORDS

REBUS

COUGH MIXTURE
DOWN IN THE DUMPS
MANY HAPPY RETURNS

LITTLE TOUGHIE

Across: 4 Eskimo,
5 Layered, 8 Strata

Down: 1 Peal, 2 Firearm, 3
Nose, 6 Apse, 7 Drat

KAKURO

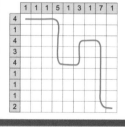

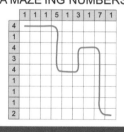

FLOWERY PHRASES

HIS BARK IS WORSE THAN
HIS BITE

LION STANDARD: 28 WORDS

UPSETTING WORDSEARCH

BATTLESHIPS

PAIR WHEELS

BUCKET, CUCKOO, NICKEL,
RECKON, TACKLE, WICKED

A'MAZE'ING NUMBERS

NATURAL NINE

PUSSYCAT STANDARD: 14 WORDS

afield afire deaf defer defier
defile defiler differ fade fail failed
fair fare fear feared federal feed
feel feral field fielder FIELDFARE
fife file filed filer fire fired flair
flare flared flea fled flee flier frail
free freed fried leaf life lifer raffle
raffled reef relief rife riff rifle
rifled

PANTHER STANDARD: 18 WORDS

NATUREGRAMS

¹O	G	R	E	S		¹G	O	R	S	E
²A	M	P	L	E		²M	A	P	L	E
³N	E	P	A	L		³P	L	A	N	E

BUG TEASE

4 INSECTS AND
3 SPIDERS

CROSSWORD

ACROSS: 1 Rose-bush, 6 Ali,
7 Spare, 9 Tote, 11 Seen, 12
Tree, 14 Cleo, 16 Spree,
18 Got, 19 Retrieve

DOWN: 1 Reassess, 2 Smite,
3 Best, 4 Sea, 5 Resettle,
8 Pete, 10 Once, 13 Rogue,
15 Leer, 17 Rue

B	D	H	A	E	I	G	F	C
C	G	A	D	B	F	H	E	I
F	E	I	C	G	H	A	B	D
D	B	G	E	H	C	F	I	A
A	I	E	B	F	G	C	D	H
H	C	F	I	D	A	E	G	B
G	A	C	F	I	D	B	H	E
I	F	B	H	C	E	D	A	G
E	H	D	G	A	B	I	C	F

ODD ONE OUT

WOLF, ALL THE REST ARE
BIG CATS

OPPOSITES ATTRACT

ATTACK,
DEFEND

PYRAMID OF EGGS

74
36 38
17 19 19
8 9 10 9
4 4 5 5 4
1 3 1 4 1 3

NINE NUMBERS

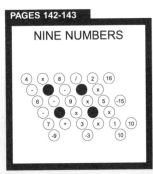

OCCUPATIONS

EXCELLENT: 26 WORDS

cent cite iciest incest incite
insect inset insist nest nett
nicest scent SCIENTIST sect
sent sett site stein stet stint
tent test testis tine tiniest tint

GOOD: 14 WORDS   VERY GOOD: 18 WORDS

THREE FOUR ALL

AGED, RANG, RAGE

HOLE, HOST, HOSE

WORD WHEEL

NUMBER HEX

WORD SPLITZ

1 ALLAN, BARRY
2 BRIAN, COLIN
3 GEOFF, JASON
4 NIGEL, RALPH

QUICK QUIZ QUESTIONS

CHICAGO
NEW YORK
LIVERPOOL
NOTTINGHAM
LONDON
AMSTERDAM

NINE NUMBERS

STEP LADDER

COLD
CORD
WORD
WORM
WARM

OPPOSITES ATTRACT

WARM AND COOL,
GOOD AND EVIL

AND THREE TO THREE

1 HAMPER
2 DISCARD
3 PISCES

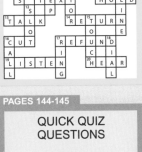

FIVE SNEAKY SNAKES

LANDLADY
ATTORNEY
COMEDIAN
SALESMAN
PRISONER

LITTLE TOUGHIE

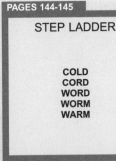

WORD WHEEL

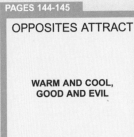

COUNTING CRITTERS

CASTLE MAZE

BIRD BOXES

CROSSWORD

ACROSS: 2 GASP, 4 SANE,
5 TEAR, 6 SAME, 7 LIES,
8 FEEL

DOWN: 1 FANFARE,
2 GET WELL, 3 STARTER

ADDING GRIDS

WINTER SPORTS SQUIRCLE

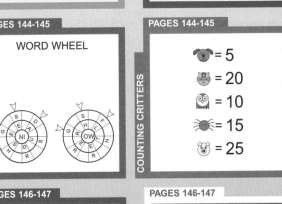

PAIR WHEELS

BOUNCE, PLUNGE,
LAUNCH, TRUNKS,
HAUNTS, COUNTS

OCCUPATIONS

EXCELLENT: 33 WORDS

acini acne acre cairn cane
canier canine cann canner
cannier care ceria cran crane
crena face facer fancier farce
fiacre finance FINANCIER franc
icer icier irenic nacre neanic
niacin nice nicer race rice

GOOD: 18 WORDS   VERY GOOD: 24 WORDS

MOVIE HOUSE

BITS AND PIECES

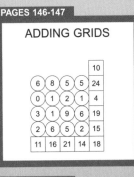

PAGES 146-147

JIG GRID

P	O	L	L	O	C	K
C	E	Z	A	N	N	E
P	I	C	A	S	S	O
V	A	N	G	O	G	H
V	E	R	M	E	E	R
H	O	C	K	N	E	Y
M	A	T	I	S	S	E

PAGES 146-147

TEA POT NUMBER PIC

PAGES 148-149

PICTURE TILES

PAGES 148-149

SITTING WORDSEARCH

PAGES 148-149 ARROWS

PAGES 148-149

LOLLIPOPS

PAGES 148-149

PICTURE PHRASES

WALK-IN WARDROBE
NEON LIGHTS
LONG TIME NO SEE
YOU WIN SOME, YOU LOSE
SOME

PAGES 148-149 SUDOKU

2	6	4	8	5	1	7	3	9
8	7	1	9	6	3	5	2	4
9	3	5	7	2	4	8	6	1
6	2	3	5	4	8	1	9	7
5	4	9	3	1	7	2	8	6
7	1	8	2	9	6	3	4	5
4	8	6	1	7	2	9	5	3
1	9	2	4	3	5	6	7	8
3	5	7	6	8	9	4	1	2

PAGES 148-149

80S SCIENCE QUIZ

1. NORTHROP
2. WORLD'S BIGGEST AEROPLANE
3. VENUS
4. GAME BOY
5. THE WORLD'S FIRST SUPERCOMPUTER

PAGES 148-149

COMMON WORDS

MARKET, REMARKED, ARKANSAS, DARK, SPARKLER — ARK

PAGES 148-149

PLACE THE PLACES

T	H	Y
R	O	E
A	L	L
P	E	P

PAGES 148-149 CROSSWORD

B	E	L	T	S		S	P	A	D	E
E		I		T		R			A	
R	U	N		S	C	A	T	T	E	R
G		E		T		B			N	
	P	A	L	E		N	A	M	E	
R	G		R	U	T		B		D	
O	B	E	Y		R	A	R	E		F
Y		F		A	I	F			F	
A	P	P	L	A	U	D		D	U	E
L		S		R	E		G	E	E	
S	P	I	K	E		S	M	E	L	T

PAGES 148-149

LETTER STEW

GIGGLE,
CHORTLE,
GUFFAW

LION STANDARD: 23 WORDS

PUSSYCAT STANDARD: 9 WORDS

PANTHER STANDARD: 15 WORDS

PAGES 150-151

NATURAL NINE

avenge avenger engrave even
ever gave give given giver
GRAPEVINE grave graven
greave grieve nave nerve never
pave paving rave raven ravine
raving riven vain vainer vane
veer veering vegan vein verge
vine vinegar viper

PAGES 150-151

NATURE TRAIL

THE HIDDEN PLANT IS A
HORSE CHESTNUT

PAGES 150-151

ANAGRAM LADDERS

EGYPT
PERU
IRAN
ROMANIA
BRAZIL
FRANCE
YEMEN

CENTRAL WORD: GERMANY

PAGES 150-151 SUDOKU

2	9	4	3	7	8	6	1	5
5	6	7	1	4	2	8	9	3
3	8	1	5	6	9	7	4	2
8	3	5	7	1	6	4	2	9
6	1	9	4	2	3	5	8	7
7	4	2	9	8	5	1	3	6
1	5	3	8	9	4	2	7	6
9	2	8	6	5	7	1	3	4
4	7	6	2	3	1	9	5	8

PAGES 150-151

CHILDREN IN NEED WORDSEARCH

PAGES 150-151

CHAIN REACTION

WELCH, CHEST, STRAW,
AWFUL, ULCER, ERRED,
EDITH, THYME, MELBA,
BANJO, JOYCE, CELEB,
EBONY, NYMPH, PHONE,
NEPAL, ALLOW, OWLET,
ETHAN, ANVIL

PAGES 150-151

CODED CROSSWORD

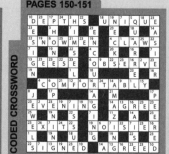

D	E	P	T	H	S		U	N	I	Q	U	E
E		H		I		E			E			A
	S	N	O	W	M	E	N		C	L	A	W	S
I		S			E		K		R			R
	G	E	E	S	E		O	B	S	E	R	V	E
N				L		U			I			E
	C	O	M	F	O	R	T	A	B	L	Y	
J		P			I		R			E		J
E	V	E	N	I	N	G		A	G	R	E	E
W			I		S		I		Z			A
E	X	I	T	S		N	O	I	S	I	E	R
L			U		G		U			N		S
S	I	G	N	E	D		A	G	R	E	E	D

PAGES 150-151

DIZZY DICTATION

1. We missed you when you were away in Greece.
2. What's your aunt's building close to?
3. Sue wore a dress because Mary borrowed her suit.

PAGES 150-151

KAKURO

6	9	8	
3	5	1	2
8	3		5	1
	1	2	4	3
	9	6	8

PAGES 150-151

HOLLYWOOD ANAGRAMS

LINK: THEY HAVE ALL WON
BEST FILM OSCARS
UNFORGIVEN
SCHINDLERS LIST
FORREST GUMP
THE ENGLISH PATIENT

PAGES 150-151

GEOGRAMS

1 DANGER   1 GRANDE
2 NERVES   2 SEVERN
3 CRADLE   3 CALDER

PAGES 152-153 SUDOKU

7	4	6	1	2	5	3	9	8
8	9	2	6	3	7	4	1	5
3	1	5	9	8	4	6	7	2
2	3	7	5	9	6	8	4	1
5	6	4	8	1	2	7	3	9
4	5	3	9	7	1	6	8	2
6	2	9	3	5	8	1	7	4
1	7	8	2	6	4	9	5	3

PAGES 152-153

NINE NUMBERS

7	-	1	-	5	1
-		+		x	
9	-	2	+	6	13
x		-		-	
4	x	3	-	8	4
-8		0		22

PAGES 152-153

CROSSWORD

ACROSS: 1 MISUSE, 5 SUE,
6 SHE, 7 LIT, 8 ART, 9 ALI,
10 GRANGE

DOWN: 1 MISHAP, 2 SHELTER,
3 SUSTAIN, 4 PETITE

PAGES 152-153

WORD WALL

WELL
TELL
TEAL
TEAM
TRAM
TRAP
WRAP

PAGES 152-153

REBUS TOWER

BED AND BREAKFAST
NO THROUGH ROAD
JUST AROUND
THE CORNER

ANAGRAM RIDDLE

1. OBLONG
2. SEGMENT
3. PRACTICE
4. LITERALLY

NATUREGRAMS

1. VOILE 1. OLIVE
2. CHEAP 2. PEACH
3. WEEDS 3. SWEDE

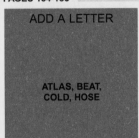

```
B A S A L T
C O P P E R
G A R N E T
S I L V E R
Q U A R T Z
G Y P S U M
```

```
L A C K   O F F E R S
O     H       O   X   T
W O O L   P R A I S E
  R     R   R   M     T
S Q U E E Z E D       M
T     S   V   R F S
      J E A L O U S Y
S     G   A   Y T M
U N A B L E   B U L B
N     M   E       R   O
G R E E D Y   S E A L
```

HOLLYWOOD ANAGRAMS

LINK: THEY ARE COUPLES
WHO USED TO BE MARRIED

BRAD PITT
BRUCE WILLIS
DEMI MOORE
JENNIFER ANISTON

ON TARGET

1 WALES, 2 REARS,
3 EARLS, 4 X-RAYS,
5 HANDS, 6 ALIAS,
7 MATHS.

OUTER WORD: WREXHAM

HIDDEN COLORS

```
W H J Q W Z G B C V H B
O I E D H A L E S N L K
I X O X T I M I F C J Y
A O U R J U E O P G Q M
E S V E N Y R A U I A O
I C Y U F K L E T E F U
B G V I S Q N O R A B I
Z P K A P M W E Z O T E
```

ADD A LETTER

ATLAS, BEAT,
COLD, HOSE

PYRAMID OF APPLES

224
96 128
40 56 72
16 24 32 40
6 10 14 18 22
2 4 6 8 10 12

NINE NUMBERS

PAIR WHEELS

ASSIST, BESIDE,
DESIGN, EASILY,
UPSIDE, VISION

```
P   S Q U A R E S   J
I   U     A   C     E
L A V A   B R A I N S
E   E   C L U E   E   U
D U S K   G L A N D S
  Y   B   Y   C       E
P U S H E S   S E W S
U   T   H O M E       T
P R E F I X   L A Z Y
I   M   N         L   L
L   S A D N E S S     E
```

```
  7 9   5 6
6 8 1 3 4 5 2
4 2 6 5   3 5
9 3   8 3 9
7 5 3   5 7 2
  4 2 9   2 5
3 1   3 6 4 8
7 9 3 5 2 1 4
  6 4   7 8
```

```
            B   D
          S H O R E       C O L
          C   U       T A R N   A
      S C A R L E T         Y   E
      A   E   D   A         O
      V   E   E   R
  S E A   D R U M L I N
      T   E     L         S   D
      O A S I S   L       L   U
      R       E   P L A N E T   N
      Y       R   O       A   E
      M O U N T A I N   D U N E
                  D
```

```
C H A U C E R
R O W L I N G
K I P L I N G
G R I S H A M
T O L K I E N
T O L S T O Y
C A R R O L L
```

PLACE THE PLACES

```
S A W
A W E
F A R
E Y E
```

CAGED ANIMALS

1 RAFT, 2 TRAM, 3 LIRA,
4 BOAR, 5 STEM, 6 ECHO,
7 HISS, 8 IDLE

CAGED ANIMAL: MARMOSET

STEP LADDER

TEA
PEA
PET
POT

BLOCKBUSTERS

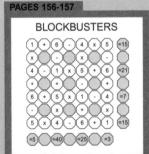

ADD THREE TO THREE

1. SESAME
2. SALOON
3. ARTERY

LION
STANDARD:
22 WORDS

NATURAL NINE

PUSSYCAT STANDARD: 9 WORDS
PANTHER STANDARD: 19 WORDS

cider circle circled cleric coir
colder cooler cord core cored
cried CROCODILE dire doer
door drool idler lord lore oiler
older oriel oriole recoil relic
rice ride rile riled rode
rodeo role rood

CROSSWORD

Across: 1 Stairway, 6 A la,
7 Graze, 9 Tree, 11 Twee,
12 Aloe, 14 Able, 16 Share,
18 Ava, 19 Get there.

Down: 1 Smartish, 2 Abate,
3 Rage, 4 Ada, 5 Renegade,
8 Real, 10 Rear, 13 Lease,
15 Beat, 17 Ace.

SPORTS QUIZ – BOXING

1. MUHAMMED ALI AND
GEORGE FORMAN
2. FRANK BRUNO
3. RED AND BLUE
4. NASEEM HAMED
5. MEXICO

COMMON WORDS

BLUNDER, ASUNDER,
PLUNDERED, LAUNDERETTE,
THUNDERSTRUCK — UNDER

CLUB HOUSE

Agassi, Henman, Kiefer,
Murray, Nadal, Roddick.

```
T M I I L G R H
R D U C Z O R E
E O F R D O B N
F J K D R T L M
E M I S S A G A
I C C P D I Y N
K G E A W Q L G
L L N H L H K Q
```

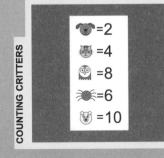

=2
=4
=8
=6
=10

WORD SPLITZ

1. BRUSH, EASEL
2. BOARD, CHALK
3. FRAME, GLAZE
4. MOUNT, PAINT

```
C L O S E T R Q
S T E N U E N D
K C A R V K I K
C H E L R S S I
O E A U H A A S
N S L G C B B I
E T A L P A I L
K N U R T H U O
```

OPPOSITES ATTRACT

ABOVE, BELOW

217

PAGES 158-159 SUDOKU

4	7	5	9	2	1	3	6	8
3	2	8	6	4	7	1	5	9
9	1	6	3	8	5	4	2	7
6	3	7	4	5	2	8	9	1
1	8	9	7	6	3	5	4	2
2	5	4	1	9	8	6	7	3
7	9	1	2	3	4	6	8	5
8	4	2	5	1	6	9	7	3
5	6	3	8	7	9	2	1	4

PAGES 158-159
BRITISH MAMMALS SQUIRCLE

H	S	S	V	C	A	L	M	P
O	T	T	E	R	D	E	E	R
B	E	U	R	E	O	A	L	O
B	A	D	G	E	R	F	O	X
Y	L	Y	E	D	E	Y	N	Y

PAGES 158-159
OCCUPATIONS

EXCELLENT: 30 WORDS

abound ammon anus band bond bonus bosun bound buna busman damn damson manus mason moan monad mound noma nomad nous numb OMBUDSMAN onus sand snob snub sound summon undam undo

VERY GOOD: 22 WORDS / *GOOD: 22 WORDS*

PAGES 158-159
FIVE SNEAKY SNAKES

1. MARATHON
2. CANOEIST
3. ROULETTE
4. LACROSSE
5. SKITTLES

PAGES 158-159 WORD FIT

PAGES 158-159
HOLLYWOOD ANAGRAMS

LINK: THEY ARE ALL MADONNA FILMS

WHO'S THAT GIRL
SHANGHAI SURPRISE
DIE ANOTHER DAY
SWEPT AWAY

PAGES 158-159
BITS AND PIECES

EA	TI	N	GO	UT
S	TA	RT	E	R
D	E	SS	ER	T
WA	I	T	E	R
N	A	PK	I	N

PAGES 158-159
RACING NUMBER PIC

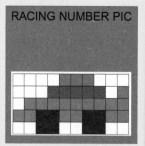

PAGES 160-161
ON TARGET

1 BACON, 2 UNION,
3 RAVEN, 4 NYLON,
5 LADEN, 6 EATEN,
7 YEARN.

OUTER WORD: BURNLEY

PAGES 160-161
ODD ONE OUT

OSTRICH,
BECAUSE IT CANNOT FLY

PAGES 160-161
CROSSWORD

ACROSS: 1 EXERCISES,
6 STATE, 7 ART, 8 LIST,
10 SEES, 13 BED,
14 AWARE, 16 DESCENDED.

DOWN: 1 EASEL, 2 ERA,
3 CHEW, 4 SLAVE, 5 SIT,
9 SIDES, 11 SPEED,
12 SAVE, 13 BID, 15 ADD.

PAGES 160-161
NURSERY BLOCKS

SING A SONG OF
SIXPENCE A POCKET
FULL OF RYE

PAGES 160-161
NOURISHING NINE

WELL DONE: 24 WORDS

ALLOW ALOE HALE HALL HALLO HALO HEAL HEEL HELL HELLO HELM HOLE HOWL LAME LOAM MALE MALL MALLOW MEAL MELLOW MOLE MOLL WALL WEAL WELL WHALE WHEEL WHOLE WHOLEMEAL

UNDERDONE: 10 WORDS / *MEDIUM: 16 WORDS*

PAGES 160-161
PAIR WHEELS

BRANCH, CHANCE, GRANNY,
ORANGE, PEANUT, PLANET

PAGES 160-161
A'MAZE'ING NUMBERS

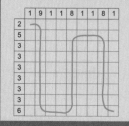

PAGES 160-161
QUICK QUIZ SELECTIONS

1 NORTH ATLANTIC TREATY ORGANISATION
2 INTERNATIONAL BUSINESS MACHINES
3 BRITISH BROADCASTING CORPORATION
4 WORLD HEALTH ORGANISATION
5 WORLD WIDE WEB
6 INTERNATIONAL OLYMPIC COMMITTEE

PAGES 160-161
PLACE THE PLACES

N	O	T
E	A	R
A	T	E
T	H	E

PAGES 160-161
LETTER SWAP

TIME AND TIDE
WAIT FOR NO MAN.

PAGES 160-161
LETTER STEW

FIERY, WARM, SPICY

PAGES 160-161
QUICK QUIZ

1. NORTH ATLANTIC TREATY ORGANISATION
2. INTERNATIONAL BUSINESS MACHINES
3. BRITISH BROADCASTING CORPORATION
4. WORLD HEALTH ORGANISATION
5. WORLD WIDE WEB
6. INTERNATIONAL OLYMPIC COMMITTEE

PAGES 162-163
LONDON STREETS WORDSEARCH

D	P	T	E	E	L	F	B
N	A	D	N	O	B	D	B
A	R	C	H	E	R	C	A
R	K	O	A	O	G	Y	K
T	S	G	F	N	B	E	E
S	L	X	A	G	N	W	R
E	O	E	U	S	T	O	N
W	B	R	E	L	D	O	N

PAGES 162-163
NINE NUMBERS

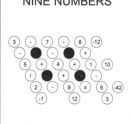

PAGES 162-163
BATTLESHIP

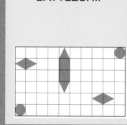

PAGES 162-163
QUICK MUSIC QUIZ

1 TAKE THAT,
2 SWEDEN, 3 POSH,
4 STAN, 5 WILL YOUNG

PAGES 162-163
CAGED ANIMALS

1 JUDO, 2 BOOK, 3 TOGA,
4 LION, 5 WING, 6 NONE,
7 PURR, 8 LUDO.

CAGED ANIMAL: KANGAROO

PAGES 162-163
LITTLE TOUGHIE

PAGES 162-163
OCCUPATIONS

EXCELLENT 40 WORDS

afield afire aidful argufied deaf delf direful earful fade fail failed failure fair faired fard fardel fare fared fear feral ferial feud feudal field figural figure figured filar file filed filer fire fired flag flair flare flared flea fled flier flue fluid fragile frail fraud fridge fried frugal fudge fuel fugal furl furled grief gulf gulfed leaf lief life LIFEGUARD lifer refugia rife rifle rifled

GOOD: 40 WORDS / *VERY GOOD: 46 WORDS*

PAGES 162-163 KAKURO

PAGES 162-163 SUDOKU

D	F	E	C	A	G	I	B	H
H	I	G	D	E	B	C	F	A
B	A	C	F	I	H	E	G	D
F	C	H	G	D	I	B	A	E
A	B	D	H	F	E	G	I	C
E	G	I	B	C	A	H	D	F
C	E	F	I	B	D	A	H	G
I	H	A	E	G	F	D	C	B
G	D	B	A	H	C	F	E	I

G	B	R	O	T	H	E	R		E
A		O		O		A		R	
Z	E	R	O		J	U	M	P	E	R
E		F	O	U	R		I		O
D	O	T	S		G	L	I	D	E	R
	R		M		Y		L		
S	Q	U	E	A	K		H	Y	M	N
W		S		N	I	C	E		C
E	X	T	E	N	D		N	O	T	E
E			E		E		C		D
P		D	E	R	I	V	E	D		S

JIG GRID

T	U	R	B	O	T
M	I	N	N	O	W
K	I	P	P	E	R
M	A	R	L	I	N
P	L	A	I	C	E
M	U	L	L	E	T

ON TARGET

1 WADER, 2 ADDER,
3 LAGER, 4 SAFER, 5 ALTER,
6 LATER, 7 LINER.

OUTER WORD: WALSALL

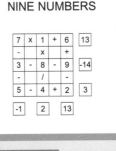

WELL DONE! 27 WORDS

NINE NUMBERS

7	x	1	+	6	13
-		x		+	
3	-	8	-	9	-14
-		/		-	
5	-	4	+	2	3

-1	2	13

NATUREGRAMS

[1] P A N E S [1] A S P E N

[2] B A S A L [2] B A L S A

[3] R A C E D [3] C E D A R

R	A	C	K	E	T		S	Q	U	I	R	T
	R		L		U		T			R		
P	L	A	T	E	A	U		E	X	A	C	T
		Z			M		E			L		L
E	G	Y	P	T		B	O	N	F	I	R	E
D			E		E			A		S		
	H	A	N	D	W	R	I	T	I	N	G	
A		L			J		R		E			
F	O	R	M	U	L	A		A	R	G	U	E
	E		N			V		L				
A	P	A	R	T		K	E	E	P	I	N	G
			D		S		L		D			
R	H	Y	M	E	S		A	S	P	E	C	T

CHAIN REACTION

PLEAD, ADAGE, GECKO,
KOALA, LARVA, VALVE,
VEGAN, ANODE, DEPTH,
THOSE, SEDAN, ANGEL,
ELATE, TEMPO, POACH,
CHASM, SMASH, SHAPE,
PEACE, CENTS

NOURISHING NINE

EAST ESTATE ESTEEM MAST
MATE MATT MEAT MEET SATE
SEAT SETT SETTEE STATE
STEAM STEM STET STEW
SWAT SWEAT SWEET
SWEETMEAT TAME TAMEST
TASTE TEAM TEASE TEAT
TEEM TEST TWEE TWEET
WASTE WATT WEST

UNDERDONE: 13 WORDS

MEDIUM: 20 WORDS

FLOWERY PHRASES

NOTHING SUCCEEDS LIKE
SUCCESS

ANAGRAM LADDERS

CLYDE
FULHAM
CELTIC
BURNLEY
WALSALL
EVERTON
ALLOA

CENTRAL WORD: CHELSEA

THREE FOUR ALL

INVERSION – IRON, VEIN,
NEON
SQUANDER – SANE, SAND,
QUAD

PYRAMID OF BRICKS

96
48 48
24 24 24
12 12 12 12
6 6 6 6 6
3 3 3 3 3 3

4	9	6	3	7	8	1	5	2
3	7	8	5	1	2	4	9	6
2	5	1	9	4	6	8	7	3
7	1	2	4	3	5	6	8	9
5	6	4	8	2	9	3	1	7
9	8	3	7	6	1	5	2	4
8	3	5	6	9	7	2	4	1
1	4	9	2	8	3	7	6	5
6	2	7	1	5	4	9	3	8

EURO TEASE

IAN HAD 4 EUROS

ZOO HUNT

THE MISSING CREATURE
IS A PORCUPINE

PAIR WHEELS

CRADLE, DEADLY, MEADOW,
TRADER, SHADED, LEADER

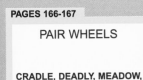

Q		W	O	R	S	H	I	P		B
U		U		A		U		A		A
E	V	E	N		J	U	M	P	E	D
U			C	O	O	L		P		G
E	L	S	E		B	E	S	I	D	E
			K	R	D	E				
P	R	I	Z	E	S		U	S	E	S
U			L		S	I	G	N		C
S	U	F	F	I	X		I	D	E	A
H			U		S			O		R
Y		L	E	T	T	I	N	G		Y

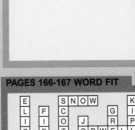

BITS AND PIECES

CO	ME	DI	E	S
F	R	AS	I	ER
C	HE	E	R	S
FR	I	EN	D	S
TH	EO	FF	IC	E

NINE NUMBERS

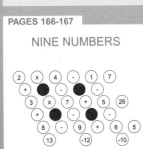

STEP LADDER

APE
APT
OPT
OAT
MAT
MAN

ARROWS

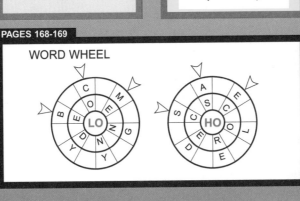

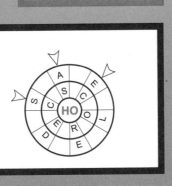

ON TARGET

1 FLORA, 2 ALPHA,
3 LARVA, 4 KOALA,
5 INDIA, 6 RUMBA,
7 KOREA.

OUTER WORD: FALKIRK

WORD WHEEL

ODD ONE OUT

POUND, BECAUSE
IT IS NOT A
UNIT OF TIME

OPPOSITES ATTRACT

SOFTEN, HARDEN

PAGES 168-169
SPORTS QUIZ

FOUR
JOHN McENROE
SUE BARKER
CLIFF RICHARD
SWISS

PAGES 168-169 SUDOKU

PAGES 168-169

BLOCKBUSTERS

PAGES 168-169
LITTLE TOUGHIE

Across: 4 Angora,
5 Assayer, 8 Asthma.

Down: 1 Ta-ta, 2 Royalty,
3 Tape, 6 Slay, 7 Reap.

PAGES 168-169

CROSSWORD

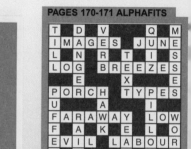

PAGES 168-169
ADD THREE TO THREE

1. HATCHET
2. LAUGHTER
3. PROBLEM

PAGES 168-169

COUNTING CRITTERS

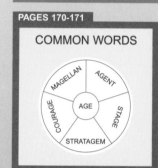

=6
=2
=4
=8
=10

PAGES 170-171
GEMS WORDSEARCH

PAGES 170-171
ADD A LETTER

BETA, SOLVE,
TITLE, GAIN

PAGES 170-171 ALPHAFITS

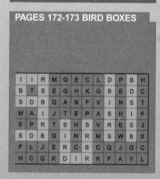

PAGES 170-171

SUDOKU

PAGES 170-171
AMPHIBIAN SQUIRCLE

FROGTOADS
EEPAHULRU
ALAMANDER
SALENCEAG
TXSSKERDE

PAGES 170-171

CODED CROSSWORD

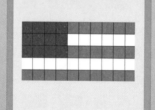

PAGES 170-171
FIVE SNEAKY SNAKES

CRUSTACEA
CROCODILE
MACKEREL
GOLDFISH
PORPOISE

PAGES 170-171
COMMON WORDS

MAGELLAN
AGENT
AGE
STAGE
STRATAGEM
COURAGE

PAGES 170-171

BITS AND PIECES

GR	AS	S	E	S
M	I	LL	E	T
B	A	M	BO	O
W	H	E	A	T
BA	R	L	E	Y

PAGES 170-171
HOLLYWOOD ANAGRAMS

LINK: THEY ARE ALL
MUSICALS
THE SOUND OF MUSIC
MARY POPPINS
CABARET
MOULIN ROUGE

PAGES 170-171
FLAG NUMBER PIC

PAGES 172-173
ON TARGET

1 PAPER, 2 ODOUR,
3 NICER, 4 TIGER,
5 ORDER, 6 OCCUR,
7 NEWER.

OUTER WORD: PONTOON

PAGES 172-173 BIRD BOXES

PAGES 172-173
ANAGRAM LADDERS

FRIDGE, THRONE
SHELF, DESK
SOFA, OVEN, CRIB

CENTRAL WORD:
DRESSER

PAGES 172-173
RIDDLE WORDS

REEL, FLING,
SALSA, LIMBO

PAGES 172-173
CHAIN REACTION

BANJO, JOUST, STILE,
LEILA, LARGO, GORSE,
SEDAN, ANDRE, REMAP,
APACE, CELLO, LOTTO,
TOAST, STEEP, EPOXY,
XYLEM, EMERY, RYDER,
ERICA, CAMEO

PAGES 172-173

ALPHAFITS

PAGES 172-173
ROTATION WORDS

CONVINCE,
OPPOSITE
CONVENIENT,
DELIGHTFUL

PAGES 172-173

MOVIE HOUSE

PAGES 172-173
PLACE THE PLACES

S	U	M
A	G	O
I	L	L
D	Y	E

PAGES 172-173

CROSSWORD

PAGES 174-175
PICTURE PHRASES

RED HERRING
BIG DEAL
CROSS ROADS

PAGES 174-175
LETTER STEW

STRIKE, THUMP, COLLIDE.

KAKURO

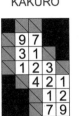

	9	7	
3	1		
1	2	3	
	4	2	1
		1	2
		7	9

EXCELLENT 21 WORDS

OCCUPATIONS

GOOD: 12WORDS — VERY GOOD: 16 WORDS

airy amir aria arid army
dairy DAIRYMAID dari
diary dram drama dray
dryad maria miry myriad
radii raid rami rimy yard

DANCE WORDSEARCH

Hidden word: Fan

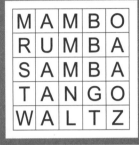

PAIR WHEELS

ISLAND, PALACE,
RELATE, SALARY,
SPLASH, INLAND.

BITS AND PIECES

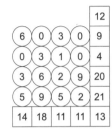

AR	T	I	ST	S
PO	L	L	OC	K
T	U	R	N	ER
H	O	CK	N	EY
M	AT	IS	S	E

CROSSWORD

ACROSS: 2 DUSK,
4 BARE, 5 SLAM, 6
HAZE, 7 REEF, 8 TEST.
DOWN: 1 WARFARE,
2 DESSERT, 3 SEAWEED.

NATURE TRAIL

HONEYSUCKLE

4	3	2	9	5	8	6	7	1
7	5	9	1	2	6	4	3	8
8	1	6	4	3	7	5	2	9
2	4	3	8	9	5	7	1	6
9	8	7	6	1	4	2	5	3
5	6	1	2	7	3	9	8	4
3	9	4	7	8	2	1	6	5
6	2	5	3	4	1	8	9	7
1	7	8	5	6	9	3	4	2

M	A	M	B	O
R	U	M	B	A
S	A	M	B	A
T	A	N	G	O
W	A	L	T	Z

ADDING GRIDS

MEDIUM KAKURO

9	8		
5	7	8	9
3	4	1	5
		9	7

80s SPORTS QUIZ

MANCHESTER UNITED
PAUL GASCOINE
1987
PAT CASH
USSR

CODED CROSSWORD

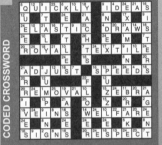

4	5	3	7	2	8	1	6	9
1	7	8	5	6	9	3	2	4
9	6	2	4	3	1	7	8	5
8	1	5	9	4	6	7	3	2
3	9	6	1	8	7	4	5	2
2	4	7	6	5	3	8	9	1
7	2	1	8	4	5	9	3	6
6	3	4	9	7	2	5	1	8
5	8	9	3	1	6	2	4	7

GEOGRAMS

RUMBA BURMA
²CHAIN ²CHINA
³PANEL ³NEPAL

POOR SEESAW
O C X O E
LACE STARVE
I U T E E K
CUPBOARD
Y Y M N L S
MAGAZINE
H S T L Q N
AUTHOR JUGS
L U E I E
FINISH ADDS

FALL WORDSEARCH

ODD ONE OUT

8, BECAUSE THE
REST ARE
ODD NUMBERS

WORD SPLITZ

CREWE, DERBY
DOVER, LUTON
POOLE, RUGBY
STOKE, WIGAN

LETTER STEW

SPEEDY
RAPID
SWIFT

WHAT COMES FIRST?

BROAD
TOOTH
GOLF
BIG

	1	2		1	2	5
	7	5	6	2	3	1	4
	3	1	2			2	1
		3	1	2	4		
		4	1	2		
		3	4	5	1	
	3	1		1	2	3
	1	7	5	6	3	2
	2	4	3	1		3	1

NINE NUMBERS

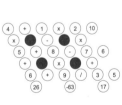

BIRTHDAY GIRL

SUE'S BIRTHDAY IS ON
DECEMBER 30TH.
THE STATEMENTS WERE
MADE ON JANUARY 1ST.

P F B Q M
UNITED JUNE E
L N E N I S
LOG FREEZES E
O E X E
PORCH TYPES
A A L
DOORWAY ASK
D V K Y I
LOAF PARENT E
E L H D E

CROSSWORD

ACROSS: 2 SCAN, 4 WEPT,
5 DELAYED, 6 THEY, 7 WEDS

DOWN: 1 DEFENCE,
2 STRAITS, 3 ADHERES

CAGED ANIMALS

1 ACRE, 2 DATA, 3 BURN,
4 SPOT, 5 TIRE, 6 BELL,
7 TRIO, 8 CHIP

CAGED ANIMAL: ANTELOPE

7	2	3	4	9	6	8	5	1
5	4	6	1	2	8	9	3	7
9	1	8	7	5	3	2	4	6
2	8	5	6	7	9	4	1	3
3	6	1	2	4	5	7	8	9
4	7	9	3	8	1	5	6	2
1	3	4	9	6	2	5	7	8
8	9	2	5	1	7	4	6	3
6	5	7	8	3	4	1	2	9

BITS AND PIECES

CH	E	E	S	E
C	HE	D	DA	R
R	IC	O	TT	A
PA	R	ME	S	AN
S	T	I	LT	ON

NATURAL NINE

PUSSYCAT STANDARD: 9 WORDS

PANTHER STANDARD: 17 WORDS

dough doughy dour drug dune dung enough euro gourd GREYHOUND ground guyed hound hour hued huge huger hung hunger hungry nude nudge rogue rogued rouge rouged rough roughed roughen round rude rued rune rung under undergo undo undoer urge urged young younger your

---

NATURE TRAIL

CAULIFLOWER

ARROWS

BATTLESHIPS

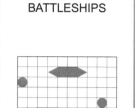

MINI MAZE

BLOCKBUSTERS

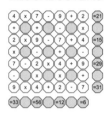

MATCH STICKS

Answer: 4 match sticks

WORD FIT

HOLLYWOOD ANAGRAMS

LINK: THEY ARE ALL BRAT PACK FILMS

THE BREAKFAST CLUB
THE LOST BOYS
PRETTY IN PINK
YOUNG GUNS

JIG GRID

```
A C T R E S S
M A T I N E E
B A L C O N Y
U P S T A G E
C U R T A I N
G A L L E R Y
M A N A G E R
```

WORD WHEEL

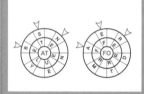

SPOT THE DIFFERENCE

1 SUN RAY MISSING,
2 CAT'S TAIL STRIPE SHADED, 3 CAT'S PATCH NOT SHADED, 4 ONE LEAF MISSING RIGHT OF TREE, 5 BUSH MISSING TO LEFT OF TREE

HIDDEN COLORS

```
Q R Y I Z Q T Z L F C V
V O W B U S O Y A R T O
E S Y D P W Q S E G K S
C U P F T Q U T H P Q U
F T X R I Y K P C R W S
B J A X H T M V L G A Y
I R J V B E H R Y S Z P
D G D P T X Q W O U X S
```

ANAGRAM LADDERS

KITTEN, FAWN
KID, PUPPY
FOAL, PIGLET
LEVERET

CENTRAL WORD:
TADPOLE

PYRAMID OF BRICKS

415
205 210
95 110 100
40 55 55 45
15 25 30 25 20
10 5 20 10 15 5

MOUNTAIN SQUIRCLE

```
A N N A P U R N A
D O A N A N E A S
M O N T B L A N C
I S N I L I L C O
T E Y C O T M Y T
```

GREEN WORDSEARCH
Hidden word: Leaf

```
C P L S B S A E
U O E U S H P B
C E D A J A P U
U S R A R M L D
M G A R C R E G
B R O C C O L I
E T N I M C V E
R B E A N K F A
```

ALPHAFITS

```
S A V E   L A S T E D
P A     W I   A
L U C K   J A M M E D
A   U B K   E   S
S Q U E E Z E S
H   M C N O   O
    O     P O W E R F U L
B S   M D F   D
E X O T I C   D I V E
E   F N   C S
S H A G G Y   B E A T
```

QUICK QUIZ QUESTIONS

MICHAEL STIPE
BONO
DAMON ALBARN
JON BON JOVI
STEVE TYLER
JUSTIN HAWKINS

NATUREGRAMS

```
¹PAGER  ¹GRAPE
²MELON  ²LEMON
³AMONG  ³MANGO
```

SKELETON CROSSWORD

```
D A P     F G
A B R O A D   M A T E
Z   M   Y B K   N
E N A   E A R N E S T
  D         A   L
S W A P S   T E A S E
T   K     K   Z
R E T A I N S   A F T
E   E   T E   L E
S L A P   M E T E O R
S   K     M A   M
```

COUNTING CRITTERS

🐶=5
🐱=8
🐵=7
🕷=9
🐨=6

```
G D C I H B F E A
I E F C A G D H B
B A H E D F G I C
E H G B F I A C D
F C D A G H I B E
A B I D E C H G F
H I E F C A B D G
D G A H B E C F I
C F B G I D E A H
```

CAGED ANIMALS

1 PART, 2 GLUE, 3 MAIL, 4 SAGE, 5 LEAP, 6 ITCH, 7 PUMA, 8 SEEN.

CAGED ANIMAL: ELEPHANT

CROSSWORD

ACROSS: 1 CACKLE, 5 ROE, 6 AIR, 7 APT, 8 FEN, 9 HID, 10 DEGREE.

DOWN: 1 CARAFE, 2 CLEANSE, 3 LEATHER, 4 FRIDGE.

ADD A LETTER

THREE, PAIL, RAPID, SIDE

NINE NUMBERS

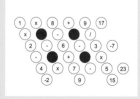

CHAIN REACTION

BRISK, SKATE, TENCH, CHEAP, APHID, IDIOT, OTTER, ERODE, DELHI, HINDU, DUMMY, MYNAH, AHEAD, ADORE, REPRO, ROUGH, GHANA, NATAL, ALONE, NEEDY

OCCUPATIONS

UNDERDONE: 13 WORDS

VERY GOOD: 18 WORDS

eerie erne inner INNKEEPER keen keener keep keeper kepi kine knee nine peek peer perk pier pike pine preen reek rein repine ripe ripen

---

COMMON WORDS

PAGES 184-185

KAKURO

PAGES 184-185

HOLLYWOOD ANAGRAMS

LINK: THEY ARE ALL ACTORS IN LORD OF THE RINGS

SEAN BEAN
VIGGO MORTENSEN
IAN MCKELLEN
CATE BLANCHETT

PAGES 184-185

JIG GRID

PAGES 186-187

NATURAL NINE

AUBERGINE bairn bane bang banger bare barge bargee baring barn bean bear bearing beau been beer began begin begun beige being berg bier binge brae brag brain bran brig brine bring bung burn garb gibe grab grebe grub urban urbane

PPAGES 186-187

ZOO HUNT

THE MISSING CREATURE IS A **WATER BUFFALO**

PAGES 186-187 ALPHAFITS

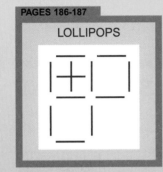

PAGES 186-187

LOLLIPOPS

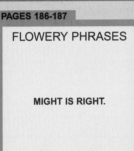

PAGES 186-187

PAIR WHEELS

ASLEEP, SELECT, SILENT, SOLEMN, TALENT, UNLESS.

PAGES 186-187

CROSSWORD

Across: 2 Learns, 5 Save, 6 Avenue, 7 Sets, 8 EEC, 11 Rose, 13 Seance, 14 Plan, 15 Svelte.

Down: 1 Pave, 2 Lease, 3 Rink, 4 Sleeve, 7 Senses, 9 Crepe, 10 Pare, 12 Snag.

PAGES 186-187

KAKURO

PAGES 186-187

THREE FOUR ALL

CATS,
CUTS, AUTO

MARE,
MALE, ABLE

PAGES 186-187

FLOWERY PHRASES

MIGHT IS RIGHT.

PAGES 186-187

BITS AND PIECES

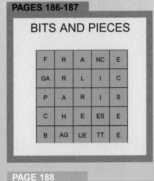

PAGES 186-187

SWEETIE TEASE

MARK HAS 2 SWEETS.

PAGE 188

WORD SPLITZ

1. BOXER, CAIRN
2. CORGI, DINGO
3. HOUND, POOCH
4. HUSKY, PUPPY

PAGE 188

ODD ONE OUT

RAVIOLI, BECAUSE IT IS NOT A CHEESE

PAGE 188 SUDOKU

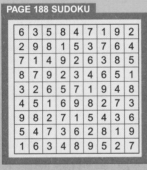

PAGE 188

FRUIT SQUIRCLE

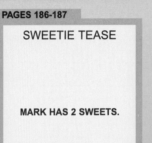

PAGE 188

CHAIN REACTION

LASSO, SOLID, IDEAL, ALAMO, MOCHA, HAREM, EMPTY, TYPED, EDITH, THIGH, GHOUL, ULTRA, RASTA, TANGO, GOOSE, SEDAN, ANDES, ESSEX, EXPEL, ELAND

PAGE 224

PAGE 224 SUDOKU

PAGE 224

CHAIN REACTION

BLAST, STARE, REACH, CHAFE, FEMME, MECCA, CACHE, HEATH, THESE, SEOUL, ULCER, ERODE, DEBAR, AROMA, MACRO, ROUTE, TELEX, EXILE, LEASH, SHOCK

PAGE 224

BITS AND PIECES

THE GRAND FINALE

It's not quite the end yet! Here are the last four puzzles for you to complete. You can find the solutions on page 223. Watch out for more books in this series.

JIG GRID ★★

Can you fit the blocks back into the grid to reveal, reading from left to right, six animals?

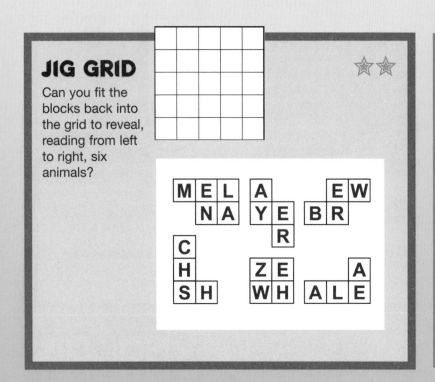

ALPHABET SUDOKU ★

To solve, fill in the grid so that every row, column and box contains the letters a to i.

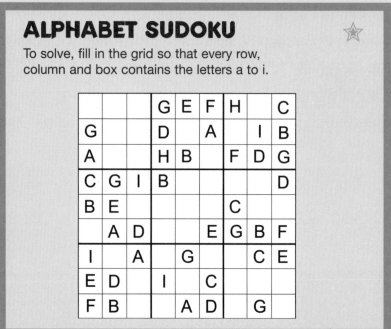

CHAIN REACTION ★★★

Solve this puzzle by creating a 'chain reaction' of 20 five-letter words that run left to right, beginning in the upper-left hand corner, using the 19 two-letter tiles in the middle. A two-letter tile that ends one begins the next. Each tile will only be used once. The single letters already entered are the middle letters of the words you are to form. Start by finishing the word that begins BLA_ _. [Tip: one of the words is French for female.]

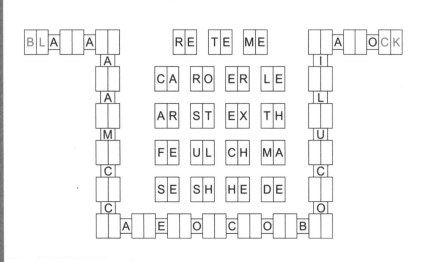

BITS AND PIECES ★★★

The tiles in the top grid are all jumbled up. Can you rearrange them in the grid below using only one tile from each column to reveal four related words and their theme?

R	E	D	O	N
S	IV	Z	R	E
AM	AN	E	B	E
D	A	I	SO	S
H	U	U	N	N